ELEMENTS OF
MODERN STATISTICS

ELEMENTS OF
MODERN STATISTICS

=============== FOR STUDENTS OF
ECONOMICS AND BUSINESS

Boyd L. Nelson, Ph.D.

University of Maryland

New York

APPLETON-CENTURY-CROFTS, INC.

SEP 28'61 0 0 8

To
LOIS

PREFACE

In writing this book, I have tried to present in a clear and concise manner those parts of statistics which are of most importance to students of economics and business, limiting the range of topics to those that can be handled in a one-semester course. The emphasis is upon basic statistical *concepts*, with an attempt being made to indicate their limitations and weaknesses as well as their strengths when brought to bear upon the problems of the business world. An understanding of such concepts is essential for both the intelligent consumer and the intelligent producer of statistics. In the former case, a list of "do's" and "don'ts" will not suffice, and in the latter, a burdensome mass of computational routines will seldom lead to real understanding. Basic concepts can be understood, I think, without rigorous derivations or proofs, although skill in mathematical reasoning is of considerable help if progress is to be made rapidly.

My definition of statistics reflects a certain approach to the subject and is, I recognize, not necessarily an all-inclusive statement. The objective is to focus the students' thinking on samples, populations, and inductive inference at the very beginning of the course.

I have included discussions of short-cut computations of the mean and variance because of the basic importance of these statistics, but the sections dealing with these methods may be omitted without serious loss of continuity.

The lists of selected references appearing at the ends of the chapters have been restricted to elementary books or those parts of advanced works which can be read and understood by beginning students.

The objectives, in sum, are (1) to help those persons who are going to be primarily consumers of statistics and (2) to give an adequate foundation to the potential producers of statistics—those students who will go on to more advanced work in such areas as sample surveys, forecasting techniques, and statistical decision-making.

For comments on various portions of the manuscript, I am indebted to John H. Cumberland, E. A. Gaumnitz, John M. Kuhlman, A. C. Rosander, and Vincent Schultz. I am also indebted to Prof. R. A. Fisher, Cambridge and Dr. Frank Yates, Rothamsted, and to Messrs. Oliver and Boyd Ltd., Edinburgh, for permission to reprint, in part, Table No. III from their book *Statistical Tables for Biological, Agricultural, and Medical Research.*

B. L. N.

CONTENTS

ELEMENTS OF
MODERN STATISTICS

1

INTRODUCTORY

DEFINITIONS

STATISTICS HAS BEEN DEFINED in many ways and has been given all sorts of names—especially by unwilling undergraduate students who have had to take the subject as a part of their required curricula. But even in the case of serious definitions, there is great diversity. This diversity suggests that there are many facets to the subject. Indeed there are, and as a result, a comprehensive definition often takes the form of a list of the various activities performed by statisticians.

However, let us define our subject, not by listing functions, but by examining two different basic meanings of the word *statistics*. From our point of view, the second of these meanings will form the more important definition.

When *statistics* is used in the plural, it means groups or batches of numerical data such as one would find in the *Statistical Abstract of the United States* or in the back pages of the *Federal Reserve Bulletin*. Numbers indicating how many people were born in 1932, married in June, 1956, or killed in auto accidents on Labor Day, 1958, are statistics, as are figures showing dollar volume of department store sales, the level of national income, or changes in wholesale prices.

When *statistics* is used in the singular, it means a body of methods for acquiring information in numerical form about *populations*.

The term *population* represents a key concept in statistics. It means any collectivity or totality of objects, real or hypothetical,

1

which we care to define. Examples of real populations readily come to mind. Thus, all of the beef cattle in the state of Nebraska on August 1, 1956, constitute a population. All of the households in College Park, Maryland, constitute another. The television tubes of type 5U4 produced by the Radio Corporation of America in January, 1950, make up still another population.

These three examples involve *finite* populations; that is, each of them consists of some definite number of objects. However, the concept of an indefinitely large (or infinite) population is also important. The indefinitely large number of measurements that could be made of the polar diameter of the earth would constitute an infinite population. In many cases finite populations are so large that for purposes of statistical analysis they may be assumed to be infinite.

The infinite population of polar diameters is also hypothetical. Another example of a hypothetical population is all of the Pioneer 301 hybrid corn that will ever be grown in Iowa.

A *statistical* population *may* consist of people but, as indicated by the examples given, it often does not. The individual persons or things which make up the population are called units or *elements*. The information we seek to acquire concerns the characteristics of these elements. For example, we may wish to know the number of the Nebraska beef cattle which are of the Black Angus *breed*, the average *income* of the College Park households, or whether it is reasonable to suppose that the percentage of *defective* 5U4 TV tubes is 4 or less.

To repeat, statistics is a body of methods for acquiring information in numerical form about populations. Such information not only adds to the general store of knowledge, but also aids us in solving problems and *making decisions*. Information about College Park incomes may be an important factor considered by a retail chain store in deciding whether to locate an outlet in the College Park shopping center. Information on the percentage of defective TV tubes can aid the manufacturer in deciding whether or not his production methods need to be improved. And, of course, the student can give examples of the numerical information which aids a college administrator in deciding whether the student is to be put on the honor roll, continued in normal good standing, or placed on probation. Often, different types of information about several populations are required for the making of one decision. Basically, then, it is the desire for new knowledge and the necessity of solving problems and making decisions that give rise to the development of statistical methods.

CENSUS TAKING AND SAMPLING

Pursuing the second definition of statistics further, we find that there are, in general, two ways of acquiring information about a population: (1) by taking a census of the population, or (2) by taking a *sample* of elements from the population. In the first case, we would collect information by making observations on each and every element in the population and, if we can imagine a census in which there were no errors in measuring, counting, collecting, or tabulating, our results would be absolutely precise. But absolutely precise census results are almost impossible in practice, particularly when the population is very large. Furthermore, census taking is often extremely expensive and time-consuming, and in some cases a census is impossible because making an observation on an element destroys that element; such a case occurs when we wish to determine how long it takes on the average to burn out a given type of light bulb. Obviously, a census is possible only for a finite population.

Thus, we find that more often than not we must acquire information about a population by taking a sample. Indeed, the sampling idea permeates all of modern statistics and, as we shall see, creates the necessity for rooting the subject in the theory of probability. A sample is a segment of the population or a limited number of the elements which make up the population. For example, if all the households in College Park constitute our population, and they are 3000 in number, then any subgroup of these households is a sample of the population, the subgroup containing anywhere from 1 to 3000 households. If our sample size is 3000, then sample size and population size coincide and our sampling procedure becomes a census.

INDUCTIVE INFERENCE, PROBABILITY SAMPLES, AND PRECISION

When we acquire information about a population by sampling, we engage in a process of inductive inference, that is, reasoning from the particular to the general, or specifically, from sample to population. A large part of what we know and much of what we believe comes to us as a result of this type of reasoning process. We generalize from samples of observations occurring in our experience.

Plato at one point has Socrates addressing himself to the question of whether virtue can be taught. Four men possessing virtue are cited by Socrates. Each of these men has a son, but Socrates notes that not one of the men has taught his son virtue. Generalizing from this small sample, then, Socrates concludes that virtue cannot be taught.[1]

The conclusion *could* be correct, but we cannot be *sure* that it is. Such is the nature of inductive inference.

Let us take another example which is a bit closer to the business world. A personnel executive recalled very vividly the case of Eriksen, who had requested and received a transfer to another plant in the company. Eriksen received notice of his transfer one month prior to the time he was to depart. During this month he accomplished very little in the way of constructive work. After this, the personnel executive was convinced that any man who knew he was going to be transferred would not work.

Here we have a sample of one element (Eriksen), but the conclusion made by the personnel man applies to *all* persons who know they are about to be transferred.

The two illustrative cases given were treated nonnumerically. Since, in statistics, we seek to acquire information in numerical form, let us illustrate an inductive inference involving numbers by going back to the case of the College Park household incomes. Suppose that from the population of all College Park households, we select a sample consisting of 400 households. Computations show that the average income for the households in the sample is $5422, and we make the inference that this figure is very close to the average income of *all* College Park households (the population average). But how close? Well, if our sample is a *probability* sample, we can find a reasonable answer to this question. Such an answer might be as follows: The odds are 19 to 1 that the sample average does not differ from the population average by more than $50. Why and how such statements of precision can be made will form an important part of the material in the chapters that are to follow. It is important to bear in mind that such statements are possible *only* if we are dealing with a special type of sample called a *probability* sample.

[1] Rex Warner, *The Greek Philosophers* (New York, Mentor Books, 1958), pp. 100–102.

The manner in which a sample is selected determines whether it is (1) a probability sample, or (2) a judgment sample. Now let us assume that each population element has some probability of getting into the sample. If our selection method enables us to know what these probabilities are, we have a probability sample. If these probabilities are not known, we have a judgment sample and we are unable to make a statement of precision about our results. We have, in other words, no idea of how far off our results might be. Sometimes judgment samples are our only source of information about a population. (The Gallup Poll and estimates of Gross National Product components are based on judgment samples.) But whenever feasible, probability samples should be employed because of the fact that their use enables us to get an objective measure of the amount by which we err in the process of inductive inference.

If each population element has the same chance of getting into the sample, the selection procedure results in a special type of probability sample called a *simple random sample*. Simple random samples are the type that we shall be primarily concerned with in this book.

The nature of probability and the procedure we go through to select a simple random sample are subjects which we will explore more fully in later chapters. At this point, common sense notions of probability or chance should be sufficient for our introductory glance at scientific sampling.

STEPS INVOLVED IN A SAMPLING STUDY

If we are going to acquire information about a population by taking a sample,[2] we must go through the following essential steps: (1) Stating the purpose of our study, the definition of the population and the nature of the information desired, (2) determining the size and design of the sample to be selected, (3) selecting the sample, (4) making observations (measuring and counting) and describing the data, (5) drawing the inference, (6) stating the degree of precision involved in the estimates or other results.

[2] The sampling process may involve either a survey or an experiment. In the former instance we have no control over the conditions under which the data arise. Thus we cannot cause the magnitudes of the observed characteristics to change or remain constant at will. But in the latter case (experiment) we do have at least partial control over some of the variables. In business and economic applications, surveys appear to be of more importance than statistical experiments, although the latter are gaining wide acceptance in industrial research.

STATISTICAL DESCRIPTION

We are going to begin our discussion at step (4), which involves what is often called statistical description. This starting point is appropriate, for statistical description will introduce us to statistical symbols and some of the simpler statistical concepts. Gradually we shall work our way to the why and how of statements of precision, treating the problems of sample size and selection after the necessary basic concepts have been introduced.

THE STRANGE NEW SUBJECT

To the undergraduate student exposing himself to statistics for the first time, the subject often appears mysterious or somewhat strange. Part of the mystery is due, we think, to the fact that statistics is a branch of applied mathematics and thus is to a large extent expressed in the symbols of mathematical language. The student has a twofold problem here; he must learn a new language and a body of fairly difficult subject matter as well. But awareness of the nature of this problem is a definite aid to the learning and appreciation of statistics.

Other reasons for the seeming strangeness of statistics have been well summed up by Rosander: [3]

Probability statistics is a strange science. It is strange because it has a checkered past, its development having been associated with gamblers on the one hand and with college professors on the other. It is strange because, due to its association with gambling casinos and ivory towers, it has lain dormant as an applied science for over two centuries. It is strange because even though it is a powerful and versatile science with revolutionary implications for industry and government, for research and management, these implications have been recognized only during the past 30 years. Finally it is strange because it removes three common activities—sampling, estimating, and inferring—from the area of common sense and intuition and puts them on a scientific basis.

It is our hope that we may dispel some of the mystery of statistics and show that the uniqueness or strangeness of the subject does indeed derive from the fact that it is an amazingly versatile and powerful tool of science and administration.

[3] A. C. Rosander, "Probability Statistics in Accounting," *Industrial Quality Control*, Vol. 11 (May, 1955), p. 26. By permission of the author and the editorial board of *Industrial Quality Control*.

SUMMARY

There are two important meanings of the term *statistics*. Used in the plural, *statistics* means numerical data. Used in the singular, *statistics* means a body of methods for acquiring information in numerical form about populations. Conceivably either censuses or sampling procedures could be used to acquire this information, but frequently censuses are not feasible. A population is any class of objects or measurements which we care to specify.

If a sampling procedure is used to acquire information about a population, the reasoning is inductive: for example, numerical estimates of a population average might be computed from the sample. Statements of precision about these estimates can be made if the sample is a probability sample.

An especially important type of probability sample is a simple random sample. This type of sample is selected in such a manner that each element in the population has the same chance of getting into the sample.

Statistics is often difficult for the beginning student because of the language problem. Statistics involves the use of many symbolical expressions which may be new to the student. He must learn the statistical language as well as the subject of statistics.

TERMS TO PONDER

1. Statistics
2. Population
3. Sample
4. Simple Random Sample
5. Judgment Sample
6. Population Element
7. Census

EXERCISES

1. Could a population defined so as to contain only one element have any practical significance? If not, why not? If so, define two such populations.
2. Discuss some of the reasons why sampling procedures may be employed in preference to censuses.
3. An executive of a large automobile corporation claims price cuts will not increase the sales of his company's automobiles. He bases this statement on the fact that at one time in the recent past his company

cut prices down almost to the level of competitors' prices but sales did not increase. What is the sample here and what is the inductive inference?

4. Learning by experience involves sampling. Discuss.

5. Indicate if you can some of the ways in which mathematics is similar to a language.

6. M. Pirie Sist is a mythical philosophy professor who claims that an individual person fundamentally is a sequence of events, these events constituting a sample drawn from the vast realm of possible experiences that could occur over the course of a lifetime. Would you go along with Sist's idea? Why or why not?

7. On the basis of sales reports from 14 bookstores, a newspaper compiles a best-seller list for the Washington, D.C., area. What is the sample and what is the population? What possible inferences are being made if a person decides to read a book because it is on the list?

8. During the well-known recession of 1958, a newspaper reporter interviewed 66 persons in order to find out if they intended to purchase any durable goods in the near future. Only one person was so inclined. The reporter concluded that because of the important role of the durable goods industries in generating recovery, the recession was going to be longer than had generally been supposed. Identify sample, population, and inductive inference.

SELECTED REFERENCES

FISHER, R. A., *Statistical Methods for Research Workers,* 12th ed. (New York, Hafner Publishing Co., 1954), Ch. I.

KENDALL, Maurice G., *The Advanced Theory of Statistics,* 5th ed. (New York, Hafner Publishing Co., 1952), Vol. I, Ch. I.

ROSANDER, A. C., *Elementary Principles of Statistics* (New York, D. Van Nostrand, Inc., 1951), Chs. I, II.

2

DATA, OBSERVATION,

AND RATIOS

TWO TYPES OF DATA

THE CHARACTERISTICS which we observe in a statistical study may be either (1) measurable or (2) nonmeasurable. Some fundamental physical characteristics which are measurable are length, weight, and time. Of fundamental importance in business and economics is money value. Other measurable characteristics (area, specific gravity, gross revenue) may be derived from the fundamental ones.

In measuring, we observe the *extent* or *amount* of a characteristic associated with a given element. For example, we may measure the heights of a group of college students, the money balances of a set of accounts receivable, or the times taken by several workmen to smooth the edges of a metal casting. Incidentally, when speaking of measurable characteristics, we sometimes do not mention the elements. Thus we may speak of a sample of incomes, a population of rents and so on. Recorded observations and computations relating to measured characteristics are called *measurement data*.

Now in the case of nonmeasurable (or qualitative) characteristics, we cannot determine amounts associated with each of the elements in our sample or population. However, it is still possible to use numbers in handling this type of characteristic. We can, for instance, count the number of elements which possess some given attribute. Examples would be (1) a count of *owner-occupied* households in College Park, Maryland, (2) a count of *defective* condensers in a sample taken from an auto parts production line, or (3)

9

a count of *seniors* in an upper division statistics class. Recorded observations and computations relating to nonmeasurable characteristics are called *attribute data*.

It is worth noting that the boundary lines separating qualitative characteristics are sometimes determined by measurement. For example, a vacuum tube that will last at least 1500 hours may be classified as acceptable, whereas a tube that will not last at least this long will be called defective. Thus tubes are sorted into the acceptable or defective categories in accordance with a certain measurable standard of minimum durability. Although the boundary line between "acceptableness" and "defectiveness" is determined by measurement, we are still dealing with attribute data, for the *amounts* of "acceptableness" or "defectiveness" are not recorded. We merely count the number of tubes falling into each category.

NONADDITIVE AND ADDITIVE MEASUREMENTS

Certain characteristics which are ordinarily thought of as qualitative may be defined so as to become measurable on a point scale or scoring basis. Measurements of such characteristics are called nonadditive. To show what we mean by the term *nonadditive*, let us take the example of the IQ, the standard measure of intelligence. Although a high IQ indicates high intelligence and a low IQ indicates low intelligence, we cannot say that a person with an IQ of 120 has the same amount of intelligence as two persons each with an IQ of 60. This situation arises because there is no constant sized unit of measure for intelligence comparable to the inch, pound, or second. We cannot, therefore, assume that one unit of IQ at the lower end of the scale is the same size as one unit of IQ at the upper end of the scale. Some other characteristics measured on nonadditive scales include (1) mechanical aptitude, which may be measured by the number of correct answers made on a set of test questions, (2) temperature, which is measured by the height of a liquid column in a tube, and (3) hardness of minerals and other materials, which is measured on a point scale called a Rockwell hardness scale. An example of an additive measurement is weight. We can indeed say that a person weighing 250 pounds is as heavy as two persons who each weigh 125 pounds.

The student should remember that a characteristic must be clearly and rigidly specified before it can be measured accurately.

And precise definitions, to say nothing of measurements, are almost impossible in many cases. "Measurements" of such things as cupidity, personality, masculinity, or courtesy should be viewed with a wary eye.

OBSERVATION AND SIGNIFICANT DIGITS

Statistical observation consists fundamentally of measuring or counting. Counting is the familiar process of matching objects with the positive whole numbers. Measurement, as we shall see, includes counting and much more. In the first place, measurement involves the comparison of a standard with the characteristic to be measured. We may make the comparison directly in the case of some physical objects. For example, we may compare the length of a table with a carpenter's rule or compare the time necessary to type a letter with the number of seconds ticked off on a stop watch. However, in the case of money value, the comparison of a good with the money standard is made by the forces of supply and demand in the market place.

All measurements are approximations, for no matter how closely we measure anything, it is possible to think of a closer measurement. Thus, the numbers used to record measurements are called "approximate numbers." These numbers, of course, are made up of digits. Now, some of these digits are said to be *significant* and others are said to be *not significant*. In order to develop rules for rounding approximate numbers, we must be able to recognize both of these types of digits.

Significant digits are those digits which indicate the number of scale segments on the standard that correspond to the characteristic we are measuring. When we say "scale segment," we mean that fraction of a unit or that multiple of a unit which represents the degree of fineness of the measuring scale. In other words, a scale segment is the smallest interval utilized on the measuring scale. Thus, if we are measuring to the nearest hundredth of an inch, the significant digits in our measurement tell us how many hundredths of an inch correspond to the thing we are measuring. If we are measuring to the nearest ten inches, the significant digits tell us how many "tens of inches" correspond to the thing we are measuring. The more finely divided the scale, the more significant digits it is possible to have in the measurement of a particular characteristic on a given element. Measurement, then, involves a standard, a process of comparison, and the counting of scale segments.

A simple example will help clarify the meaning of approximate numbers and significant digits. Suppose that we are measuring the length of the carriage of a calculating machine in the statistical laboratory and that we are using as our standard a yardstick marked off in tenths of an inch.[1] We place the zero mark of the measuring stick at one end of the carriage and note the reading on the stick at the other end of the carriage. Suppose the position of this other end of the carriage is indicated by the arrow in Figure 2–1.

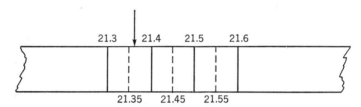

FIGURE 2–1. Measuring Length of Calculator Carriage

Our measurement would be recorded as 21.4 inches and called a measurement "to the nearest tenth" because the end of the calculator carriage is closer to 21.4 than to either 21.3 or 21.5. In other words, the measurement recorded as 21.4 inches may range anywhere from 21.35 to 21.45, for any measurement within this interval on our yardstick would be written down as 21.4 inches. The maximum possible error in such a measurement (assuming the half-tenth marks—dotted lines in Figure 2–1—to be fixed precisely) is ±.05 inch. That is, we *could be* as much as five hundredths of an inch off in either direction.

Now in considering our measurement of 21.4 inches, how do we decide which ones of its three digits are significant? Well, we are sure that the carriage is at least 20 inches long, and since there are two more digits to the right of 2, the 2 indicates that the carriage length corresponds to *at least* 200 tenths of an inch. Similarly, we will readily agree that the carriage is at least 210 tenths of an inch in length, and thus that the 1 is significant. Finally, from our discussion of the meaning of the measurement 21.4, we know the limits (21.35 and 21.45) within which the .4 is accurate. Thus all of the digits or figures in our measurement are significant. The

[1] The discussion to follow will assume that our measuring instruments are calibrated in units subdivided by integral powers of 10, that is, the units are subdivided into tenths, hundredths, thousandths, and so on.

length of the carriage, then, corresponds to 214 tenths of an inch, or (as we ordinarily write) 21.4 inches.

The last significant digit in a measurement will always be accurate only within certain limits. This "fuzziness" gives rise to errors in our answers when we compute with approximate numbers.

HOW TO RECOGNIZE SIGNIFICANT AND NONSIGNIFICANT DIGITS

In general, digits other than zero are always significant. Zeros are sometimes significant and sometimes not. Thus, the only digit we have to worry about is zero; and zero means nothing, so really we have nothing to worry about!

Let us think of any measurement as having "beginning digits" on the extreme left and "ending digits" on the extreme right. Then adjacent ending zeros which are to the right of the decimal point are always significant, as in the numbers 134.00, 134.0, or 15.60. It is readily seen, incidentally, that the measurements written as 134.0 and 134.00 are not the same if we observe that 134.0 means a measurement between 133.95 and 134.05, whereas 134.00 represents a measurement falling between 133.995 and 134.005.

Zeros which are "surrounded" by larger digits, as in the numbers 120.01, 13.04, and 10.2, are always significant.

Adjacent beginning zeros which are to the right of the decimal point are never significant. Such a case is the number .000374 or the number .012. The student should have little trouble convincing himself that such zeros are not significant if he reviews our definition of significant digits. Using the notation of fractions may also help, for example, thinking of .012 as 12/1000. However, the student should not assume that nonsignificant zeros are so unimportant that they can be neglected. They must be indicated so that the decimal point will be properly located.

Adjacent ending zeros which are to the left of the decimal point, as in 3200, may or may not be significant. The uncertainty arises because of the fact that a number such as 3200 may represent a measurement to the nearest 100, to the nearest 10, or to the nearest unit. If stated to the nearest 100, 3200 would represent a range extending from 3150 to 3250 and neither zero would be significant. But if stated to the nearest 10, 3200 would represent a value somewhere between 3195 and 3205, and the zero adjacent to the 2 would be significant. The remaining case is obvious.

To avoid confusion, it is wise to indicate nonsignificant zeros by using words if possible. In our example, 3200 should be stated as "32 hundred" when both of the zeros are not significant. However, we are at a loss for words which would satisfactorily express 3200 when only the last zero is not significant; it seems unlikely that "320 ten" would gain wide acceptance.

In general, we may avoid confusion arising from nonsignificant zeros by adopting *standard notation,* using integral powers of 10. In this notation 3200 with neither zero significant would be stated as 3.2×10^3 and 3200 with both zeros significant would be stated as 3.200×10^3. The measurement .000374 would appear as 3.74×10^{-4}. The rule underlying this system tells us to write the significant digits in our measurement with one digit to the left of the decimal point and then to write the factor (expressed as a power of 10) required to shift the decimal point to its proper place.

EXACT NUMBERS; APPROXIMATIONS ARISING FROM COUNTS

We have said that measurements are approximations and that the numbers representing them are approximate numbers. But frequently in statistical work we find numbers which are called exact. These numbers arise most often, perhaps, from counts of persons or other things occurring in units which are not logically divisible. Such counts, of course, are involved when we observe qualitative characteristics. For instance, when we say that there are 24 juniors in a class, we do not mean that there are between 23.5 and 24.5 juniors; we mean *exactly* 24. Now, exact numbers are "infinitely significant." That is, we can think of the 24 just mentioned as having an indefinitely large number of significant zeros following the decimal point. However, we must recognize the fact that counts which are stated ("rounded back") to the nearest 10 or 100 or 1000 units are approximate. When, for example, we say the population of Denver is 416 thousand, we mean the population of Denver is somewhere between 415,500 and 416,500. Thus counting as well as measuring yields approximations when the count is in terms of a multiple (greater than 1) of units. Such a multiple may be called the "scale segment of count."

ROUNDING: RULE FOR PRODUCTS OR QUOTIENTS

Let us now consider the problem of how to round answers resulting from computations with approximate numbers. We shall consider first the case of products or quotients. Suppose that the statistical laboratory is 30.5 feet long and 21 feet wide, the first of these measurements being taken to the nearest tenth of a foot and the second to the nearest foot. The product of these two numbers represents the laboratory floor area in square feet. How many significant digits should this product contain? Some readers may be willing to state the area figure as 640.5 square feet. But we know that the figure 30.5 signifies a measurement between 30.45 and 30.55, and that the figure 21 represents a measurement somewhere between 20.5 and 21.5. Thus the product of the two given figures *could* represent an area as small as $30.45 \times 20.5 = 624.225$ or as large as $30.55 \times 21.5 = 656.825$ square feet. In comparing these two results we note that only the digit on the extreme left (6) is the same in both products. We cannot be absolutely sure of the value of the digit following immediately after this 6, but it is subject to less variation than the remaining portion of the product. In view of these facts, it appears reasonable that we round our product to two significant digits; it should be stated as 640 square feet (with the zero being not significant) instead of 640.5 square feet. Quotients should be rounded in a similar fashion.

We may avoid the retention of digits representing questionable accuracy by observing the following general rule for rounding products or quotients:

Round a product or quotient to the same number of significant digits as contained in that one of the given figures (multiplier, multiplicand, dividend, or divisor) having the fewer or fewest significant digits.

To illustrate the application of this rule, suppose we have the following computation to perform. (All figures are approximate numbers.)

$$\frac{1.96 \times 45.1}{3.0} = 29.4653 \text{ or } 29$$

From the three numbers lying to the left of the equal sign, we pick out the one having the fewest significant digits. The selected number is 3.0. Since this number has two significant digits, we round our answer to two significant digits. Counting from the extreme left, we find that the second significant digit is in the units place. Thus the answer properly rounded is 29.

To see more clearly why the rule works, let us take a simple example involving only the multiplication of two approximate numbers: 512×43. According to the rule, the answer should be rounded to two significant digits. Now let us do the computation by the pencil and paper method:

$$5\,12 \text{ (Top figure)}$$
$$43 \text{ (Bottom figure)}$$

$$1\,536 \text{ (First row)}$$
$$204\,8 \text{ (Second row)}$$

$$22016$$

The answer properly rounded is 22,000, with the zeros being not significant. To get the answer, we begin multiplying by taking 3×2. From our knowledge of the measurement process, we know that both 3 and 2 contain an error. Thus it is wise to assume that their product (6 in the first row) will be in error. We continue multiplying by 3 to form the entire first row, but because of the error in the 3, each digit (except the 1) in the first row will be in error. (The margin of error in the 3 is not sufficiently large to alter the 1 in the first row.) To form the second row, we begin by multiplying 4×2. The 4 contains no error but the 2 does, so 8 in the second row will probably be in error. However, the other digits in the second row will *not* be in error. All digits not in error have been enclosed by straight lines in the computational scheme.

Now, in adding the two rows of digits to get the final answer, we assume (as above) that the 6 will be in error. Errors are very probably present in the 0 and the 1. However, the final 2 (extreme left) in the answer is not in error, and the digit next to it (also 2) is likely to be only slightly in error, so our rule is justified.

Now, had the bottom figure in the example contained three digits, we would have formed three rows in multiplying, and very probably the first two digits on the extreme left in the answer would have been without error; also, the third digit from the left would have had only a small error. Thus, in that case, rounding to three significant digits (as required by the rule) would have been justified. In general, if the figure containing the fewer significant digits is thought of as the bottom figure, the pencil and paper method readily reveals a pattern demonstrating the reasonableness of the rounding rule for any multiplication problem. The student will, we hope, be able to satisfy himself that the product-quotient rounding rule is appropriate for division problems also.

PRECAUTIONS

In order to avoid a common pitfall, the student should remember that in rounding to a given place, we are usually governed only by the digit in the next place to the right. For example, in rounding 29.4653 to two significant digits, we are rounding to the units place, which is occupied by 9. Rounding of the 9 is governed by 4, the next digit to the right. Since this digit is less than 5, we leave the 9 alone. Had the digit following 9 been greater than 5, we would have added 1 to the 9. Only if the digit following the 9 had been 5, would we have paid attention to the remaining digits. Then if any of these remaining digits had been greater than 0, we would have rounded up, that is, added 1 to the 9. If all digits to the right of the 5 had been zero, we would have had the general borderline case, which is discussed on page 19.

The above precaution applies to all cases of rounding, regardless of the rule being applied, and it will enable us to avoid the common mistake of rounding by the "hop, skip, and jump" system, whereby one starts at the digit farthest to the right and rounds back to the left one place at a time.

One other precaution is in order. Note that a process of multiplication or division involving an exact number and an approximate number yields an answer that should always be rounded to the number of significant digits contained in the approximate number. Recall that exact numbers contain an indefinitely large number of significant zeros, even though the zeros are unwritten.

ROUNDING: RULE FOR SUMS OR DIFFERENCES

We have yet to develop a rule of rounding for sums or differences of approximate numbers. Suppose we wish to add the following column of numbers, all of which represent measurements:

No.		Maximum possible error in each number
250.	(zero significant)	±.5
12.36		±.005
23.4		±.05
285.76		±.555

The tabulation of the amounts of error in the numbers added indicates that the error in the sum is equal to the sum of the errors in the numbers added. We can readily see that the (maximum possible) error in the sum ($\pm.555$) is enough to throw our answer off in every place to the right of the decimal point and very probably in the units place as well.

Taking into account the maximum possible errors in each of the numbers added, we may write a column of their minimum values and a column of their maximum values, as follows:

Minimum values	Maximum values
249.5	250.5
12.355	12.365
23.35	23.45
285.205	286.315

We notice that in both of the sums the 2 and the 8 do not change, but that a slight divergence does begin in the next digit thereafter. Our answer properly rounded would be 286. Similar considerations apply to the case of subtraction.

Before stating a rule for rounding sums and differences, let us define the term "degree of accuracy" as the size of scale segment indicated by the "place" of the last significant digit in an approximate number. For example, the degree of accuracy of 20.1 is a tenth and the degree of accuracy of 150 (zero not significant) is "a ten." We now state the rule as follows:

To round a sum or difference, find the least accurate number in the computation and locate the place indicating its degree of accuracy. Round the answer to this same place.

To illustrate the application of the rule, suppose we are adding the following column of measurements:

$$4.053$$
$$37.2$$
$$6.54$$
$$1.36$$
$$\overline{49.153}$$

The number 37.2 is the least accurate of all numbers in the column. Its degree of accuracy is indicated by the tenths place.

Therefore, the sum should be rounded to the nearest tenth to appear as 49.2.

INTERMEDIATE CALCULATIONS

In the case of a computation that involves a great many different operations, it is advisable to determine in advance by tracing through the various steps how the final answer should be rounded. Then, at each stage of the actual computation at least two more digits should be carried in the computing machine than would have been indicated by the rounding rule at that stage. The final answer should be rounded back to the point determined in advance of computation.

ROUNDING: GENERAL BORDERLINE CASE

If the number we are rounding (be it product, quotient, sum, or difference) is, say, 456.75 and we wish to round to the nearest tenth, the properly rounded result would be 456.8. On the other hand, if we wished to round 456.65 to the nearest tenth, the correct result would be 456.6. These borderline cases occur only where the digit 5 follows immediately after the digit in the place to which we are rounding and where there are no digits or only zeros following the 5. The rule to apply in such cases is sometimes called the "nearest-even" rule, according to which we round to the nearest even digit (in the place immediately preceding the 5). Some students years ago learned to state the rule as follows, "If the digit preceding the five is odd, round up; if it is even, drop the 5."

DUBIOUS DIGITS

The discussion of measurement and the rules of rounding we have developed should serve as guides in helping the student avoid being duped by dubious digits, that is, digits that appear to be significant but really are not. Final answers containing a great many such digits may appear impressive and seem to represent a study carried out with meticulous care, but the dubious digits merely represent the extent to which the investigator is deceiving himself—and perhaps others as well. Above all, the student should bear in mind that no amount of statistical analysis or mathematical manipulation will put more accuracy into final answers than there was in the raw data. Data stated to the nearest thousand dollars do not yield results accurate to the nearest cent.

CONTINUOUS VARIABLE: MODEL FOR MEASUREMENT DATA

At the beginning of this chapter, the student will recall, we distinguished between measurement data and attribute data. Measurement data in their raw form are simply figures representing the *amount* of height, weight, income received, rent paid, or some other characteristic associated with each of several elements.

Due to the nature of a measurable characteristic, measurement data are often said to be values of a continuous variable. A "variable" is simply a symbol, say, x, which may take on any of the values in a specified set. For example, we could let the variable x represent the height measurements of a sample of college students. Now a *continuous* variable can take on *any* value within a given *range*. Thus, if the college students ranged in height from 62 inches to 78 inches, *any* height, say, 65.00563 inches, between these two values would be a permissible value of x. Of course, we don't ordinarily measure height out to 5 decimal places, but theoretically we could, and thus a continuous variable is an appropriate theoretical model for a measurable characteristic. In statistical parlance, the term *variable* is often applied to the characteristic itself as well as the symbol representing it. Thus we speak of such variables as price, quantity, and time.

DISCRETE VARIABLE: MODEL FOR ATTRIBUTE DATA

In contrast with measurement data, attribute data in their raw form indicate the *numbers* of elements possessing a given non-measurable, qualitative characteristic or the *number* of instances of a given attribute associated with some element. To give an example of the latter case, if we are counting the number x of defects per product in a sample of carburetors, the values of x can be only positive whole numbers or zero: that is, values lying between two successive positive integers are not allowed. The possible range of x is 0 to d, where d is the total number of defects that have been defined by the production control engineers. If a carburetor has no defects, it is given the value 0; if it has one defect, it is given the value 1, and so on. The largest value that could be assigned a carburetor is d.

It is interesting to note that though we may treat them otherwise, *all* of the data which we meet in practical problems are in fact discrete because of the limits of accuracy of our measuring instruments. This means that if our instruments allow us to measure only to the nearest pound, we are going to have data which vary in jumps of a pound or whole multiples of a pound, but not less than a pound.

SIMPLE RATIOS AND PERCENTAGES

Perhaps the simplest computation that can be made from a set of raw data—aside from summing it—is a ratio. A simple ratio is a device for making a comparison between two quantities. These quantities may involve measurement data, attribute data, or a combination of both. The ratio of a company's net profit to its sales and the ratio of the number of unemployed persons to total number of persons in the labor force are two very common ratios in business and economic statistics. Ratios are expressed as percentages merely by shifting the decimal point two places to the right, or to put it another way, by multiplying the ratio by 100.

The comparison embodied in a ratio is the result of a process of division and is subject, in general, to two interpretations. The first interpretation treats both the quantities as aggregates or "lump sums." The second interpretation involves the idea of an average called the arithmetic mean.

Let us begin with the first interpretation. Take, for example, any two quantities, a and b, which we wish to compare. If we wish b to serve as the basis of comparison, b is placed in the denominator and we form the ratio of a to b (a/b). If a is larger than b, the ratio is greater than 1 and tells us how many times larger a is than b. If a is smaller than b, the ratio is less than 1 and tells us what proportion or fraction a is of b. If a is equal to b, the ratio, of course, is equal to 1.

Under this first interpretation, it is important to know the value of b, the denominator of the ratio. To illustrate, an advertisement extolling the merits of a stomach tablet claims that the product "takes care of twice as much stomach acid." The question that immediately comes to mind—if we are rash enough to assume we know what "takes care of" means—is "twice as much as what?" The answer is "twice as much as some value, b, which we don't know." Maybe b is only .00001 ml. of acid. (The strength of the acid is of course unknown.) Maybe it is much larger. Maybe "twice as much" is significant. Maybe not. The potential customer's imagination supplies the value of b.

To take another example, if we learned that 25% of the machinists in the Ajax Metal Works Company died of industrial accidents in 1957, we might be unduly outraged until we learned that there was a total of only four machinists working for the company in that year.

Let us now examine the ratio, a/b, under the second interpretation. In this view, the numerator of the ratio (a) is thought of as being divided into b equal parts. In other words, the ratio tells us the average (or mean) amount of a per unit of b.

The ratio of net profits to sales of a business enterprise is subject to both of the interpretations we have discussed above. Say, for instance, that the ratio of net profits (after taxes) to sales for the Blitz Company was .035 or 3.5% in 1956. This means that the aggregate of net profit amounted to 35 thousandths of the total dollar volume of sales. Or, using the second interpretation, we may say that for each dollar of sales, 35 thousandths of a dollar (3.5 cents) of net profit was made by the company.

As a rule, the information conveyed by a ratio is limited. In particular one net profit ratio is not sufficient to convey a complete picture of the profit position of a business enterprise. The Blitz Company, although it is making only 3.5% on sales, may be making 15% on invested capital. Also, the Blitz rate of profit (in either form) may or may not compare favorably with last year's rate, and it may or may not compare favorably with the profit rates of comparable firms.

This example, incidentally, also points up the necessity for care in defining the basic concepts relating to the numerator and denominator of a ratio. The numerator of the profit ratio is *accounting* net profit *after taxes*. Net profit before taxes would lead to a higher rate, and profit as defined by an economist might include portions of executive salaries and other items that are ordinarily treated as business expenses by accountants.

The ratio of annual domestic airline fatalities to annual domestic revenue miles flown is a ratio rendered meaningful under the second interpretation. Here, incidentally, the numerator is so small compared to the denominator that we take 1,000,000 revenue miles as our unit of division. That is, we divide the denominator by 1,000,000 before computing the ratio. This ratio was .289 for United States domestic airlines in 1955. It represents the average (or mean) number of fatalities per million revenue miles.   In 1955 there were 179 domestic airline fatalities in revenue operations and the number of revenue miles flown was 619,796 thousand.   The computation of the ratio, then, is as follows: [2]

$$\frac{179}{619.796} = .289$$

In this particular example, the ratio is very helpful in safeguarding us from drawing unwarranted inferences when we are making comparisons over time.   If, for instance, we were comparing the *number* of domestic airline fatalities in 1934 with the number in 1955, we would find that there were only 29 in 1934 but 179 in 1955. We might be tempted to make the hasty inference that airlines were less safe in 1955 than in 1934.   However, after computing the ratio of airline fatalities to millions of revenue miles flown for 1934, we find that the ratio is .70, which is much higher than the 1955 ratio of .289.[3]

Vital statistics are often expressed in ratios similar to the airline fatalities ratio.   Thus we find death rates expressed as so many deaths in a given year per thousand persons in the population.

PERCENTAGE INCREASE AND DECREASE

We read in the *New York Times* for June 12, 1957, that the May, 1957, volume of sales for department and chain stores has risen 6.2% over the May, 1956, figure.   How was the 6.2% computed? We find that the *New York Times* has conducted a sample survey. The estimated volume of sales for the stores covered by the survey was $1422 million in May, 1957, and $1339 million in May, 1956. The difference between these figures is $83 million, which is the *absolute* increase.   This figure is expressed as a proportion or percentage of the 1956 figure to give the *relative* increase in sales.   We may summarize the computation as follows:

May, 1957   May, 1956

$$\frac{1422 - 1339}{1339} = .062 \text{ or } 6.2\%$$

May, 1956

---

[2] Data from U.S. Bureau of the Census, *Statistical Abstract of the United States: 1956*, 77th ed. (Washington, D.C., U.S. Government Printing Office, 1956), p. 576.
[3] *Ibid.*

An alternative computation would be:

$$\frac{1422 - 1339}{1339} = \frac{1422}{1339} - \frac{1339}{1339} = \frac{1422}{1339} - 1 = 1.062 - 1 = .062 \text{ or } 6.2\%$$

By noting the last two steps, the reader can see how the second method would save considerable time compared to the first method.

Computations are similar for a percentage decrease except that the earlier figure will be larger than the later figure. For example, the farm population in the United States decreased from 32.0 million persons in 1920 to 22.2 million in 1955.[4] The percentage decrease is computed as follows:

$$\frac{\overset{1920}{\diagdown}\ 32.0 - 22.2\ \overset{1955}{\diagup}}{\underset{\substack{|\\1920}}{32.0}} = .31 \text{ or } 31\%$$

An alternative computation would be:

$$\frac{32.0 - 22.2}{32.0} = \frac{32.0}{32.0} - \frac{22.2}{32.0} = 1 - .69 = .31 \text{ or } 31\%$$

The latter computation is more convenient, especially on a desk calculator. It is carried out by a method sometimes called "negative division." By dividing 22.2/32.0 "negatively" we get one minus the quotient that would result from ordinary division, that is, 1 − .69 or .31.

Note that in computing both percentage increase and percentage decrease, the figure occurring earlier in time serves as the denominator of the ratio.

In business and economic statistics, percentage increases and decreases are often stated so that two types of comparisons over time can be made. Let us refer to the above example of department and chain store sales. One comparison given was the May, 1957, figure as compared to the May, 1956, figure. Also, in such cases, one would frequently find a comparison of the May, 1957, sales with those of April, 1957. Thus, percentage changes from a comparable period occurring one year earlier as well as percentage changes from the immediately preceding period are usually given.

[4] *Ibid.* Table No. **762**, p. **618.**

AVERAGING RATIOS AND PERCENTAGES

Perhaps since his eighth grade arithmetic classes, the student has heard the oft-repeated rule: "Never average a group of ratios unless they all have the same base." We may revise this rule to read: "Never average a group of ratios without weighting them properly." In the event that all of the ratios had the same denominator (or base), each would have the same weight in the computation of the average. But when denominators are different, each ratio must be multiplied by its denominator, or a number proportional thereto, in order that it will have the proper weight.

Suppose we have tabulated three ratios which we desire to average. Each ratio represents the proportion of unemployed persons who were unemployed 4 weeks or less in the given year. The numerators of the ratios are given in column (3) of Table 2–1 and the denominators in column (4).[5] Note that column (5) is merely a repetition of column (4), that is, the denominators are the weighting factors. Again, in order to compute the average, we must know what the denominators of the ratios are, or we must have a set of weights which are proportional to the denominators.

TABLE 2–1

Example of Averaging Ratios

Year	Ratio	Persons unemployed four weeks or less (millions)	Persons unemployed (millions)	Weighting factor	Ratio × weighting factor
(1)	(2)	(3)	(4)	(5)	(6)
1950	.417	1.31	3.14	3.14	1.31
1951	.532	1.00	1.88	1.88	1.00
1952	.557	.93	1.67	1.67	.93
	1.506	3.24	6.69	6.69	3.24

The computation of the weighted average (or weighted arithmetic mean) of the ratios is made as follows:

$$\frac{.417 \times 3.14 + .532 \times 1.88 + .557 \times 1.67}{3.14 + 1.88 + 1.67} = \frac{3.2397}{6.69} = .484$$

[5] Basic data from *Economic Report of the President* (Washington, D.C., U.S. Government Printing Office, 1957), Table E-20, p. 144.

By comparing column (3) with column (6) in the table, we can see that the process of weighting yields the numerators used in computing the ratios in the first place. In effect, the weighted average allows us to get the ratio for all three years combined, that is, the sum of the numerators divided by the sum of the denominators.

If we had made the mistake of assigning equal weights to all of the ratios, our average would have been computed by summing the ratios and dividing this sum by 3. That is, each ratio would have been given a weight of 1. The result would have been .502 = 1.506/3, which is quite different from the properly computed result.

In a later chapter we will discuss certain other types of averages used for combining ratios or rates of change.

RATIOS AND DECISIONS

Ratios and percentages are important elements in the making of many business decisions. Let us take a few highly simplified examples.

Creditors make extensive use of ratios in determining whether or not to grant loans. Suppose, for example, that a savings and loan association is considering loan applications for the purchase of houses in the $18,500-to-$22,500 range. Past experience has shown the association's credit committee that for houses in this price range it is unwise to act favorably on a loan application unless the applicant's annual income is at least $\frac{1}{3}$ of the price of the house.

Ratios are important to insurance companies as an element in the determination of premiums. If a company has 1500 straight life policies of $1000 each on persons aged 50 at the beginning of 1959 and it is known that 1.4% of persons aged 50 die before reaching the age of 51, then $21,000, that is, .014 × 1500 × $1000, are likely to be paid out in claims during 1959. Premiums must be sufficient to cover such claims plus costs of administration.

Real-estate firms make use of ratios in deciding whether or not to construct new apartment buildings. In particular, they pay a good bit of attention to the vacancy ratio, that is, the ratio of the number of vacant apartments to the total number of apartments. If the vacancy ratio is 5% or less in a given area, the apartment will probably be built, but if the ratio is greater than 5%, the new structure may very well be postponed.

SUMMARY

Essentially, statistical observation involves measuring and counting. Recorded observations and computations relating to measurable characteristics are called measurement data, whereas recorded observations and computations relating to nonmeasurable characteristics are called attribute data.

Significant digits are those digits in a recorded measurement (or other approximation) which tell us how many standard scale segments correspond to the characteristic we are measuring or counting. In general, digits other than zero are significant, while zeros are sometimes significant and sometimes not. Examples of the various cases of significant and nonsignificant zeros were given. There are two particularly important rules of rounding, one relating to products or quotients and the other to sums or differences.

A continuous variable serves as a model for measurement data. A discontinuous or discrete variable serves as a model for attribute data.

Simple ratios and percentages are subject to two basic interpretations, one involving the comparison of aggregates and the other the idea of an average. Often absolute as well as relative figures are necessary in order to give a complete picture of the situation we seek to describe. In some cases more than one ratio or other type of information may be necessary to complete the picture. When the denominator of a ratio is extremely large compared to the numerator, this denominator may be divided by 1,000,000 or 1000 or some other integral power of 10 before the ratio is formed. Such cases arise frequently in the field of vital statistics.

Percentage increases and decreases are very commonly used to show certain comparisons in business and economic statistics. These comparisons concern observations of like kind made at two or more different points in time.

In finding the mean of several ratios, we may assign a weight of 1 to each ratio only if the bases or denominators of all the ratios are equal. Otherwise, a weighted average (mean) must be computed. The weighting factors are the denominators of the ratios or numbers proportional thereto. The weighted ratios are summed and this sum is divided by the sum of the weights to get the required result.

TERMS TO PONDER

1. Measurement Data
2. Attribute Data
3. Significant Digit
4. Exact Number

5. Continuous Variable
6. Discrete Variable
7. Weighted Average

EXERCISES

1. It has been said that measurement includes counting and much more. Can you justify this statement?
2. A series of measurements taken to the nearest ½ ounce is recorded as follows:

$$16.5 \quad 15.0 \quad 17.5 \quad 15.0 \quad 14.5 \quad 17.0$$

Is there anything misleading about these figures? Why or why not?
3. Round each of the given figures as indicated. (Use words to indicate nonsignificant zeros.)
   a. $1,404,000 (round to two significant digits).
   b. 5285 ft. (round to the nearest 10 units).
   c. .00378 kg. (round to one significant digit).
   d. 170,981,000 (round to the nearest million units).
   e. 170,981,000 (round to four significant digits).
   f. 156.375 (round to the nearest hundredth of a unit).
4. Using the words "significant," "not significant," or "questionable," indicate the status of the zeros in each of the following approximate numbers:
   a. $369,000.
   b. 1.00320 tons.
   c. .00031 meters.
   d. 690.0 lbs.
5. Express each of the following approximate numbers in standard notation:
   a. 420 (zero not significant).
   b. .00678.
   c. 269.
   d. $694,500 (zeros not significant).
6. Perform the following subtractions and round the answers properly:
   a. 62,359 − 128.3 (both figures represent measurements).
   b. 21.00 − 19.4 (both figures represent measurements).
7. Multiply the following sets of numbers and round the products properly. (Numbers represent measurements unless a different designation is made.)
   a. 17.0×23.
   b. 72×5 (exact number).
   c. $58,976 \times .0000003$.
   d. $3.2 \times 10^3 \times 4.26 \times 10^2$.

8. Perform the following indicated divisions and round the answers properly. (Numbers represent measurements unless a different designation is made.)

   a. $\dfrac{2349}{602 \text{ (exact number)}}$.

   b. $\dfrac{.0056}{.003}$.

   c. $\dfrac{2.94 \times 10^2}{1.32 \times 10^3}$.

9. Perform the following computation and round the answer properly. (All figures are exact except 58.5.)

$$40 + \frac{58.5}{200} \times 5.$$

10. Figures relating to traffic safety in 1949 and 1954 are given below:

	1949	*1954*
Traffic deaths	31,701	36 thousand
Motor vehicles	44,029 thousand	58,065 thousand
Vehicle miles	42,268 ten millions	56,250 ten millions
U.S. population	149 million	161 million

Source: U.S. Bureau of the Census, *Statistical Abstract of the U.S.: 1956*, 77th ed. (Washington, D.C., U.S. Government Printing Office, 1956), pp. 10, 549.

   a. Compute the number of traffic deaths per 10,000 motor vehicles.
   b. Compute the number of traffic deaths per 100 million vehicle miles.
   c. How many deaths were there for each 100,000 persons in the population?
   d. If the ratios for 1949 are to be compared with those for 1954, how should they be rounded?

11. Mr. Green tells his competitor, Mr. Ferguson, that his (Green's) May sales volume had decreased 200% from his April sales volume. Ferguson says that this is nonsense, for the only conceivable interpretation of Mr. Green's statement would be that he had sold nothing in May and bought back everything that he had sold in April. Furthermore, Ferguson says that percentage decreases computed from positive numbers can never exceed 100%. Is Ferguson correct? If not, what could Green mean?

12. Selected items from the *1958 Annual Report of the General Electric Company* are given below:

	Millions of dollars
Net sales billed	$4120.8
Net earnings (after taxes)	242.9
Dividends declared	173.7
Capital invested	1617.3

a. How many dollars of net earnings were made per dollar of net sales billed?

b. What was the rate of return or profit (after taxes) on capital invested?

c. Dividends declared were what percentage of net earnings?

d. What multiple of capital invested were net sales billed?

13. The following data are taken from the *Annual Report of the Pacific Gas and Electric Company* for 1957:

Customers—by Departments

	December 31	
	1956	*1957*
Electric department	1,753,278	1,801,479
Gas department	1,468,779	1,517,823
Water department	25,194	24,590
Steam sales department	678	678
Totals	3,247,929	3,344,570

a. Water department customers made up what proportion of total customers in 1957?

b. Electric and gas department customers together made up what percentage of total customers in 1956?

c. Find the percentage decrease in steam sales department customers from 1956 to 1957.

d. Did the ratio of gas department customers to water department customers change between December 31, 1956, and December 31, 1957? If so, by how much?

e. How many water department customers were there for every 100,000 electric department customers on December 31, 1957?

14. In 1956, 34.6% of the gross income of the Radio Corporation of America was paid out for wages and salaries. In 1955 the comparable figure was 32.7%. These figures show an increase of 1.9 percentage points from 1955 to 1956. What was the *percentage increase* in these ratios? (Data from *Annual Report of the Radio Corporation of America* for 1956.)

15. In 1955, the Radio Corporation of America sold 228.6 million dollars' worth of goods and services to the U.S. Government. In 1956, this sales figure increased to 240.2 millions. However, the 1955 figure represented 21.7% of total sales, whereas the 1956 figure represented 21.3% of total sales. How could the absolute figures increase and the percentage figures decrease? (Source of data same as for Exercise 14.)

16. If the temperature in Fairbanks, Alaska, was 80° on July 21, 1958, and 20° below zero on January 21, 1959, would it be correct to say that the difference in the two temperatures represented a decline of 125%?

SELECTED REFERENCES

CROXTON, F. E., and COWDEN, D. J., *Applied General Statistics*, 2d ed. (Englewood Cliffs, N.J., Prentice-Hall, Inc., 1955), Ch. VII and Appendix T.

LEWIS, Edward E., *Methods of Statistical Analysis in Economics and Business* (Boston, Houghton Mifflin Co., 1953), Ch. I, Sec. 1.5; Ch. II, Sec. 2.2.

SCARBOROUGH, James B., *Numerical Mathematical Analysis*, 3d ed. (Baltimore, The Johns Hopkins Press, 1955), Ch. I.

WAUGH, Albert E., *Elements of Statistical Method*, 3d ed. (New York, McGraw-Hill Book Co., Inc., 1952), Ch. II.

3

A WORD

ABOUT SYMBOLS

BEFORE PROCEEDING FURTHER with statistical description, the student will need to know the meanings of a few fundamental symbols of statistical language. He is familiar already with the conventional symbols of elementary algebra. He knows, for example, that letters toward the end of the alphabet are commonly used to represent the variables of a function or the "unknowns" in an equation, and that letters toward the beginning of the alphabet are used to represent constants or coefficients.

SUMMATIONS

However, some students may not be familiar with the Greek capital letter, sigma (Σ). This symbol is not entirely unfamiliar to all college students, for it frequently appears in mathematics books or over the front doors of fraternity houses. As used in statistics, Σ is an operator, that is, it tells one to perform the operation of summing or adding. We may think of it as a sequence of plus signs condensed into a single symbol.

In order that we may demonstrate the use of summation symbols, suppose that we have a small sample of measurements (ages of 10 students, say) which can be conveniently handled without resorting to the use of a frequency distribution.[1] Let the sample be as follows:

$$19, 20, 25, 19, 20, 20, 32, 40, 21, 18$$

[1] Frequency distributions are the subject of Chapter 4.

The symbol x_i represents any one of the values. And the subscript i may be assigned any one of the whole numbers from 1 to 10 inclusive so as to designate a *particular* value of the variable x_i. For example, x_3 is the symbol for 25 because 25 is the third value in the list. The order in which the data are listed makes no difference as long as the order remains the same throughout a given problem or discussion.

Now suppose we wish to symbolize the operation of adding all ten of the values of x_i. The appropriate symbol is $\sum_{i=1}^{10} x_i$. It means "add the values of x_i from the first through the tenth." We know that we are to add all ten of the values in the sample, for directions to do just this are given by the symbols written above and below the sigma. The symbols "$i = 1$" and "10" indicate that x_1 is the first value in the sum and that all other values are to be added (x_2, x_3, x_4, $\cdots$ and so on) until we reach the tenth one. Quite obviously, $\sum_{i=1}^{10} x_i$ is just a shorthand expression for ($x_1 + x_2 + x_3 + \cdots + x_{10}$). For the data given, $\sum_{i=1}^{10} x_i = 19 + 20 + 25 + 19 + 20 + 20 + 32 + 40 + 21 + 18 = 234$.

The formula for the summation of *all* the values in a sample of *any* size is $\sum_{i=1}^{n} x_i$, where n represents the number of observations in the sample. In such cases, the "$i = 1$" and "n" are often omitted from the symbol Σ, and the subscript i may be omitted from x. Thus, $\Sigma x = \Sigma x_i = \sum_{i=1}^{n} x_i$. Each of these symbols may be read as "the summation of x sub i with i running from 1 to n." The subscript "$i = 1$" in the example is called the lower limit of the summation and the symbol above the sigma is called the upper limit of the summation. Partial summations are readily symbolized by means of the upper and lower limits. If we wish to add only the third, fourth, and fifth values, for example, we symbolize the operation by $\sum_{i=3}^{5} x_i$.

The symbol x_i is used not only to represent any one of the observations in a set of data but also to represent any one of the midpoints in a frequency distribution. This latter use of x_i will be illustrated in Chapter 4.

SUMMATION RULES

Now, suppose that we want to sum a constant instead of a group of varying quantities. We might use the symbol $\sum_{i=1}^{n} k$. We have not attached the subscript i to the k, for all k's are the same. But the upper and lower limits are necessary in order to tell us how many k's are to be included in the sum. Quite obviously, $\sum_{i=1}^{n} k = nk$. But let us demonstrate that this identity holds, so that we may get a little more practice in manipulating symbols.

By definition, $\sum_{i=1}^{n} k = (k + k + k + \cdots + k_n)$, letting k_n represent the nth k.

Factoring out k, we have, $\sum_{i=1}^{n} k = k(1 + 1 + 1 + \cdots + 1_n)$.

The quantity in parentheses equals n, which gives the required result:

$$\sum_{i=1}^{n} k = nk$$

We may call this result Summation Rule I: *Summing a constant from 1 to n is accomplished by multiplying the constant by n.* An application would be $2 + 2 + 2$ equals 3×2.

Next suppose that we wish to add n two-factor products, where each product consists of a constant times a value of a variable. We may use the following identity to accomplish our purpose: $\sum_{i=1}^{n} kx_i = k \sum_{i=1}^{n} x_i$. The validity of this formulation is often not obvious at first glance.

By definition, $\sum_{i=1}^{n} kx_i = (kx_1 + kx_2 + kx_3 + \cdots + kx_n)$.

Factoring out the k, we have: $\sum_{i=1}^{n} kx_i = k(x_1 + x_2 + \cdots + x_n)$.

But the quantity in parentheses equals $\sum_{i=1}^{n} x_i$.

Therefore, $\sum_{i=1}^{n} kx_i = k \sum_{i=1}^{n} x_i$.

This identity we shall call Summation Rule II: *Summing a group of n two-factor products, where each product consists of a*

*constant times a variable, is accomplished by multiplying the sum-
mation of the variable by the constant.*

The use of this rule in computations can be illustrated if we
assign values to x_i and k. Let $k = 2$ and let x_i take on the values
indicated in Table 3–1.

TABLE 3–1

Illustration of Summation Rule II

x_i	kx_i
2	$2 \times 2 = 4$
5	$2 \times 5 = 10$
4	$2 \times 4 = 8$
7	$2 \times 7 = 14$
18	36
Σx_i	Σkx_i

Σx_i is equal to 18. And $k \sum_{i=1}^{n} x_i = 2 \times 18 = 36$. And we see
also that $\sum_{i=1}^{n} kx_i = 36$.

This particular summation $\left(\sum_{i=1}^{n} kx_i \right)$ is much easier to do, therefore, if we follow the rule and add all of the x_i values first, then
multiply this sum by k.

Now let us combine the results of Summation Rules I and II
to prove a very useful general result, which we shall call Summation Rule III. Suppose we wish to add n algebraic quantities, each
quantity consisting of a variable plus another variable minus a
constant plus the product of another constant and a variable.
(After such a sentence, perhaps the reader will consider with an
open mind the statement that mathematical symbols are better
than words for expressing clearly and concisely certain statistical
formulations.) In symbols, this sum of quantities can be indicated
as follows:

$$\sum_{i=1}^{n} (x_i + y_i - k + bz_i)$$

We wish to show that this summation equals $\sum_{i=1}^{n} x_i + \sum_{i=1}^{n} y_i - nk$
$+ b \sum_{i=1}^{n} z_i$. The demonstration is as follows:

By definition, $\sum\limits_{i=1}^{n} (x_i + y_i - k + bz_i) = (x_1 + y_1 - k + bz_1)$
$+ (x_2 + y_2 - k + bz_2) + (x_3 + y_3 - k + bz_3) + \cdots + (x_n + y_n - k + bz_n)$.

After removing the parentheses, we may write:

$$\sum_{i=1}^{n} (x_i + y_i - k + bz_i) = x_1 + x_2 + x_3 + \cdots + x_n + y_1 + y_2 + y_3 + \cdots$$
$$+ y_n - k - k - k - \cdots - k_n + bz_1 + bz_2 + bz_3 + \cdots + bz_n$$

Collecting like terms and recalling Summation Rules I and II, we have:

$$\sum_{i=1}^{n} (x_i + y_i - k + bz_i) = \sum_{i=1}^{n} x_i + \sum_{i=1}^{n} y_i - nk + b \sum_{i=1}^{n} z_i$$

which is the result required. We shall call this result Summation Rule III: *Summing an algebraic quantity from 1 to n is accomplished by first summing the individual terms in the quantity and then adding these sums.*

Let us illustrate the use of this rule by means of a set of simple whole numbers (Table 3–2).

TABLE 3–2

Illustration of Summation Rule III

x_i		y_i	k		bz_i		
2	+	4	-2	+	3×5	=	19
5	+	3	-2	+	3×7	=	27
7	+	2	-2	+	3×4	=	19
4	+	9	-2	+	3×2	=	17
18	+	18	-8	+	3×18	=	82
Σx_i		Σy_i	nk		$b\Sigma z_i$		

A moment's study of Table 3–2 will reveal that all Summation Rule III tells us is that adding the algebraic quantities "across and then down" is the same as adding the quantities "down and then across." And we utilize Summation Rules I and II in certain of the "adding down" operations.

After becoming familiar with the three rules on summations, the student should satisfy himself that $\sum\limits_{i=1}^{n} x_i y_i$ does *not* equal

$\sum\limits_{i=1}^{n} x_i \sum\limits_{i=1}^{n} y_i$. [Hint: $\sum\limits_{i=1}^{n} x_i y_i = (x_1 y_1 + x_2 y_2 + x_3 y_3 + x_4 y_4 + \cdots +$

$x_n y_n)$, whereas $\sum\limits_{i=1}^{n} x_i \sum\limits_{i=1}^{n} y_i = \left[(x_1 + x_2 + x_3 + \cdots + x_n)(y_1 + y_2 + \right.$

$y_3 + \cdots + y_n).]$

We shall call this negative rule Summation Rule IV: *The summation of the product of two variables from 1 to n is not equal to the product of the sums of the variables.* Though some students may persist, wishing won't make it otherwise.

USE OF SYMBOLS TO DISTINGUISH STATISTICS FROM PARAMETERS

In addition to furnishing a convenient shorthand expression for indicating summations, abstract symbols can help us to distinguish between quantities relating to samples and quantities relating to populations.

A particular quantity that we may use for purposes of illustration is the arithmetic mean. The arithmetic mean is a type of average that we met briefly in Chapter 2 and which we shall take up in detail in Chapter 5. It is sufficient here to know that the symbol $\bar{x}$ denotes the arithmetic mean of a *sample*, whereas $\bar{X}$ or μ denotes the arithmetic mean of a *population*. The symbol μ is the lower case Greek letter mu. The rule requiring the use of lower case Roman letters to denote sample quantities and capital Roman or lower case Greek letters to indicate population quantities should be borne in mind, even though a few notable exceptions will develop later on.

The sample quantities such as $\bar{x}$ are called *statistics*—giving us a third meaning of the word—and the population quantities such as μ are called *parameters*. The term *parameter* conveys the notion of a certain amount of fixity, the parameter being fixed for a given population but subject to change from one population to another. Incidentally, if we wish to speak of a group of data in general without indicating whether it constitutes a sample or a population, we shall use the phrase *set of data*.

STANDARDIZATION OF SYMBOLS

If perchance the reader ever peruses more than one book on statistics, he will undoubtedly come to feel that there is a great need for standardizing statistical symbols according to one simple, logical system. But such a set of symbols will perhaps not develop in the near future, for it is quite difficult to standardize symbols in a body of subject matter changing as rapidly as statistics. New concepts require new formulations and new formulations require new sets of symbols.

Recently two trends in symbol standardization have become discernible. In the field of statistical quality control a formal attempt at standardization of symbols has been made, but in that case, past customs of the trade seem to have been the dominant influences. In the field of sample surveys, the use of small letters to denote statistics and capital letters to denote parameters has been quite consistently followed. As implied above, we shall, in general, follow sample survey notation in this book.

SUMMARY

Summation notation is an essential part of the statistical vocabulary. $\sum_{i=1}^{n} x_i$ or Σx_i means "add all the values of x_i from the first through the nth." In short, $\Sigma x_i = (x_1 + x_2 + x_3 + \cdots + x_n)$.

Partial summations may be indicated if necessary by means of the subscript and superscript on Σ.

There are four important elementary summation rules:

I. *Summing a constant from 1 to n is accomplished by multiplying the constant by n.*

II. *Summing a group of n two-factor products, where each product consists of a constant times a value of a variable, is accomplished by multiplying the constant by the summation of the variable.*

III. *Summing an algebraic quantity from 1 to n is accomplished by first summing the individual terms in the quantity and then adding these sums.*

IV. *The summation of the product of two variables from 1 to n is not equal to the product of the summations of the variables.*

Descriptive values which relate to samples are called *statistics*. Descriptive values relating to a population are called *parameters*. Lower case Roman letters are used to denote statistics and capital Roman or lower case Greek letters are used to denote parameters. No generally acceptable system of symbols has as yet been devised by statisticians. But within the field of statistical quality control a limited formal attempt at symbol standardization has been made.

TERMS TO PONDER

1. Summation
2. Statistics
3. Parameters

EXERCISES

1. Write $\sum_{i=1}^{n} k$ in a different form. If $n = 25$ and $k = 6$, evaluate the summation.
2. If $k = 3$ and x_i takes on the values 3, 9, 8, 7, 10, find $\Sigma k x_i$ and $k \Sigma x_i$.
3. Write $\Sigma(x_i - a)$ in a different form. The letter a represents a constant.
4. Write $\sum_{i=1}^{n} (x_i + y_i)$ in a different form. Use Summation Rule III.
5. Write the summation $\sum_{i=1}^{n} (x_i{}^2 - 2x_i\bar{x} + \bar{x}^2)$ in a different form. The figure 2 and $\bar{x}$ are both constants. Use Summation Rule III.
6. Explain the difference between $\Sigma x_i{}^2$ and $(\Sigma x_i)^2$. If x_i takes on the values 3, 9, 6, 4, 10, 1, compute both of the summations.

SELECTED REFERENCES

FREUND, John E., *Modern Elementary Statistics* (Englewood Cliffs, N.J., Prentice-Hall, Inc., 1952), Ch. I.

HANSEN, M. H., HURWITZ, W. N., and MADOW, W. G., *Sample Survey Methods and Theory* (New York, John Wiley and Sons, Inc., 1953), Vol. II, Ch. II, Sec. 2.

KENDALL, M. G., and BUCKLAND, W. R., *A Dictionary of Statistical Terms* (New York, Hafner Publishing Company, 1957).

KENNEY, J. F., *Mathematics of Statistics*, 2d ed. (New York, D. Van Nostrand, Inc., 1947), Part I, Ch. III, Sec. 2.

WALKER, Helen M., *Mathematics Essential for Elementary Statistics*, rev. ed. (New York, Holt, Rinehart and Winston, Inc., 1951), Ch. VII.

4

FREQUENCY

DISTRIBUTIONS

THE NATURE OF A FREQUENCY DISTRIBUTION

IF WE HAVE SELECTED a large sample, say, 75 elements or more (or even if we have taken a complete census of a relatively *small* population), a frequency distribution will be a useful aid to us in describing our data. By using this device, we can condense or group our data and arrange them in an orderly scheme which reveals their pattern of variation.

To illustrate the use of a frequency distribution, suppose that from the population of all the male freshmen at Gonsocki College, we have selected a sample of 82 and weighed each of them. The 82 measurements rounded to the nearest pound are, let us say, as follows:

119	101	213	155	135	135	171	151	144
150	165	156	149	153	151	150	145	145
201	155	153	153	165	172	171	172	
150	136	139	143	143	141	131	129	
150	151	149	153	122	124	130	129	
180	183	186	192	191	185	151	150	
158	160	140	139	142	168	135	181	
169	129	132	152	158	149	161	162	
133	148	102	159	160	112	199	186	
152	153	154	155	156	157	142	143	

Leaving these data in their present form, we could not, even if we stared at them for an hour or so, learn much about the distribution or pattern of weights in our sample. We could, with a little effort, discover the smallest value in the sample and the largest value, but that is about all. In order to condense the data into a meaningful pattern, we must make use of the frequency distribution.

CONSTRUCTING A FREQUENCY DISTRIBUTION

The first step in grouping the data into a frequency distribution is to find the range of the data, which is nothing more than the highest value minus the lowest value. In our sample, we have $213 - 101 = 112$. Now we know that our data are scattered over an expanse of 112 pounds. But we do not know whether they are scattered evenly, and if they aren't we do not know where the points of concentration and sparseness are.

Thus our next step is to divide the range (or the approximate range) into a number of equal parts called class intervals or cells. We can picture the range as a straight line marked off in units of one pound. We want to divide this line into a series of intervals, each interval representing an equal number of pounds. If we then indicate how many of our measurements fall within each interval, we have constructed our frequency distribution, and the form of the distribution of the weights over the range becomes evident. But the important question which usually pops into the students' minds at this point is, "How many class intervals should we have in our distribution?"

There is no simple, straightforward answer to this question. The number of intervals we decide to use is arrived at quite arbitrarily. We do not want the data to be too highly condensed (all of the data sorted into only two or three intervals), nor do we want too little condensation (so many intervals that there are no more than one or two measurements in any one interval). It is desirable beyond these considerations to divide the range so that the interval size (or length) will be a whole multiple of the scale segment representing the degree of accuracy in our measurements. That is, if our measurements are stated (or rounded) to the nearest tenth of a unit, the cell length should be a whole number of tenths. The first interval must, of course, begin at a point low enough to include the smallest measurement in the sample. Any one of several starting points would satisfy this requirement. But the starting point must be chosen with care, for once the size of the interval is determined, the starting point of the first class interval determines the positions or locations of all the other intervals.

It appears that about eight class intervals would be satisfactory for the data we are working with. If we divide the range (112) into exactly 8 equal parts, each part (interval) will be 14 units in length. For convenience, let us choose an interval of 15 units in length and start the first interval at 95. The data are then sorted into their appropriate class intervals by means of the following *tally sheet* (Table 4–1):

TABLE 4–1

Tally Sheet.   Weights of Gonsocki Freshmen

Class interval no. (i)	Class limits	Tally	Frequency (f_i)
1	95–109	//	2
2	110–124	////	4
3	125–139	Ⅳ Ⅳ ///	13
4	140–154	Ⅳ Ⅳ Ⅳ Ⅳ Ⅳ Ⅳ /	31
5	155–169	Ⅳ Ⅳ Ⅳ //	17
6	170–184	Ⅳ //	7
7	185–199	Ⅳ /	6
8	200–214	//	2
			82

The frequencies (f_i) are the sums of the tally marks for each given interval. The frequency (13) for the third interval tells us how frequently we found a student weighing between 125 and 139 pounds inclusive. The subscript i tells us which cell a particular frequency refers to. Thus, 17, the frequency of the fifth interval, is symbolized by f_5.

CLASS LIMITS AND CLASS BOUNDARIES

Class *limits* are approximate numbers used to indicate the length and locations of the various class intervals. In the case of the second interval in Table 4–1, the lower limit is 110 and the upper limit is 124. Note that limits are *inclusive,* that is, both a measurement equal to 110 and a measurement equal to 124 would be included in the interval labeled 110–124.

Class *boundaries* are exact numbers used to indicate the lengths and locations of the various class intervals. Boundaries, furthermore, are the precise points of division which separate a given interval from the interval lying immediately above and the interval lying immediately below. For the second interval in our distribution (Table 4–1) the lower boundary is 109.5 and the upper boundary is 124.5, with 109.5 lying exactly halfway between the limits 109 and 110, and with 124.5 similarly located between 124 and 125. Notice that the lower boundary for any interval is the same as the upper boundary for the next lower interval.

Here again a perennial question pops up. For example, if we have a measurement exactly equal to 124.5, in which interval does it belong, the second or the third? The reader is invited to search through our original raw data (p. 40) and find any value that ends in .5. The search is fruitless, for all our sample measurements have been rounded to the nearest pound. Thus there is no basis for such a question if class limits are stated to the same degree of accuracy as our original measurements. Class limits should always be so stated.

With the class intervals indicated by boundaries, our frequency distribution appears as follows (Table 4–2):

TABLE 4–2

**Weights of Gonsocki Freshmen;
Class Intervals Indicated by Boundaries**

Class interval no. (i)	Class boundaries	Frequency (f_i)
1	94.5 and 109.5	2
2	109.5 and 124.5	4
3	124.5 and 139.5	13
4	139.5 and 154.5	31
5	154.5 and 169.5	17
6	169.5 and 184.5	7
7	184.5 and 199.5	6
8	199.5 and 214.5	2
		—
		82

DIRECTED BOUNDARIES

There is still another method of indicating the size and location of intervals in a frequency distribution. This method employs the phrase "and under" to separate the boundaries. For want of a better term, we shall call such boundaries "directed boundaries." Suppose, for example, a frequency distribution in which the interval size is 10 units, the boundaries for the first few intervals being stated as follows:

20 and under 30

30 and under 40

40 and under 50

The boundaries of the second interval tell us that all the items it contains must be at least 30 and some amount (however small) less than 40. This means, then, that a value, 29.99, belongs in the first interval, and that a value of 40.0000001 belongs in the third. This type of boundary is especially appropriate for distributions of a variable such as age stated as of the *last* birthday. Taking the boundaries given, we see that anyone having passed his twentieth birthday but not his thirtieth would fall in the first interval. If we measure in this manner, a separate indication of limits is unnecessary. However, if we measure to the *nearest* unit instead of the *last* unit, we are ignoring the differences between the actual boundaries and the directed boundaries. Measuring age to the nearest unit (or birthday), we see that a person past his twentieth birthday and within ½ year of his twenty-first is taken as 21 years old, whereas he would be taken as 20 years old if he were less than ½ year beyond his twentieth birthday. Suppose that in grouping such ages, we are using directed boundaries with the first interval stated as "20 and under 30." Since we are measuring to the nearest unit, the actual or true boundaries would be 19.5 and 29.5. This is so because a person barely over 19½ years old would be recorded as 20 years of age; 20 would go in the interval "20 and under 30." Similarly, an age slightly over 29.5 would be rounded to 30 and go in the next interval, "30 and under 40."

Thus in using directed boundaries, when measurements are made to the *nearest* unit or segment, we have shifted the true boundaries half a scale segment "to the right." However, the error is relatively small, and becomes smaller as the size of scale segment decreases, so in practice we ignore it in favor of the convenience of the directed boundaries.

In order to reduce the chance of confusion between limits and boundaries, we shall observe the rule that limits are pairs of numbers separated by dashes and that boundaries are pairs of numbers separated by the word *and* or the words *and under*.

THE SIZE OF THE CLASS INTERVAL; CLASS MIDPOINTS

The length or size of the class interval is symbolized by the letter c and measured by the difference between the upper and lower boundaries of any given interval. Thus in our frequency distribution of weights of college freshmen, we may subtract the lower boundary of the fourth interval (139.5) from the upper boundary (154.5) to get 15. For any distribution having intervals of equal size, the length of the interval is also given by the difference between any two successive lower boundaries or the difference between any two successive upper boundaries. Similarly, the length of the interval is given by the difference between any two successive lower *limits* or the difference between any two successive upper limits. Finally, the length of the interval is given by the difference between any two successive *midpoints*.

The midpoint of any class interval is the number lying halfway between the class boundaries. Thus we add the lower and upper boundaries of an interval and divide by 2 in order to find the midpoint of that interval. We find, accordingly, that the midpoint of the first class interval in the freshmen weight distribution is $\dfrac{94.5 + 109.5}{2} = \dfrac{204}{2} = 102$. Midpoints are given the symbol x_i, where the subscript i indicates the particular interval in which the midpoint is located. Thus x_3 is the midpoint of the third interval.

Midpoints are extremely important, for when computing various descriptive measures from a frequency distribution, we make the assumption that each value in a given interval is equal to the midpoint of that interval. For purposes of computation, therefore, we often present our distribution by listing only the class midpoints and their corresponding frequencies. For our sample of weights of college freshmen, we have:

x_i	f_i
102	2
117	4
132	13
147	31
162	17
177	7
192	6
207	2
	82

This assumption that each value in a given interval is equal to the midpoint of that interval should be kept in mind when one is deciding upon the size of the class interval and the starting point of the first interval, for we want the grouped data to conform to the assumption as closely as possible.

Incidentally, there exists an interesting special case in which limits cannot be stated. This situation occurs when the size of the interval is equal to the fraction or multiple of a unit representing the degree of accuracy in the data, that is, when the interval is equal to the "scale segment." For example, if we had a distribution of measurements stated to the nearest hundredth of a unit, and if the size of the interval were also a hundredth of a unit, boundaries could be stated but not limits. A hypothetical example of such a distribution follows:

x_i	f_i	Boundaries
.05	2	.045 and .055
.06	5	.055 and .065
.07	17	.065 and .075
.08	32	.075 and .085
.09	4	.085 and .095

We might say in a case of this kind that the limits of an interval have been squeezed from both sides to such an extent that they become equal to the midpoint.

FREQUENCY DISTRIBUTIONS OF ATTRIBUTE DATA

The frequency distribution of weights of Gonsocki freshmen was, of course, a distribution of measurement data. We often encounter certain forms of attribute data in sufficient numbers that "grouping" is quite helpful. Such data, of course, involve counts of people, defects, accidents, diseases, or other qualitative characteristics. In such distributions the counts are designated by x_i and the number of times each count occurs is given by f_i. There are no class limits or boundaries; we still know exactly the value of each of the original observations. An example of this type of distribution is given in Table 4–3.

TABLE 4–3

Distribution of Number of Defects in Eighty-five Assembled Carburetors

Defects (x_i)	Carburetors (f_i)
0	40
1	21
2	14
3	6
4	3
5	1
	85

UNEQUAL INTERVALS AND OPEN-END DISTRIBUTIONS

Some distributions containing data which vary over an extremely wide range have very small frequencies in many large portions of the range. An example is the family income distribution of the United States. If we grouped these incomes into a frequency distribution having a uniform class interval of $1000 in length, we would have to provide for an extremely large number of intervals, and the intervals for the higher incomes would have very small frequencies. The number of intervals required would, of itself, make it impossible to write down the distribution without the use of many sheets of paper taped together end-to-end. In this particular case we simply use larger intervals as we progress into the higher brackets of the income distribution. A recent family income distribution for the United States is given in Table 4–4.[1]

We could, of course, have used equal intervals of a size considerably larger than $1000, but the resulting distribution would have introduced a greater degree of condensation and thus greater approximation in the lower and middle income levels. Since most incomes are in the lower and middle levels, it is desirable to have relatively small intervals for grouping those portions of the distribution.

The family income distribution (Table 4–4) has not only unequal intervals but also open ends. An open-end distribution shows

[1] Adapted from U.S. Bureau of the Census, *Current Population Reports,* Consumer Income (Washington, D.C., U.S. Government Printing Office, April, 1958), Series P-60, No. 27, p. 1.

TABLE 4–4

**Number of Families by Family Income,
for the United States: 1956**

Family income	No. of families (millions)
Under $1000	2.9
$1000–$1999	3.9
$2000–$2999	4.4
$3000–$3999	5.4
$4000–$4999	6.4
$5000–$5999	6.0
$6000–$6999	4.2
$7000–$9999	6.7
$10,000–$14,999	2.6
$15,000 and over	.9
	43.4

no lower boundary or limit for the first interval or no upper boundary or limit for the last interval. Of course, we cannot determine the midpoints of such intervals. However, open-end distributions (as well as distributions with unequal intervals) are seldom used as a basis for computations. They are used most often to summarize data for presentation in statistical reports.

CUMULATIVE FREQUENCIES; RELATIVE FREQUENCIES

In presenting grouped data, we may wish to indicate the number of observations which are less than each of certain points in the distribution. If we take the upper class boundaries as such points and then for each such boundary write the number of items which are less than that boundary, we have cumulated our frequencies on a "less-than" basis. For example, in the distribution of the weights of 82 college freshmen, there are 2 values in the first interval; obviously these two measurements are both less than the upper boundary of the interval. There are 4 values in the second interval. Thus 2 + 4 or 6 values are less than the upper boundary of the second interval. (Six freshmen weigh less than 124.5 pounds.) We proceed in like fashion until we have cumulated the frequencies for all intervals in the distribution. The cumulative frequency opposite the last interval will, of course, be equal to n, for all the values are less than the upper boundary of the last interval.

It is possible also to cumulate the frequencies on a "more-than" basis. In this case, we take the lower boundaries as our reference points and indicate how many data are more than each such boundary.

Cumulative frequencies (symbolized by F_i) of the less-than type are given in the fourth column of the distribution of weights of college freshmen as shown in Table 4–5. This use of a capital letter to denote sample quantities is an important exception to the notation rules we have adopted.

TABLE 4–5

Weights of Gonsocki Freshmen.
Cumulative Frequencies; Relative Frequencies

Class interval no. (i)	Class boundaries	f_i	F_i	f_i/n	F_i/n
(1)	(2)	(3)	(4)	(5)	(6)
1	94.5 and 109.5	2	2	.0244	.0244
2	109.5 and 124.5	4	6	.0488	.0732
3	124.5 and 139.5	13	19	.1585	.2317
4	139.5 and 154.5	31	50	.3780	.6098
5	154.5 and 169.5	17	67	.2073	.8171
6	169.5 and 184.5	7	74	.0854	.9024
7	184.5 and 199.5	6	80	.0732	.9756
8	199.5 and 214.5	2	82	.0244	1.0000
		82			

Both the noncumulative frequencies (f_i) and the cumulative frequencies (F_i) can be expressed as proportions of the total number of items (n) in the distribution. These proportions have been computed for the distribution and are listed in the fifth and sixth columns of Table 4–5. Such proportions are called relative frequencies. They may, of course, be readily changed to percentages. Table 4–6 [2] is an example of a distribution with frequencies expressed as percentages.

[2] U.S. Bureau of the Census, *Statistical Abstract of the United States: 1958*, 79th ed. (Washington, D.C., U.S. Government Printing Office, 1958), Table No. 711, p. 559.

TABLE 4–6

**Age of Automobiles Owned
by Spending Units * (U.S., 1957)**

Age (years)	%
1 or less	14
2–3	24
4–7	40
More than 7	22

* A spending unit consists of a group of persons living together who pool their incomes.

GRAPHS OF FREQUENCY DISTRIBUTIONS; HISTOGRAM

In order to convey a vivid visual impression of the pattern of variation in a frequency distribution, we employ various graphical devices. First, let us consider the histogram. The histogram is nothing more than a modified form of bar chart. To construct such a graph, we use a layout consisting of two co-ordinate axes intersecting at a 90° angle. The horizontal axis is the scale for the characteristic under consideration (weight in our example), with the class boundaries or other appropriate figures laid off along its length. The vertical axis is the scale for the frequencies. The frequencies are represented by vertical bars of appropriate lengths, each bar being one class interval in width and centered over the midpoint of its corresponding interval. The zero point for the vertical scale must be shown in order to convey an accurate impression of the relative sizes of the bars.

The histogram of the weights of Gonsocki freshmen is shown in Figure 4–1.

Expressing the frequencies as proportions of n (or as percentages of n) does not alter the shape of the histogram. The only adjustment necessary is a change in the vertical scale and its heading so as to indicate the proportions or percentages.

We wish to emphasize that the frequency of a given class interval is represented by the *area* of its histogram bar. The area of any bar is found, of course, by multiplying its height by its width. If all the intervals of the distribution are of the same size, all bars will have equal widths and frequencies will be proportional to bar lengths as well as areas. But if we happen to have a distribution with unequal intervals, such would not be the case.

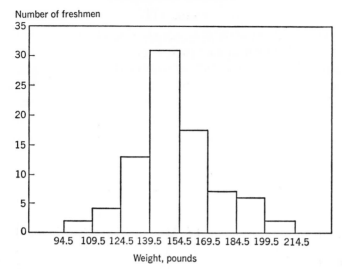

Number of freshmen

FIGURE 4–1. Histogram. Measurement Data. Weights of Gonsocki Freshmen

To illustrate, suppose we have a frequency distribution as follows:

Class limits	f_i	Area of histogram bar	Height of histogram bar
10–19	3	$3 \times 10 = 30$	3
20–29	6	$6 \times 10 = 60$	6
30–44	6	$4 \times 15 = 60$	4

Here the first two intervals both have a size of 10 units, but the third has a size of 15. Thus the bar of the third interval will be 1½ times as wide as the bar for the second interval. Now, since the second and third intervals have the same frequency, the areas of their histogram bars should be equal. The area of the second bar is 60 square units. Since the width of the third bar is 15 units, it will have to have a height of 4 units if its area is also to be 60 square units.

FREQUENCY POLYGON

Another form of graphical representation of the frequency distribution is the frequency polygon. The layout of this graph is similar to that of the histogram, and it may easily be drawn on the same axes as the histogram. The frequency polygon of the weights of Gonsocki freshmen (with the histogram sketched in dashed lines) is shown in Figure 4–2.

We recall from elementary geometry that a polygon is a closed plane figure bounded by straight lines, the term *polygon* meaning "many-sided." In a frequency polygon, the horizontal axis serves as one of these lines. The other lines are formed by connecting adjacent dots, the dots being located at the centers of the lines

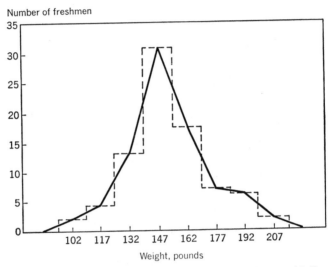

FIGURE 4–2. Frequency Polygon. Weights of Gonsocki Freshmen

forming the tops of the histogram bars. The dots standing above the midpoints of the first and last intervals do not, of course, touch the horizontal axis, so we must find a logical method of closing the polygon. We locate a point on the horizontal axis one class interval below the first midpoint and draw a line to there from the dot above the first midpoint. In a similar fashion, we draw to the horizontal axis at a point one class interval above the last midpoint in the distribution. Closing the frequency polygon in this manner is logical, for we can imagine an interval with a frequency of 0 lying immediately below the first interval and another interval with a frequency of 0 lying immediately above the last interval. It is, of course, not necessary to superimpose the frequency polygon on a histogram.

If we construct a "frequency polygon" of a cumulative frequency distribution, we will no longer have a closed plane figure, but the graph is, nevertheless, sometimes called a cumulative polygon. Another name for it is the *ogive*. In plotting the ogive of the less-than cumulative frequency distribution, we locate dots directly above the various upper boundaries. The vertical heights of the dots are determined, of course, by the cumulative frequencies. Joining the sequence of dots by straight lines completes the ogive. For the distribution of weights of Gonsocki freshmen (or for any distri-

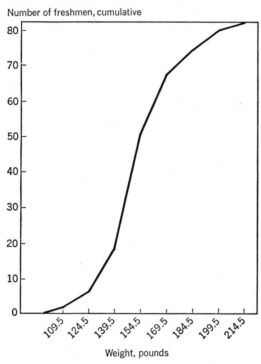

FIGURE 4–3. Cumulative Polygon (Less-Than). Weights of Gonsocki Freshmen

bution that is approximately bell-shaped), the ogive will look roughly like an S-curve. The ogive of the less-than cumulative frequency distribution of the Gonsocki freshmen is shown in Figure 4–3. The more-than cumulative distribution for this same sample of data would be shaped approximately like a reverse S, sloping from the upper left-hand corner of the graph to the lower right-hand corner.

We note that the largest of the cumulative frequencies in Figure 4–3 is 82 units on the vertical scale. If we erect another vertical scale of this length on the right-hand side of the graph and divide it into 100 equal segments, we can "box in" the cumulative polygon and read either cumulative frequencies as such (left-hand scale) or per cent cumulative frequencies (right-hand scale) from the same graph. The "boxed-in" ogive is shown in Figure 4–4.

A horizontal line is drawn across the graph in Figure 4–4 at the 50% level. This level, obviously, corresponds to a cumulative frequency of 41, and the point at which the line intersects the polygon indicates that 50% or 41 of the observations are less than

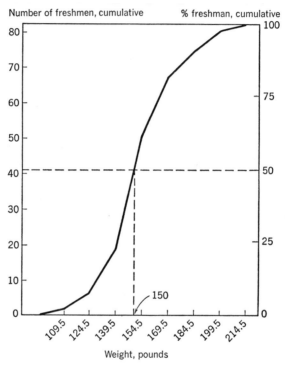

FIGURE 4–4. Cumulative Polygon (Less-Than). Weights of Gonsocki Freshmen

about 150. If 50% of the observations are less than 150, then 50% of them must be greater than 150. A value centered in a distribution in this fashion is known as the *median* of the distribution. By definition, there are as many items above the median as there are below it. Later on, we shall explain a nongraphical method of estimating the median of a frequency distribution.

Knowing that the median is the value which divides the observations into two equal groups, the student should estimate three values which divide the data into four equal groups. These three values are called the quartiles of the distribution. The second quartile is, of course, equal to the median. The first quartile (q_1) separates the lowest 25% (lowest quarter) of the items from the rest of the distribution. The third quartile (q_3) separates the highest 25% of the items from the rest of the distribution.

FREQUENCY CURVE

To understand the nature of a frequency curve, suppose we round off the tops of the bars in a histogram by bending the lines of the frequency polygon (superimposed) to conform to a given smooth curve. Now if we can imagine the intervals of the distribution becoming smaller, the bars of the histogram becoming narrower and narrower, and the total number of data getting larger and larger, we eventually have bars which approach a thickness of 0. The tops of these very thin bars would lie along the continuous frequency curve. Now the frequency of observations in any range or interval would be given by the area under the curve standing directly on top of that range. And if the frequencies are thought of as relative frequencies, their sum is 1 or 100%.

Sometimes we use a frequency curve to represent an indefinitely large population from which we are sampling. In such cases we may desire to "fit" the population curve to the frequency distribution of the sample. Standard methods of curve fitting and testing the "goodness of fit" are available to the statistician. A very important frequency curve called the *normal curve* is fitted to the distribution of freshmen weights in Figure 4–5.

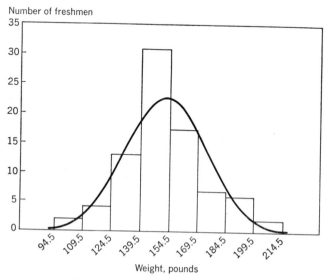

FIGURE 4–5. Normal Frequency Curve and Histogram. Weights of Gonsocki Freshmen

In modern statistics two types of frequency curves are particularly important, one of them corresponding to a distribution with relative frequencies and the other to a distribution having relative cumulative frequencies. A curve of the former type (for which a frequency polygon is an approximation) is said to represent a frequency function; and a curve of the latter type (for which an ogive is an approximation) is said to represent a cumulative frequency function. Both of these curves represent "ideal" or theoretical models which are realized more or less imperfectly in practice. We shall learn more about them when we take up the subject of probability distributions.

GRAPH OF A DISTRIBUTION OF ATTRIBUTE DATA

We might ask ourselves what kind of a graphical device we would employ to picture the distribution of attribute data given in Table 4–3. In this case we do not have data grouped in intervals; we have data equal to certain specified whole numbers only. Instead of using bars to represent frequencies, therefore, we use vertical lines. The first value in the distribution is *exactly* 0. The frequency of this value is 40. Thus, a vertical line 40 units long and standing directly above 0 represents the first frequency. Representing the frequencies of the other values in like fashion, we have Figure 4–6.

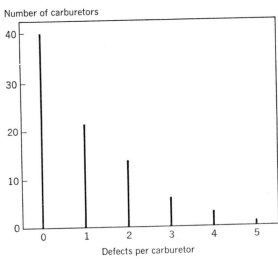

FIGURE 4–6. Histogram. Attribute Data. Carburetor Defects

A graph of the cumulative frequency distribution of carburetor defects is readily constructed if we first cumulate the frequencies as follows:

x_i	F_i
0	40
1	61
2	75
3	81
4	84
5	85

In this type of distribution, the frequencies are cumulated with reference to the x_i. Thus the F_i values tell us how many carburetors had a count of defects *equal to or less than* the corresponding x_i values. The graph of this cumulative frequency distribution is given in Figure 4–7.

Theoretical models of attribute data distributions are called

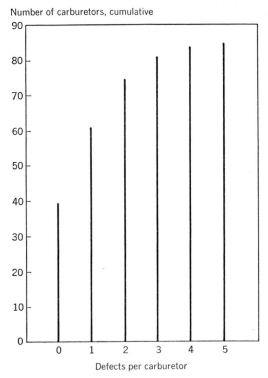

FIGURE 4–7. **Cumulative Graph (Less-Than). Carburetor Defects**

discontinuous frequency functions because of the "gaps" in the horizontal scale for which there are no frequencies.

SUMMARY

A frequency distribution is a device for condensing or grouping a relatively large set of data into a meaningful, manageable arrangement. To form the frequency distribution, we find the range of the observations, divide it into a number of class intervals or cells, and then sort the observations into the intervals by means of a tally sheet. The decision as to how many intervals we should have is essentially an arbitrary one, but we do want to avoid excessive grouping (too few intervals) or inadequate grouping (too many intervals). Factors of convenience influence the decision as do alternative locations of the class midpoints.

Class limits denote the size and locations of the intervals. They are approximate numbers stated to the same degree of accuracy as the original data. Class boundaries also denote the size and locations of the intervals. In addition, they indicate precise points of division between successive intervals. They are exact numbers.

Class intervals are sometimes denoted by directed boundaries. Whenever the interval size is an even number of units, in this case, the midpoint is a whole number.

Some frequency distributions have unequal intervals or open ends or both.

Frequency distributions may be used to group attribute data where one has counted the number of defects or other characteristics per object. An example is the number of defects per unit for a sample of several carburetors. The identity of the original observations is not lost in such a distribution.

Frequencies may be cumulated to show the number of observations in the distribution that are less than the various upper boundaries of the intervals. In the case of attribute data, cumulated frequencies tell us how many elements have a count equal to or less than 0 or some given whole number.

Graphical devices may be used to convey visual impressions of frequency distributions. The histogram, a form of bar chart, is used to represent a noncumulative distribution. Frequency polygons may be either of the cumulative or noncumulative form. A frequency curve may be fitted to a sample of data if it represents the population from which the sample was selected. In general, frequency curves are theoretical models in the form of continuous mathematical functions. The two types representing relative frequency distributions—noncumulative and cumulative—are of special importance in modern statistics.

TERMS TO PONDER

1. Tally Sheet
2. Class Limits
3. Class Boundaries
4. Class Midpoints
5. Open-End Distribution
6. Cumulative Frequencies
7. Relative Frequencies
8. Histogram
9. Frequency Polygon
10. Cumulative Polygon or Ogive
11. Frequency Curve

EXERCISES

1. The following data represent service lives (in hours) of a sample of standard flashlight batteries.

58	62	58	62	62	55	55	60	56	42	40	53	55	57	55
53	46	46	43	43	40	42	57	51	46	44	44	46	40	48
46	46	46	55	52	49	46	49	50	48	49	47	65	46	52
49	51	50	51	51	51	66	66	60	58	58	60	61	60	58
57	55	44	50	52	51	49	49	51	40	54	54	52	50	67

63	64	62	60	59	62	40	53	53	53	51	45	51	51	53
60	57	54	42	44	48	45	50	43	56	54	55	53	54	55
46	44	56	58	44	56	66	55	53	47	50	65	47	50	57
40	47	40	62	46	50	53	62	44	64	53	53	46	64	64
53	53	50	60	51	48	49	53	49	48	51	46	48		

  a. Using a tally sheet, arrange the data in a frequency distribution having equal intervals of 5 hours each. Begin the first interval at 40. Use limits.
  b. Sort the data into another frequency distribution having intervals which are 20 hours in length. Begin the first interval at 40. Use limits.
  c. Which distribution conveys the best description of the pattern of variation? Why?
2. For the distribution in Exercise 1a, express the frequencies as percentages of n.
3. Cumulate the frequencies of the distribution in Exercise 1a. Express these cumulated frequencies as percentages of n.
4. Draw a histogram of the frequency distribution in Exercise 1a on graph paper. Use ink.

5. The following data represent a sample of pieces of woven fabric. Each figure indicates the number of defects found in a piece of cloth.

```
0  1  0  0  0  1  5  0  1  0  0  1  3  7  0  0  7  6  2  1
1  1  0  2  1  0  0  1  3  0  0  2  0  1  5  2  0  3  4  0
0  0  6  0  5  0  0  4  1  3  2  1  0  1  1  2  3  1  0  0
6  1  5  0  1  2  3  1  1  0  0  0  0  1  2  0  0  2  1  0
2  2  4  0  0  1  2  3  6  5  5  3  0  3  3  2  1  2  3  0
```

   a. Group these data into a frequency distribution.
   b. Draw a histogram of the distribution. Use graph paper and ink.
6. In what fundamental way do the battery data differ from the cloth data? (Refer to Exercises 1 and 5.)
7. What important disadvantage does the *distribution* of battery lives have that the *distribution* of cloth defects does not have?
8. What are some of the factors one should take into consideration when deciding upon the size of the intervals for a frequency distribution?
9. Which of the following three sets of data are frequency distributions? Why?

   a. Family Characteristics and Life Insurance Ownership, 1956

Age of family head	% of families insured
18–24	69
25–34	88
35–44	89
45–54	85
55–64	80
65 or over	56

Source: *Life Insurance Fact Book*, 1959 (New York, Institute of Life Insurance, 1959), p. 17.

   b. Value of Nonfarm Owner-occupied Houses, 1959

Amount	% of houses
$1–$2499	4
$2500–$4999	8
$5000–$7499	12
$7500–$9999	15
$10,000–$12,499	16
$12,500–$14,999	11
$15,000–$19,999	19
$20,000 and over	16

Source: "1959 Survey of Consumer Finances, Housing of Nonfarm Families," *Federal Reserve Bulletin* (Vol. 45), September, 1959, p. 1108.

c. Speed of Motor Vehicles, 1958

Vehicles exceeding	%
40 m.p.h.	90
45 m.p.h.	76
50 m.p.h.	54
55 m.p.h.	32
60 m.p.h.	15

Source: U.S. Bureau of the Census, *Statistical Abstract of the United States: 1959*, 80th ed. (Washington, D.C., U.S. Government Printing Office, 1959), p. 561.

10. *a.* State the boundaries of the intervals in the following frequency distribution:

Class limits	f_i
15.00–27.99	3
28.00–40.99	7
41.00–53.99	5

b. State, if possible, the limits of the intervals in the following frequency distribution:

Class boundaries	f_i
$1000 and under $2000	69
$2000 and under $3000	42
$3000 and under $4000	25

c. State the size of the interval, the boundaries, and the limits of the following frequency distribution. (State limits to the nearest unit.)

x_i	f_i
9	4
16	5
23	9
30	2

11. *a.* Refer to the data on value of nonfarm owner-occupied houses, 1959, Exercise 9. What percentage of the houses were valued at $10,000 or more?

b. Refer to the data on speed of motor vehicles, 1958, Exercise 9.
(1) In general terms, what kind of a distribution is this?

     (2) What per cent of the vehicles did *not* exceed 40 miles per hour?

     (3) Could a frequency polygon of these data be drawn? If so, what would it look like?

  c. Refer to the data on family characteristics and life insurance ownership, 1956, Exercise 9. Is it possible to find, from the data given, the proportion of families insured where the head of the family was aged from 25 to 54 years inclusive? Why or why not?

SELECTED REFERENCES

McCarthy, Philip J., *Introduction to Statistical Reasoning* (New York, McGraw-Hill Book Co., Inc., 1957), Ch. III, Secs. 3.2, 3.3.

Paden, D. W., and Lindquist, E. F., *Statistics for Economics and Business*, 2d ed. (New York, McGraw-Hill Book Co., Inc., 1956), Ch. IV.

5

AVERAGES

In Chapter 4 we showed how to group numerical data into a frequency distribution and construct graphical devices in order to convey a clear visual impression of the pattern of variation. Now whether the data are grouped or not, it seems reasonable that a single number—a sort of summarizing value—denoting or locating the middle of the sample (or population) would be extremely useful in describing our data. But we find that the "middle" of a set of data can be defined in several ways, and this fact leads to the formulation of several measures of central tendency or averages.

THE ARITHMETIC MEAN ($\bar{x}$)

The arithmetic mean is *the* average that most of us first encountered in junior high school arithmetic classes. It is, by definition, simply the sum of n numbers divided by n. We will need to know how to compute it for both ungrouped and grouped data. First we shall show these computations by so-called "long" methods, that is, methods stemming directly from the definition of the arithmetic mean. Subsequently we shall explain indirect, short-cut methods of computation. Incidentally, whenever we use the term *mean* without a qualifying adjective we mean the arithmetic mean.

COMPUTATION OF THE ARITHMETIC MEAN; LONG METHOD; UNGROUPED DATA

Let us utilize our knowledge of summation symbols to write the definition of the arithmetic mean (ungrouped data) in shorthand form:

$$\bar{x} = \frac{\sum\limits_{i=1}^{n} x_i}{n} = \frac{\Sigma x_i}{n} \quad \text{(Arithmetic mean of a sample)}$$

$$\overline{X} = \mu = \frac{\sum\limits_{i=1}^{N} X_i}{N} = \frac{\Sigma X_i}{N} \quad \text{(Arithmetic mean of a finite population)}$$

Although we have shown the formulas for both the sample and population means, we shall, in the remainder of this section, use only the symbols referring to the sample mean.

Now suppose we have an ungrouped sample of egg prices, each price from a different retail store and referring to one dozen Grade A large eggs:

Symbol	Price (cents)
x_1	62
x_2	64
x_3	59
x_4	60
x_5	60

From our formula:

$$\bar{x} = \frac{\Sigma x_i}{n} = \frac{62 + 64 + 59 + 60 + 60}{5} = \frac{305}{5} = 61$$

The arithmetic mean of the egg prices is 61 cents.

Incidentally, in the above computation, the denominator, 5, is an exact number. Why?

Now, we may ask in what sense the mean locates the middle of a set of data. The mean is centered in the set so that the sum of positive deviations equals the sum of negative deviations. A deviation is the difference between the mean and an observation, with the mean always bearing the minus sign. In the example of egg prices, if we subtract the mean (61) from each of the observations, we get 1, 3, −2, −1, and −1. The sum of positive deviations is 4 and the sum of negative deviations is −4. Positive and negative sums of this type will always be equal when the deviations are measured from the arithmetic mean.

COMPUTATION OF THE ARITHMETIC MEAN; LONG METHOD; GROUPED DATA

In computing the arithmetic mean of a frequency distribution, we make the important assumption that was mentioned in Chapter 4 (p. 45). We assume, that is, that each value in a given interval is equal to the midpoint of that interval.

In order to illustrate readily the computation of the arithmetic mean from grouped data, let us use the frequency distribution developed in Chapter 4, that is, weights of Gonsocki freshmen. The midpoints and frequencies of our distribution are given in the first two columns of Table 5–1.

TABLE 5–1

Computation of Arithmetic Mean, Long Method, Grouped Data

x_i	f_i	$f_i x_i$
(1)	(2)	(3)
102	2	204
117	4	468
132	13	1716
147	31	4557
162	17	2754
177	7	1239
192	6	1152
207	2	414
	82	12,504

$$\bar{x} = \frac{\Sigma f_i x_i}{n} = \frac{12,504}{82} = 152.5 \text{ lbs.}$$

Now, in order to get the arithmetic mean, we know that we must add all of the measurements in the sample and divide by n. The assumption that we have made regarding midpoints makes it very easy to get the required total, for following down the first two columns of Table 5–1, we find we have 2 observations equal to 102; 4 observations equal to 117; 13 measurements equal to 132; and so on. We could get the total of all values by taking $102 + 102 + 117 + 117 + 117 + 117$ and so on, but this would be a very laborious process, so we set up column (3) in the table. This column gives the product of frequency and midpoint for each of the various intervals and is, therefore, headed $f_i x_i$. Now, under our assumption, the total of this $f_i x_i$ column is the total of all observations in the frequency distribution and is written in symbols as $\Sigma f_i x_i$ or $\displaystyle\sum_{i=1}^{k} f_i x_i$, where k is the number of intervals in the distribution. (Note that this total is not equal to $f_i \Sigma x_i$.) It follows, of course, that the formula for the arithmetic mean for grouped data by the long method is:

$$\bar{x} = \frac{\Sigma f_i x_i}{n}$$

Substituting the appropriate numbers as shown in Table 5–1, we have:

$$\bar{x} = \frac{12{,}504}{82} = 152.49 \text{ or } 152.5 \text{ lbs.}$$

Using frequencies expressed in *relative* terms, we may compute the mean from the following formula:

$$\bar{x} = \Sigma \left(\frac{f_i}{n}\right) x_i$$

The outstanding feature of the computation in Table 5–1 is, perhaps, that it involves a lot of work. Eight multiplications and a long addition process are required, as well as the final division by n. Now, an electric computing machine can shorten the time of this computation, but there still remains a fairly high probability that a mistake will creep in somewhere because the numbers are so large. Thus, we wish to show next how short-cut methods can be used in computing the arithmetic mean. We will begin with ungrouped data, for they illustrate the basic principles of the method best.

COMPUTATION OF THE ARITHMETIC MEAN; SHORT METHOD; UNGROUPED DATA

Short methods of computing the arithmetic mean are merely elaborations of the old idea of finding a mean by "splitting the difference." Suppose, for example, a student has received a 95 on one statistics examination and a 75 on another. To get the arithmetic mean of these two grades he may split the difference between them in half and add the result to the 75. The difference between 95 and

75 is 20. One-half of 20, that is, 10, added to 75 equals 85. This result, of course, checks with the long method, whereby $\bar{x} = \dfrac{95 + 75}{2} = 85$.

Now let us look at this business of splitting the difference in a slightly different light. Using the example of the two grade scores again, it is easy to interpret the process as meaning that we have subtracted 75 from *both* to yield 20 and 0; then we have found the arithmetic mean of 20 and 0 and added it to 75. So we were really splitting the *sum of the differences* into n equal parts (here $n = 2$) and adding the result to the lower score ($75 + 10 = 85$).

The 75 in our example is called an arbitrary constant, "arbitrary" because *any* number would have worked in place of the 75. To illustrate, suppose we had selected 90 as our arbitrary constant and subtracted it from both 95 and 75. The results would be $+5$ and -15. Adding these numbers together, we have -10. Splitting -10 into n parts ($n = 2$), we have -5. We add -5 (algebraically) to 90 (our arbitrary constant) to get 85.

Now let us apply this method to the sample of five egg prices used in the first illustration of computing the arithmetic mean. (Note that n is no longer equal to 2.) Since all of the prices (62, 64, 59, 60, 60) are close to 60, let us choose that number as our arbitrary constant. This choice will make smaller the numbers that we have to work with in our computation. Subtracting out the 60 gives us the five numbers, 2, 4, -1, 0, 0, respectively. Adding the numbers and dividing by five (splitting the sum five ways), we have:

$$\frac{2 + 4 + (-1) + 0 + 0}{5} = \frac{5}{5} = 1$$

Adding the 1 to the 60, we have 61, which checks with the result obtained by the long-method computation (p. 64).

We can get a general formula for the short method of computing the arithmetic mean (ungrouped data) by assigning symbols to the various numbers entering into the computation. First of all, let the arbitrary constant be x_0.

Next let the differences between the arbitrary constant and the observations be called u_i, so that $(x_i - x_0) = u_i$. We have as our formula then:

$$\bar{x} = x_0 + \frac{\Sigma u_i}{n}$$

(The arbitrary constant plus the sum of the differences split n ways; or the arbitrary constant plus the *mean of the differences*.)

To show that the short method is equivalent to the long method, we write:

$$\bar{x} = \frac{\Sigma x_i}{n} = x_0 + \frac{\Sigma u_i}{n}$$

Since

$$u_i = (x_i - x_0)$$

then

$$\frac{\Sigma x_i}{n} = x_0 + \frac{\Sigma (x_i - x_0)}{n}$$

Remembering that x_0 is a constant and recalling Summation Rule III, we may write:

$$\frac{\Sigma x_i}{n} = x_0 + \frac{\Sigma x_i - n x_0}{n}$$

Carrying out the division by n in the second term, we have:

$$\frac{\Sigma x_i}{n} = x_0 + \frac{\Sigma x_i}{n} - x_0 = \frac{\Sigma x_i}{n}$$

which completes the demonstration.

Subtracting an arbitrary constant from each of the data before carrying out further computations is sometimes called "coding" or "partial coding." And the reader will no doubt readily agree that the device would be especially useful where each of the observations contained, say, four digits yet was fairly close to some constant value. For example, suppose a sample of 100 measurements that ran as follows: 2051, 1952, 1848, 2103, and so on, all fairly close to 2000. Subtracting 2000 from each of the measurements would greatly simplify the work of computing the arithmetic mean as well as other statistics.

COMPUTATION OF THE ARITHMETIC MEAN; SHORT METHOD; GROUPED DATA

The short method of computing the arithmetic mean is easily adapted to grouped data if we (again!) bear in mind the assumption that the values in each interval are equal to the midpoint of that interval.

In view of the assumption, we will find that computations are simplified if we select one of the class midpoints as our arbitrary constant. Also, the numbers in the computation will usually be easier to handle if we select an arbitrary constant near the middle of the distribution. Taking the frequency distribution of weights of college students again as an illustration, suppose we select the midpoint 147 as our arbitrary constant. The worksheet in Table 5–2 illustrates all the subsequent steps involved in the computation.

TABLE 5–2

Computation of the Arithmetic Mean, Short Method, Grouped Data

x_i	f_i	u_i	v_i	$f_i v_i$	
(1)	(2)	(3)	(4)	(5)	
102	2	-45	-3	-6	$\bar{x} = x_0 + \dfrac{\Sigma f_i v_i}{n} c$
117	4	-30	-2	-8	
132	13	-15	-1	-13	
147	31	0	0	0	$\bar{x} = 147 + \dfrac{30}{82} (15)$
162	17	$+15$	1	17	
177	7	$+30$	2	14	$= 147 + 5.49$
192	6	$+45$	3	18	
207	2	$+60$	4	8	$= 152.49$, or 152.5
	82			$+30$	

Column (3) of Table 5–2 is the result of subtracting 147 from each of the midpoints in column (1). And, of course, since successive midpoints are one class interval apart, the u_i values of column (3) are one class interval apart.

In getting from column (3) to column (4), we have introduced an additional step into our short-method computation. But we have done nothing more than divide each of the figures in column (3) by 15, the length of the interval. It is therefore advisable, after the student is familiar with the method, to write down column (4) immediately on his worksheet without going through the intermediate step of putting down column (3). He can think of the process as a rewriting of the column of midpoints with one of them called zero and the others denoted by the number of class intervals they lie from this zero. Essentially we have changed the midpoints to a new scale having a new zero point and a unit equal to the class interval. The new midpoints (column 4) are symbolized by v_i. The symbol v_i is used instead of u_i because of the division of each u_i by c, the length of the interval.

The next step in the computation is to multiply the v_i values by the corresponding frequencies. Recalling our assumption and locating corresponding figures in columns (2) and (4), we find we have 2 measurements which lie -3 intervals from 147; 4 values which lie -2 intervals from 147; 13 observations which lie -1 intervals from 147; and so on. Carrying out these multiplications we arrive at the final column of our worksheet, column (5), which is headed $f_i v_i$.

The short-method formula for computing the mean for grouped data gives directions for getting the answer from the worksheet we have compiled. The formula, as shown in Table 5–2, is:

$$\bar{x} = x_0 + \frac{\Sigma f_i v_i}{n} c \qquad \text{or} \qquad \bar{x} = x_0 + \bar{v}c$$

where $\Sigma f_i v_i$ is simply the total of column (5) or the sum of the differences and c is the size of the interval. The term $\dfrac{\Sigma f_i v_i}{n}$ is the mean of the v_i and denotes the splitting of the sum of the differences. We must multiply it by c (which we previously divided by) and add in x_0 (which we previously subtracted) in order to get the arithmetic mean in the original units of measurement.

We are indeed still splitting the sum of differences taken from an arbitrary constant and adding the result to the constant. But, to repeat, for grouped data we have measured our differences in units of one class interval.

Substituting in the formula as shown in Table 5–2, we have $\bar{x} = 152.5$, which checks with the result obtained by the long method (p. 65). A glance at the worksheet of Table 5–2 will confirm the fact that the computation can readily be carried out without the aid of a computing machine.

The simplicity of the short method is readily brought out if we list the steps involved in using the method:

1. Select one of the midpoints of the frequency distribution as an arbitrary constant. Place a zero opposite this midpoint and convert all other midpoints to a new scale by writing the number of class intervals each lies from the zero. (This process is the same thing as subtracting the constant from each midpoint and dividing each of the resulting differences by the size of the class interval.)

2. Call the new list of midpoints v_i. Find the $f_i v_i$ values and use them to compute the arithmetic mean of the v_i. (This is the same thing as splitting the sum of the differences n ways.)

3. Multiply the arithmetic mean of the v_i by c and add the result to x_0, the arbitrary constant.

We wish to emphasize that the short method is perfectly general. That is, any midpoint (or, indeed, any number whatsoever) may be chosen as the arbitrary constant. As we have pointed out, however, computations are easier if the constant is a midpoint (instead of some other number) and if it lies near the middle of the distribution. Essentially, the idea is to choose the constant so that the total of column (5), $\Sigma f_i v_i$ (Table 5–2), will have as small an absolute value as possible.

It is not difficult to show that the short method is equivalent to the long method of computation; and the demonstration will give us more practice in the manipulation of statistical symbols. We wish to show that:

$$\frac{\Sigma f_i x_i}{n} = x_0 + \frac{\Sigma f_i v_i}{n} c$$

Recall the steps that we went through to get the v_i. They may be summarized symbolically as $v_i = \dfrac{x_i - x_0}{c}$.

Substituting this expression for v_i, we have

$$\frac{\Sigma f_i x_i}{n} = x_0 + \frac{\dfrac{\Sigma f_i (x_i - x_0)c}{c}}{n} = x_0 + \frac{\dfrac{\Sigma (f_i x_i - f_i x_0)c}{c}}{n}$$

And applying Summation Rule III, we have

$$\frac{\Sigma f_i x_i}{n} = x_0 + \frac{\dfrac{(\Sigma f_i x_i - \Sigma f_i x_0)\cancel{c}}{\cancel{c}}}{n}$$

$$= \frac{\Sigma f_i x_i - x_0 \Sigma f_i}{n} + x_0$$

$$= \frac{\Sigma f_i x_i - x_0 n}{n} + x_0$$

$$= \frac{\Sigma f_i x_i}{n} - \frac{x_0 \cancel{n}}{\cancel{n}} + x_0$$

$$= \frac{\Sigma f_i x_i}{n}$$

which completes the demonstration.

WEIGHTED ARITHMETIC MEAN

Suppose we wish to compute the mean age at death of 15 re-nowned business executives. If 5 of them died at 68 years; 2 at 59; 4 at 65; 3 at 60; and 1 at 70; how do we get the mean? Since 5 of the people died at 68; 68 must be included 5 times in the total. Fifty-nine must be included 2 times and so on. In other words we must "weight" each observation by the number of times it occurs. Our computation is as follows:

$$\frac{5 \times 68 + 2 \times 59 + 4 \times 65 + 3 \times 60 + 1 \times 70}{5 + 2 + 4 + 3 + 1} = \frac{968}{15} = 64.5 \text{ years}$$

Fundamentally, this process is the same as that we used for "averaging ratios" in Chapter 2. The denominator in such compu-tations is always the sum of the "weights."

A moment's reflection on the long-method computation of the mean for grouped data will bring home the similarity between the f_i and the weights we have just mentioned.

We have dwelled at length on the arithmetic mean and dis-cussed in detail the various methods of computation, for this mean is the measure of central tendency that the student will perhaps have to compute and interpret more frequently than any other in practical work. We will summarize the characteristics of all the different averages at the end of this chapter.

THE MEDIAN

The median is the central value in a ranked set of data. If we rank the observations in a row, that is, arrange them in the order of size from left to right, then the median is the value that has the same number of observations to its right as to its left.

We shall use the symbol m to denote the median of a sample and M to denote the median of a population.

COMPUTATION OF THE MEDIAN; UNGROUPED DATA

To illustrate the computation of the median for ungrouped data, let us take the sample of egg prices that we used in computing the arithmetic mean. We rank the observations as follows: 59, 60, 60, 62, 64, such an arrangement being called an *array*. Since we have five prices, the third one from either end of the array stands in the center and is the median. Median = 60.

But suppose we had an *even* number of observations, say 6, in the sample. Let us add another egg price, 66, to the previous 5 prices. Now our array is 59, 60, 60, 62, 64, 66. In this case, the median is the figure lying halfway between the *two* prices in the center. The prices in question are 60 and 62. The value halfway between them (their arithmetic mean) is 61, the median of the sample.

To sum up, if we have an odd number of data, the median is the central observation in the ranked data. But if we have an even number of data, the median is the value lying halfway between the two center values in the array.

This simple process requires no formula nor further elaboration.

COMPUTATION OF THE MEDIAN; GROUPED DATA

The computation of the median for grouped data involves two distinct steps. First, we must locate the interval in which the median lies. Second, we must find the value of the median by a process of interpolation. In order to accomplish this second step we make an assumption that is related somewhat to the one made in connection with the arithmetic mean. We assume, in short, that the observations in the interval containing the median are spaced out evenly over the length of that interval. The spacing is done in such a manner that the largest observation in the interval is equal to the upper boundary.

Using again the frequency distribution of weights of Gonsocki freshmen, we have illustrated the computation of the median in Table 5–3.

Taking the first step in the computation, we locate the interval containing the median by dividing n in half. Recall that there are just as many observations above the median as there are below it and that the frequency distribution is a form of array. Now $n/2 = 82/2 = 41$. This means that the median is located at the "end point" of observation number 41 in the distribution, counting from the lower end of the scale. (Note that the conventional arrangement of frequency distributions is somewhat paradoxical in that the lower end of the scale is higher on the page than the upper end of the scale.) If we cumulate the first three frequencies (f_1, f_2, and f_3), we have a total of 19. But if we add

TABLE 5–3

Computation of the Median.   Grouped Data

Class limits	f_i		
95–109	2		$n/2 = 82/2 = 41$st observation
110–124	4		
125–139	13	19	$g = 41 - 19 = 22$
140–154	31	50	$m = B_L + \dfrac{g}{f_m} c$
155–169	17		$m = 139.5 + \dfrac{22}{31} \cdot 15 = 139.5 + 10.645$
170–184	7		
185–199	6		$m = 150.14$, or 150.1
200–214	2		
	$n = 82$		

in f_4, we get 50.   Therefore, the 41st observation, lying between the 19th and the 50th, must be in the fourth interval.   The next problem is to find out precisely where in the fourth interval the median lies.   We know that it is at least as large as 139.5, the lower boundary of the fourth interval.   But since we have counted a total of only 19 observations in the first three intervals, we have $41 - 19$ or 22 values left to go to reach the median.   This figure 22 is the value we will substitute for g in the general formula, g representing the *gap* that we have to close to reach the median. Now all of these 22 values lie in the interval containing the median, the total frequency of this interval being 31; and since all of them are spaced evenly, we must travel 22/31 of the distance across this interval to reach the median.   The distance across the interval is, of course, 15.

Let B_L be the lower boundary of the interval containing the median.

Let f_m be the frequency of the interval containing the median. Then the median is found by the following formula:

$$m = B_L + \frac{g}{f_m} c$$

Filling in the appropriate numbers as shown in Table 5–3, we have:

$$m = 139.5 + \frac{22}{31} \cdot 15$$

$$m = 150.14, \text{ or } 150.1.$$

Note that the median of the frequency distribution (150.1 lbs.) is different from the arithmetic mean (152.5 lbs.). These two statistics are indeed different ways of describing the middle of the distribution.

Now if we wish to compute the median for a frequency distribution of attribute data, such as the distribution of carburetor defects on page 47, we need not use the estimating formula discussed above. In the attribute data distribution, we have not lost the identity of the original observations, so we may treat them as though they were ungrouped. There are 85 items or observations in the carburetor distribution. Thus item number 43 is the median item. The first 40 items are each equal to 0 and the next 21 items are each equal to 1. The median, therefore, must be 1.

THE MODE

The mode is the most frequently occurring observation in a set of data. We shall use the symbol "mo" to indicate the mode of a sample and the symbol "Mo" to indicate the mode of a population.

It is quite simple to pick out the mode from a sample of ungrouped data, especially if the data are arranged in an array. In our sample of egg prices (59, 60, 60, 62, 64), 60 is the mode because it occurs twice in the sample, while all other prices occur only once each. Some sets of data may have no mode, while others may have more than one mode. In the latter case, one value may occur most frequently, but another value may occur an equal or only slightly smaller number of times.

CRUDE MODE

Often when we need only a rough estimate of the mode of a frequency distribution, the *crude mode* will suffice. This statistic is simply the midpoint of the interval which contains the most observations. The value of the crude mode is 147 for the distribution of weights of Gonsocki freshmen. The crude mode should be computed only for distributions having class intervals of equal size.

Although various other methods exist for estimating the mode of a frequency distribution, we shall use only the crude mode in this book.

COMPARATIVE SIZES OF THE MEAN, MEDIAN, AND MODE

We have found in the illustrative computations that the mean, median, and mode differ for the distribution of weights of Gonsocki freshmen. This is not surprising, for differences in these averages will occur unless the distribution is perfectly symmetrical. A symmetrical distribution is represented by a histogram or frequency curve that may be divided by a vertical axis into two halves which are mirror images of each other. In the case of symmetry, then, $\bar{x} = m = $ mo. But if the distribution is skewed to the right (frequency curve or histogram has a long tail on the right side), $\bar{x} > m > $ mo. The opposite order obtains for a distribution which is skewed to the left, that is, mo $> m > \bar{x}$. Note that in skewed distributions, the mean is always toward the "tail end" of the distribution, the mode is toward the opposite end, while the median is always in between. These relationships of mean, median, and mode are illustrated graphically in Figure 5–1. The income distribution

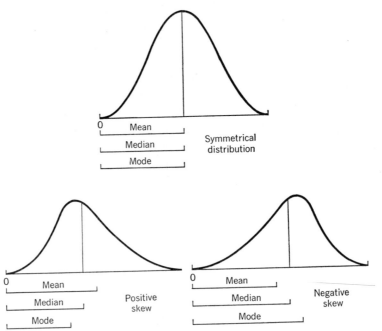

FIGURE 5–1. Order of Size of Mean, Median, and Mode for Symmetrical and Skewed Distributions

shown in Chapter 4, page 48, is a classic example of a positively skewed distribution.

STILL MORE AVERAGES

We shall examine two more measures of central tendency, namely, the geometric mean and the harmonic mean. These averages are used only in certain special kinds of problems, but the applications occur often enough that we should be able to tell when to use these averages and when not to use them.

We shall show computations only for ungrouped samples of data.

THE GEOMETRIC MEAN (gm)

The geometric mean is the nth root of the product of n numbers. To illustrate the computation, we need a set of n numbers, say, 5, 7, and 10. The product of these three numbers is 350. Now since $n = 3$, we must take the cube root of 350 in order to get the geometric mean. Using logarithms, we find that the cube root of 350 is about 7.0473, the geometric mean of 5, 7, and 10.

The formula for the geometric mean summarizes in general terms the operations we have just performed:

$$\text{gm} = \sqrt[n]{x_1 \cdot x_2 \cdot x_3 \cdot \ \cdots \ \cdot x_n}$$

The logarithm of the geometric mean is given by

$$\log \text{gm} = \frac{\log x_1 + \log x_2 + \log x_3 + \cdots + \log x_n}{n}$$

In economics and business, the geometric mean is sometimes used for averaging relative rates arising out of a time series. A time series is a set of observations taken at equal intervals of time, such as monthly sales figures or annual gross national product figures. Relative rates are formed from such a series by expressing each observation as a proportion of the one immediately preceding.

Now if each observation is a constant proportion or multiple of the one preceding, the series forms a geometric sequence and the relative rate of change is constant. That is, each value in the series may be found by multiplying the preceding value by a constant. A geometric sequence with a constant multiplier of 2 is 4, 8, 16.

In averaging *relative rates* formed from a time series, we are seeking to find the constant multiplier that would apply if the time series *did* form a geometric sequence having the same starting and ending values as the observed series. The geometric mean of the relative rates gives us this constant multiplier.

Suppose we have computed the relative rates in a series of five arbitrary one-digit numbers as follows:

Time period	No.	Relative rate
1	1	—
2	2	2
3	4	2
4	5	$5/4$
5	9	$9/5$

The geometric mean of the *relative rates* is computed as follows:

$$\text{gm} = \sqrt[4]{2 \cdot 2 \cdot \tfrac{5}{4} \cdot \tfrac{9}{5}} = \sqrt[4]{4 \cdot \tfrac{45}{20}}$$

$$= \sqrt[4]{\tfrac{45}{5}} = \sqrt[4]{9}$$

$$\doteq 1.732$$

This result means that in a 5-term geometric sequence starting with 1 and ending with 9, each figure—beginning with the second —is 1.732 times the preceding figure. Again the geometric mean of the relative rates gives the constant multiplier that would be appropriate if the original observations were in the form of a geometric sequence but having the same beginning and ending values as those observed. It is easy to see that $1 \times 1.732 \times 1.732 \times 1.732 \times 1.732$ does indeed equal 9, if the student recalls that $(1.732)^2 = 3$.

Now the average rate of *increase* in the series is 0.732. To put it another way, each figure—beginning with the second—has increased on the average 0.732 times or 73.2% over the preceding figure.

We could have reached the same result, that is, 1.732, by dividing the last term in the sequence by the first and taking the fourth root of the ratio so formed. That is, we could have computed as follows:

$$\text{gm} = \sqrt[4]{\tfrac{9}{1}}$$

This result may be generalized. That is, when computing the geometric mean of relative rates arising from a time series, we need only divide the last number in the series by the first and then take the $(n-1)$th root of this ratio, where n is the number of data in the series. The following demonstration shows why this result holds (the letter y is customarily used instead of x for time series data):

Time period	Data	Relative rates
1	y_1	—
2	y_2	y_2/y_1
3	y_3	y_3/y_2
4	y_4	y_4/y_3
.	.	.
.	.	.
.	.	.
n	y_n	y_n/y_{n-1}

$$\text{gm of relative rates} = \sqrt[n-1]{\frac{y_2}{y_1}\frac{y_3}{y_2}\frac{y_4}{y_3}\cdots\frac{y_n}{y_{n-1}}}$$

$$= \sqrt[n-1]{\frac{y_n}{y_1}}$$

Now suppose an economist tells you that the Gross National Product (at constant prices) for 1946 was $290.6 billion and that it was $401.7 billion for 1955. Furthermore, suppose he says that for the 10-year period in question the average relative rate of *increase* in the GNP was .0366 or 3.66% per year. What relationship does the figure 3.66% have to a geometric mean?

We may easily show how the figure .0366 was arrived at if we utilize the method of computation which we previously generalized. We have:

$$\text{gm} = \sqrt[10-1]{\frac{401.7}{290.6}} = \sqrt[9]{1.382}$$

$$\log \text{gm} = \frac{\log 1.382}{9} = \frac{.140508}{9} = .015612$$

$$\text{gm} = \text{antilog } .015612 = 1.0366$$

This result means that for a time series of 10 data beginning with 290.6 and ending with 401.7, the average relative rate is 1.0366.

That is, on the average each observation (beginning with the second) is 1.0366 times as big as the one immediately preceding it. The average rate of *increase* or average growth rate is thus .0366 or 3.66%.

THE HARMONIC MEAN (hm)

The harmonic mean is used in special cases for averaging rates of change expressed in terms of two different characteristics such as units of output per hour, miles per gallon, feet per second, and so on. As used in practice it is really an indirect method of computing the arithmetic mean, or, as one student put it, "a sneaky way of reversing and averaging a bunch of rates."

The harmonic mean is defined as the reciprocal of the arithmetic mean of the reciprocals. To compute it for a set of data, then, we (1) take the reciprocal of each datum, (2) compute the mean of these reciprocals, and (3) take the reciprocal of this mean.

The formula is:

$$\text{hm} = \frac{1}{\dfrac{\Sigma(1/x_i)}{n}} = \frac{n}{\Sigma(1/x_i)}$$

Suppose, for purposes of illustration, that we wish to find the length of time that it will take to get out an order of 500 metal base plates in a metals manufacturing plant where Smith, Jones, and Riley are the workers to be put on this particular job. The production time for the order will, of course, be 500 times the average number of minutes required to produce each base plate. The question for us to decide is how to compute this average.

The industrial engineer gives us the following rates on the production of base plates:

	Minutes per plate
Smith	8
Jones	5
Riley	4

Now note that in the rates given, the numbers of the plates are constant, and equal to 1: for example, Smith takes 8 minutes on the average to produce *one* plate. As a result, the mean of these rates $(8 + 5 + 4)/3 = 17/3 = 5.67$, would be weighted implicitly to show average minutes per plate under the assumption that all workers produced the same number of plates (with differing times, of course). Actually, however, we know that it is more common for workers to work the same length of time with differing levels of output. In order to solve our problem, then, we need to find the mean of the rates under the assumption that all workers work the same length of time. There are two methods of finding such an average. Under Method 1, we could reverse the given rates and then find the arithmetic mean number of minutes per plate. Under Method 2, we could compute the harmonic mean of the rates as given originally. These two methods are equivalent. They are illustrated as follows:

Method 1		*Method 2*	
Arithmetic mean		*Harmonic mean*	
Rate	*Reversed rate*	*Rate*	*Reciprocal*
8 min. per plate	0.125 plate per min.	8	0.125
5 min. per plate	0.200 plate per min.	5	0.200
4 min. per plate	0.250 plate per min.	4	0.250
	0.575 plate per 3 min.		0.575

$$\bar{x} = 3/0.575 = 5.22 \text{ min. per plate} \qquad \text{hm} = \frac{n}{\Sigma(1/x_i)} = \frac{3}{0.575}$$

$$\text{hm} = 5.22 \text{ min. per plate}$$

The required estimate of production time would be 500 plates at 5.22 minutes per plate. The computation is $500 \times 5.22 = 2610$ minutes or 43.5 hours.

Note that the arithmetic mean of the *nonreversed* rates would have given us a higher estimate, that is, $5.67 \times 500 = 2835$ minutes or 47.3 hours.

A quick comparison of the two methods shows that in Method 2 we automatically reverse the rates by taking reciprocals as required for the harmonic mean. Thus, we verify the fact that Method 1 is equivalent to Method 2.

When we wish to find the arithmetic mean of several rates of this type—under the assumption that the constant factor in the stated rate becomes variable—we should use the harmonic mean.

CHARACTERISTICS OF THE VARIOUS AVERAGES

In addition to the definitions of the various averages, we should know some of the important characteristics peculiar to each one. The definitions tell us what the averages are; the characteristics show us how the averages behave.

CHARACTERISTICS OF THE ARITHMETIC MEAN

First, from the basic formula for the arithmetic mean, we see that $\Sigma x_i = n\bar{x}$. Imagine that the observations in the first interval of a frequency distribution constitute a separate set of n_1 values. Then $n_1\bar{x}_1$ equals the total of all the values in the first interval. The same may be said of each of the other intervals. Thus the assumption previously made in computing the mean of a frequency distribution may be altered to read: We assume that the *mean* of the values in a given interval is equal to the midpoint of that interval. For the first interval, our assumption means that $n_1\bar{x}_1 = f_1x_1$.

Second, we already know that the arithmetic mean is the center of gravity of the data for which it is computed. The center of gravity of a physical object is the point at which we may consider all of its weight to be concentrated or the point on which it balances. As stated earlier, if we were to subtract the arithmetic mean from each observation in a set of data, the sum of the positive differences would equal the sum of the negative differences. The total of all the differences would be equal to zero. The data would "balance" about the arithmetic mean. Using symbols to indicate this phenomenon in shorthand, we have:

$$\Sigma(x_i - \bar{x}) = 0$$

The reader should verify this characteristic by doing the computation with a small set of whole numbers, say, 4, 5, 9, and 2.

Third, the arithmetic mean is the average of least squares. Suppose that after subtracting the mean from each observation, we squared each of the differences. The sum of these squared differences would be a minimum. That is, subtracting a number other than the mean from each datum would yield a sum of squared differences which would be equal to or larger than the sum based on the mean. Symbolically, this characteristic is expressed as $\Sigma(x_i - \bar{x})^2 = $ a minimum.

Fourth, the arithmetic mean is sensitive to extreme values. In skewed distributions, we recall, the mean was always "pulled" from the median toward the tail of the curve, having been influenced by the relatively few extremely large (positive skewness) or extremely small (negative skewness) data.

CHARACTERISTICS OF THE MEDIAN

First, we should know that the sum of the absolute differences from the median is a minimum. In symbols, $\Sigma|x_i - m| = $ a minimum. When the parentheses ( ) of such an algebraic quantity are straightened out | |, they indicate that all differences should be taken as absolute, that is, treated as though they were positive.

Second, the median is not very sensitive to extreme values. We recall from our discussion of the relative sizes of the mean, median, and mode that in skewed distributions, the median is always between the other two averages.

Third, we should note that the median can be computed for frequency distributions having unequal intervals.

Fourth, the median can be computed for open-end distributions, provided it does not fall in one of the open-end intervals.

Finally, a median can be found for qualitative characteristics, provided they can be ranked. It is possible, for example, to select the median shade of the color blue.

CHARACTERISTICS OF THE MODE

First, the mode is the most probable value in the distribution. That is, if we were to select one observation out of a set at random, we would be more likely to get the mode than any other value.

Second, we have noted already (p. 75) that there may be no mode in some sets of data, while in others there may be more than one.

Third, the mode may be found for qualitative data that can be ranked or categorized. For example, the modal rank in the army is private. The modal student classification in most colleges is freshman.

THE GEOMETRIC AND HARMONIC MEANS

Neither of these averages can be computed when one or more of the observations is equal to zero. Furthermore, the geometric mean may be meaningless if some of the data are negative. Both means are sensitive to extreme values.

THE UNSPECIFIED AVERAGE

As we have seen, the word *average* is a general term which can mean any one of at least five specific averages, each having its own particular definition and characteristics. But sometimes a person uses the term *average* without elaboration, as though it were perfectly clear just *which* average he meant. We hear such expressions as average wages, average hourly earnings, grade point average, the average student, average frequency of accidents, and so on, to say nothing of the average man and the average woman. Perhaps more often than not the arithmetic mean is the unspecified average, but we can never be absolutely sure of this. On occasion, the unspecified average may be used intentionally to support a foregone conclusion.

If an economic interest group wishes to show that "average wages" have gone up faster than prices, for example, it may select mean hourly wage rates in (high-wage) manufacturing industries as the statistic to represent average wages. The particular manufacturing industries covered will probably be unspecified, and probably the question of whether an increase in average wage rates is an appropriate quantity to compare with a price increase will be neglected. Median weekly income after compulsory deductions could be a more appropriate variable to compare with prices, for a worker spends his take-home pay, not his wage rate. And take-home pay, of course, depends not only on the hourly rate, but also on the number of hours worked and the amount of deductions.

On the other hand, if another interest group wished to show that prices had gone up faster than average wages, it might select modal net income in certain (low-wage) clerical types of work as the unspecified average for purposes of supporting its contention.

Probably it is impossible to define the average man and the average woman in a clear and meaningful fashion. Suffice it to say that the average woman, nowadays, would probably be described as 34-28-36. Most people would not care which types of averages were involved here. But they would grasp immediately the important inference that the average woman will never get far in Hollywood.

SUMMARY

In general, an average denotes or locates the middle of a set of data. The term *middle*, of course, may be defined in several ways. Three of these definitions give us respectively the mean, median, and mode, measures of central tendency having widespread applications in modern statistics.

The mean, which is the sum of n numbers divided by n, may be computed by long methods, that is, from formulas which are direct symbolic expressions of the definition of the mean. Alternatively, the mean may be computed by short methods or coded computations. The latter save us considerable time and labor, especially in the case of frequency distributions of measurement data.

The median (the center value in an array) is easily found for ungrouped data, and it is readily computed for grouped data under the assumption that the observations in the interval containing the median are spaced out evenly across that interval.

The mode is the most frequently occurring value in a set of data. It is easily found for ungrouped data, especially if they are ordered in an array. Several methods may be used to estimate the mode for grouped measurement data, but we shall use only the crude mode in this book.

Two additional averages having rather specialized uses are the geometric mean and the harmonic mean. The geometric mean is used to average relative rates of change, these rates usually having been computed from a time series.

The harmonic mean is used to find indirectly the arithmetic mean of several rates where the rates are expressed in terms of two characteristics, for example, production rates stated in minutes per unit. In the given rates, one of the characteristics is variable and the other is constant. If we desire the mean of such rates under the assumption that the variable characteristic has become constant, we use the harmonic mean.

Each average has its own peculiar characteristics. A discussion of these traits gives an insight into the meaning and significance of the various measures of central tendency. The term *average* should never be used without making clear what particular type of average is meant and what variable is being averaged.

TERMS TO PONDER

1. Ungrouped Data
2. Grouped Data
3. Splitting the Sum of the Differences
4. Arbitrary Constant

  5. Array
  6. Geometric Sequence
  7. Relative Rate of Change
  8. Center of Gravity
  9. Average of Least Squares

EXERCISES

1. Find the mean, median, and mode of the following set of ungrouped
   data.   (All data are expressed in pounds.)

6149	3498	3906	2698	2539	2379	5311	3137	7578	4995
7107	7555	7331	4997	8842	4254	7067	5187	9699	1312

2. The following frequency distribution represents the gross weekly
   earnings (in dollars) of employees in a manufacturing plant for the
   week ended July 27, 1957:

Weekly earnings	f_i
60 and under 65	3
65 and under 70	9
70 and under 75	11
75 and under 80	38
80 and under 85	30
85 and under 90	59
90 and under 95	21
95 and under 100	7
	178

   a. From the appearance of the distribution, estimate the relative
   sizes of the mean, median, and mode.
   b. Compute the mean, median, and mode of the distribution.   Check
   your answers to a.
3. Find the mean, median, and mode for the distribution of cloth defects
   in Exercise 5a of Chapter 4.   Do you need the grouped data formulas
   to find the median and mode?   Why or why not?
4. The median income in 1955 for men in the United States was $3354.
   The median income for women in the same year was $1116.   Explain
   what each of these figures means.   (Source of data: U.S. Bureau of
   the Census, *Current Population Reports*, Labor Force, Series P-50,
   No. 75 (Washington, D.C., U.S. Government Printing Office, July,
   1957), p. 10.)
5. The figures for the Gross National Product (at 1956 prices) for the
   years 1951 through 1955 are given in the following table:

Year	GNP (billions)
1950	$329.9
1951	354.2
1952	366.6
1953	381.6
1954	374.6
1955	401.7

Source: *Economic Report of the President,
January 1957* (Washington, D. C., U.S.
Government Printing Office, 1957), p. 124.

a. Compute the relative rates of change in the GNP figures.

b. Using logarithms, find the geometric mean of the relative rates.

c. Explain the meaning of the result found in *b.*

d. Find the fifth root of (401.7/329.9). Compare this result with that of *b.*

6. If productivity in the United States keeps rising at the present rate, the income of every family in the country will soon be above the average. Is there any sense to this statement? Why or why not?

7. Suppose there are exactly 48,000,000 families in the United States. Theoretically, would it be possible for all families but one to have incomes above the average,

a. if the term *average* meant the median?

b. if the term *average* meant the mode?

c. if the term *average* meant the arithmetic mean?

8. Find the median of the following frequency distribution:

Money Income of Spending Units in 1957

Income	Number of spending units
Under $1000	233
$1000–1999	336
$2000–2999	310
$3000–3999	310
$4000–4999	310
$5000–7499	646
$7500–9999	258
$10,000 and over	181
	2584

Source: *Federal Reserve Bulletin*, Vol. 44 (March, 1958), p. 250.

9. Find the mean, median, and crude mode of the following frequency distribution:

Annual Earnings of General Help Workers Employed 46 Weeks or More in the Philadelphia Knitted-Outerwear Industry During 1951

Earnings	No. of workers
1200 and under 1400	3
1400 and under 1600	22
1600 and under 1800	35
1800 and under 2000	20
2000 and under 2200	19
2200 and under 2400	8
2400 and under 2600	6
2600 and under 2800	1
2800 and under 3000	4
3000 and under 3200	3
	121

Source: Paul E. Warwick, "Annual Earnings of Knitted-Outerwear Workers in 1951," *Monthly Labor Review* (March, 1953), p. 252.

10. The geometric mean of three relative rates (computed from a time series) is 1.05. If the first value in the time series is 30, what is the last value?

11. The following figures represent ratings of 4 different water pumps in gallons per minute:

$$6.3 \qquad 8.5 \qquad 12.5 \qquad 15.8$$

Use the harmonic mean to find the arithmetic mean of all four rates under the assumption that equal *amounts* of water are pumped by all pumps.

SELECTED REFERENCES

LEWIS, Edward E., *Methods of Statistical Analysis in Economics and Business* (Boston, Houghton Mifflin Co., 1953), Ch. III.

McCARTHY, Philip J., *Introduction to Statistical Reasoning* (New York, McGraw-Hill Book Co., Inc., 1957), Ch. IV.

MILLS, Frederick C., *Introduction to Statistics* (New York, Holt, Rinehart and Winston, Inc., 1956), Ch. IV.

PADEN, Donald W., and LINDQUIST, E. F., *Statistics for Economics and Business*, 2d ed. (New York, McGraw-Hill Book Co., Inc., 1956), Ch. VI.

SPROWLS, R. Clay, *Elementary Statistics* (New York, McGraw-Hill Book Co., Inc., 1955), Ch. VII, Sec. 7.7.

6

MEASURES OF

VARIABILITY

An AVERAGE, we recall, is a descriptive measure that locates the middle of a set of statistical observations. But an average by no means *completely* describes the data. In particular, it gives us no idea of how widely the data are *scattered from* the middle of the set. For example, suppose that on the day before mid-term examinations, Brown, Johnson, Reed, Wright, and Lautzenheiser each studied exactly 4 hours. Each of the five study times is exactly equal to their mean, which is 4 hours. There is no variability or scatter. Now, suppose that on the third day after examinations the respective study times of these students were 0, 1, 6, 9, and 4. The mean (20/5) is still equal to 4, but most of the values differ widely from the mean. Variability now is great. The data are scattered far and wide.

In order to measure the extent of variability, we should like to have a descriptive measure (a statistic or parameter) that increases as variability increases and decreases as variability decreases. In short, we seek a sort of thermometer of scatter. Several such measures have been devised, but the two which the student will perhaps encounter most often are the *range* and the *standard deviation*.

THE RANGE

We are already familiar with the range from our study of frequency distributions. It is, of course, the difference between the largest and smallest values in a set of data. As a measure of variability, however, the range suffers from the weakness that it depends upon only two values. In general, a measure of variability computed from all of the data in a set is to be preferred. Such a measure is the standard deviation. The square of the standard deviation is known as the *variance*.

THE VARIANCE (s²) AND STANDARD DEVIATION (s) OF A SAMPLE

In seeking a measure of variability that depends upon every observation in the sample, we might apply our knowledge of averages and compute the mean amount by which the data differ from the mean. In order to make such a computation, we would first have to subtract the mean from each observation in the sample to get the $(x_i - \bar{x})$ differences. Then we would add these differences and divide the sum by n. But we know from our study of the characteristics of $\bar{x}$ that $\Sigma(x_i - \bar{x}) = 0$. Thus the mean of the differences, $\Sigma(x_i - \bar{x})/n$, would also equal zero.

We could get around our difficulty in either one of two ways: We could (1) take the mean of the *absolute* differences, that is, $\dfrac{\Sigma|x_i - \bar{x}|}{n}$ or (2) compute the mean of the *squared* differences. Because of the fact that the first result is inconvenient to handle mathematically, we take the second course. Thus we compute the "mean" of the squared differences to get the *variance*, s^2, but it is a very special type of mean, for we divide by $n - 1$ instead of n. The formula is:

$$s^2 = \frac{\Sigma(x_i - \bar{x})^2}{n - 1}$$

There is a very good reason for dividing the sum of the squared differences by $n - 1$, but we will not be ready for the explanation until we reach the chapter on statistical estimation.

The *standard deviation* is the positive square root of the variance; its formula is:

$$s = \sqrt{\frac{\Sigma(x_i - \bar{x})^2}{n - 1}}$$

Being a positive square root, the standard deviation, of course, never has a value less than zero.

The student is invited to write a clear, concise definition of the standard deviation in English if he can. Perhaps the best we can do is this: The standard deviation is the square root of a ratio consisting of the sum of the squares of the deviations of the observations from the mean, divided by one less than the number of observations.

If the data are grouped, the formula for the standard deviation is:

$$s = \sqrt{\frac{\Sigma f_i(x_i - \bar{x})^2}{n - 1}}$$

where x_i represents the class midpoints, f_i represents the frequencies, and the summation runs from 1 to k, k being the number of class intervals. The corresponding variance formula is:

$$s^2 = \frac{\Sigma f_i(x_i - \bar{x})^2}{n - 1}$$

The standard deviation is the "thermometer of scatter" in the sense that it becomes smaller as the data become more nearly clustered about the mean and larger as the data become more widely scattered from the mean. But even if we know the mean and standard deviation of a distribution, we cannot from this information alone infer the precise shape of its histogram or frequency curve. However, in general, a distribution with a large standard deviation will have a frequency curve of wide horizontal dimensions, as in Figure 6–1. On the other hand, a frequency distribution having a standard deviation of 0 will graph as shown in Figure 6–2.

A more meaningful interpretation of the variance is possible if we utilize an appropriate theoretical model for the distribution of the data at hand. If a particular frequency distribution model called the *normal distribution* is appropriate, then we know that

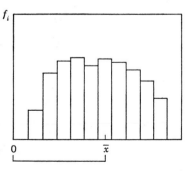

FIGURE 6–1. Distribution with Large Standard Deviation

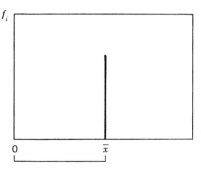

FIGURE 6–2. Distribution with Standard Deviation of Zero

the standard deviation should be equal to about $\frac{1}{6}$ of the range and that about $\frac{2}{3}$ of the observations should lie within 1 standard deviation of the mean. We shall have more to say about the normal distribution in Chapter 7.

Knowing the standard deviation has a minimum value of 0, we may ask if it has an upper limit. The answer is that theoretically the standard deviation can be indefinitely large or infinite. However, the distributions which are the most useful theoretical models in statistics have finite standard deviations.

We wish to emphasize that there is no fixed relationship between the standard deviation and the mean for all sets of data. In some samples of data, s is bigger than $\bar{x}$; in others, the order of size is reversed. Two distributions with equal means can have widely differing standard deviations, and two distributions with the same standard deviation can have very different means.

COMPUTATION OF THE SAMPLE VARIANCE AND STANDARD DEVIATION; LONG METHOD; UNGROUPED DATA

To illustrate the computation of the variance and standard deviation of an ungrouped sample of data, let us take a small set of whole numbers. The study times of Brown, Johnson, Reed, Wright, and Lautzenheiser on the third day after examinations (p. 89) will do. These data and the steps in the computation are set forth in Table 6–1.

TABLE 6–1

**Computation of the Variance,
Long Method, Ungrouped Data**

	x_i	$(x_i - \bar{x})$	$(x_i - \bar{x})^2$
	(1)	(2)	(3)
Brown	0	-4	16
Johnson	1	-3	9
Reed	6	2	4
Wright	9	5	25
Lautzenheiser	4	0	0
	20		54

$$\bar{x} = \frac{\Sigma x_i}{n} = \frac{20}{5} = 4 \qquad s^2 = \frac{\Sigma(x_i - \bar{x})^2}{n-1} = \frac{54}{4} = 13.5 \text{ hrs.}$$

$$s = +\sqrt{13.5} = 3.67, \text{ or } 3.7 \text{ hrs.}$$

The appropriate formula is, of course, $s^2 = \dfrac{\Sigma(x_i - \bar{x})^2}{n - 1}$. To get the numerator of this expression, we must first find the arithmetic mean. It is 4. Next, in column (2) of the table, we subtract the mean from each observation in the sample. Then, in column (3), we square each of the differences of column (2). Finally, we add column (3) to get the sum of the squared differences, 54. Since $n = 5$, the denominator of the formula $(n - 1)$ is equal to 4. We have $s^2 = 54/4$ $= 13.5$ hrs. The standard deviation (s) equals $\sqrt{13.5} = 3.67$, or 3.7 hrs.

COMPUTATION OF THE SAMPLE VARIANCE AND STANDARD DEVIATION; SHORT METHOD; UNGROUPED DATA

In the formula for the sample variance of ungrouped data, the numerator is, as we have seen, the sum of n squared differences. If we carry out the squaring operation and then sum the resulting quantities by applying Summation Rule III (Ch. 3, p. 36), we have the corresponding short-method formula. Since no changes are made in the denominator, let us for the moment disregard that portion of the formula. We may square and sum the numerator as follows:

$$\Sigma(x_i - \bar{x})^2 = \Sigma(x_i - \bar{x})(x_i - \bar{x}) = \Sigma(x_i^2 - 2x_i\bar{x} + \bar{x}^2)$$

Now we apply Summation Rule III:

$$\Sigma(x_i - \bar{x})^2 = \Sigma x_i^2 - \Sigma 2\bar{x}x_i + \Sigma\bar{x}^2$$

Since $2\bar{x}$ and $\bar{x}^2$ are constants, we have $\Sigma(x_i - \bar{x})^2 = \Sigma x_i^2 - 2\bar{x}\Sigma x_i + n\bar{x}^2$.

From the formula for the arithmetic mean, we know that $\Sigma x_i = n\bar{x}$.

Thus, if we substitute $n\bar{x}$ for Σx_i in the second term of the right member, we have:

$$\Sigma(x_i - \bar{x})^2 = \Sigma x_i^2 - 2n\bar{x}^2 + n\bar{x}^2$$

Adding the last two terms, we have:

$$\Sigma(x_i - \bar{x})^2 = \Sigma x_i^2 - n\bar{x}^2$$

The last term in this expression may be written $\dfrac{n(\Sigma x_i)^2}{(n)^2}$.

Dividing numerator and denominator of this term by n, we have: $\dfrac{(\Sigma x_i)^2}{n}$.

Thus, the numerator of the variance formula may be written either as $\Sigma x_i{}^2 - n\bar{x}^2$ or $\Sigma x_i{}^2 - \dfrac{(\Sigma x_i)^2}{n}$, and the formula for the sample variance takes on the two forms:

$$s^2 = \frac{\Sigma x_i{}^2 - n\bar{x}^2}{n-1} = \frac{\Sigma x_i{}^2 - \dfrac{(\Sigma x_i)^2}{n}}{n-1}$$

Notice that in the second formula the mean does not appear; all we need for the computation is the sum of the observations and the sum of their squares. Some students find this formula easier to remember if they state the numerator in words: "The sum of the squares minus the square of the sum over n." Observe that the n in the numerator is *not* squared.

To illustrate the use of this formula, let us utilize the data of Table 6–1. The appropriate worksheet is set out in Table 6–2.

TABLE 6–2

Computation of the Sample Variance by the Short Method, Ungrouped Data

x_i	$x_i{}^2$
0	0
1	1
6	36
9	81
4	16
$\Sigma x_i = 20$	$\Sigma x_i{}^2 = 134$

$$s^2 = \frac{\Sigma x_i{}^2 - \dfrac{(\Sigma x_i)^2}{n}}{n-1} = \frac{134 - \dfrac{(20)^2}{5}}{5-1}$$

$$= \frac{134 - 80}{4} = \frac{54}{4} = 13.5 \text{ hrs.}$$

Our result, of course, checks with that obtained by the long method (p. 92).

COMPUTATION OF THE SAMPLE MEAN AND VARIANCE; SHORT METHOD WITH CODING; UNGROUPED DATA

We recall that in computing the *mean* of a sample by the short method we subtracted a constant from each of the observations. This operation has the effect of reducing the mean by the amount of the constant, but it has *no effect on the variance*. This important rule is proved by a bit of elementary algebra in the appendix at the end of this chapter (p. 103). Thus we may subtract a constant x_0 from each observation in a sample to get the values $u_i = (x_i - x_0)$. We may then compute the mean and variance from the following formulas:

$$\bar{x} = x_0 + \frac{\Sigma u_i}{n} \qquad s^2 = \frac{\Sigma u_i^2 - \dfrac{(\Sigma u_i)^2}{n}}{n - 1}$$

We are already familiar with the first of these formulas. The second is merely the short-method variance formula with u_i substituted for x_i. To illustrate the computations, let us take a new set of data.

Suppose that a cigarette manufacturer wishes to estimate not only the mean tar content of his product but also the amount of variability in tar content from one cigarette to another. In other words, he is interested in the degree of uniformity in his product. He takes samples of cigarettes from the production line from time to time for laboratory analysis and computes the mean tar content and the variance for each sample. Let us suppose a sample of 10 cigarettes results in the observations (x_i) given in Table 6–3. The observations represent milligrams of tars found in each of the cigarettes. Letting the arbitrary constant be 12 milligrams, we may carry out the computations as shown.

If the manufacturer were trying to maintain a process variance of 9 milligrams or less, this *sample* result (as we shall see later) could reasonably be supposed to arise from a population having such a degree of uniformity.

In this particular sample, it is easy to verify that the long-method formulas for the mean and variance yield equivalent results, for the mean here turns out to be 15, which is very convenient to work with. But in most cases the mean will be in such form that the computation of the $(x_i - \bar{x})$ differences becomes very troublesome.

TABLE 6–3

Computation of Sample Mean and Variance, Short Method with Coding, Ungrouped Data

x_i	$u_i = (x_i - x_0)$	u_i^2
9	-3	9
12	0	0
12	0	0
14	2	4
16	4	16
16	4	16
17	5	25
17	5	25
18	6	36
19	7	49
150	30	180

$$\bar{x} = \frac{\Sigma u_i}{n} + x_0 = \frac{30}{10} + 12 = 3 + 12 = 15$$

$$s^2 = \frac{\Sigma u_i^2 - \dfrac{(\Sigma u_i)^2}{n}}{n-1} = \frac{180 - \frac{900}{10}}{10 - 1} = \frac{180 - 90}{9}$$

$$= \tfrac{90}{9} = 10$$

The verification of the coded computations is shown in Table 6–4.

We have in Table 6–3 illustrated the coded computation of the sample mean and variance from the same worksheet because these two statistics must often be computed as a matter of routine for samples of measurement data. It is a good idea, therefore, to know how to compute them with a minimum of time and effort.

TABLE 6–4

**Computation of Sample Mean and Variance,
Long Method: Verification of Short-
Method Computations**

x_i	$x_i - \bar{x}$	$(x_i - \bar{x})^2$
9	−6	36
12	−3	9
12	−3	9
14	−1	1
16	1	1
16	1	1
17	2	4
17	2	4
18	3	9
19	4	16
150	0	90

$$\bar{x} = \frac{\Sigma x_i}{n} = \frac{150}{10} = 15$$

$$s^2 = \frac{\Sigma(x_i - \bar{x})^2}{n-1} = \frac{90}{9} = 10$$

COMPUTATION OF THE SAMPLE VARIANCE FOR GROUPED ATTRIBUTE DATA; SHORT METHOD

The formula for the variance of a frequency distribution, $s^2 = \dfrac{\Sigma f_i(x_i - \bar{x})^2}{n-1}$, may readily be transformed to the form

$$s^2 = \frac{\Sigma f_i x_i^2 - \dfrac{(\Sigma f_i x_i)^2}{n}}{n-1}$$

Notice that this latter formula is the same as that for ungrouped data except for the f_i factors; it is very convenient to use for computing the variance of a frequency distribution of attribute data. As an example suppose we wish to compute the variance for a distribution of defects of aluminum castings. The computation is shown in Table 6–5.

TABLE 6–5

Computation of Sample Variance.
Grouped Attribute Data

Defects per casting (x_i)	No. of castings (f_i)	$f_i x_i$	$f_i x_i^2$
0	10	0	0
1	4	4	4
2	4	8	16
3	2	6	18
	20	18	38

$$s^2 = \frac{\Sigma f_i x_i^2 - \frac{(\Sigma f_i x_i)^2}{n}}{n-1} = \frac{38 - \frac{(18)^2}{20}}{19} = \frac{38 - 16.2}{19}$$

$$= 21.8/19 = 1.147, \text{ or } 1.15$$

From the variance we readily find the standard deviation by taking the square root of 1.15. Thus $s = 1.07$.

COMPUTATION OF THE SAMPLE VARIANCE FOR GROUPED MEASUREMENT DATA; SHORT METHOD WITH CODING

In computing the mean by the short method for a distribution of measurement data (Ch. 5), we transformed the data to a new scale labeled v_i by using the following formula:

$$v_i = \frac{x_i - x_0}{c} = \frac{u_i}{c}$$

where x_0 is an arbitrary constant and c is the length of the class interval. We know that subtracting the constant (x_0) from each of the midpoints (x_i) will have no effect upon the variance or standard deviation. This rule is proved in Part A of the appendix at the end of this chapter (p. 103). However, dividing the differences (u_i) by c will cause the standard deviation to be divided by c; the mean will also be divided by c, and the variance will be divided by c^2.

This rule is proved in Part B of the appendix at the end of this chapter. Thus if we write the variance formula in terms of v_i, it must be multiplied by c^2 in order to compensate for the division by c^2. The short-method formula for the variance of a frequency distribution may be written:

$$s^2 = \left[\frac{\Sigma f_i v_i^2 - \dfrac{(\Sigma f_i v_i)^2}{n}}{n-1} \right] c^2$$

Carrying out the multiplication by c^2, we have

$$s^2 = \frac{\Sigma f_i v_i^2 c^2 - \dfrac{(\Sigma f_i v_i)^2 c^2}{n}}{n-1}$$

The numerator of the formula may be written as

$$\Sigma f_i v_i^2 c^2 - \frac{(\Sigma f_i v_i) c (\Sigma f_i v_i) c}{n}$$

But since $v_i = \dfrac{u_i}{c}$, $u_i = v_i c$ and $u_i^2 = v_i^2 c^2$, we may rewrite the the numerator as $\Sigma f_i u_i^2 - \dfrac{(\Sigma f_i u_i)^2}{n}$.

Substituting $(x_i - x_0)$ for u_i, we would arrive at $\Sigma f_i x_i^2 - \dfrac{(\Sigma f_i x_i)^2}{n}$ as the expression for our numerator.

This formulation is, as we noted earlier, merely the expansion of $\Sigma f_i(x_i - \bar{x})^2$. Thus, if we divide this numerator by $n - 1$, we have retraced our steps to the long-method formula for the variance of a frequency distribution:

$$s^2 = \frac{\Sigma f_i(x_i - \bar{x})^2}{n-1}$$

In short:

$$s^2 = \left[\frac{\Sigma f_i v_i^2 - \dfrac{(\Sigma f_i v_i)^2}{n}}{n-1} \right] c^2 = \frac{\Sigma f_i(x_i - \bar{x})^2}{n-1}$$

Taking as our data the distribution of weights of Gonsocki freshmen, we may compute both the mean and variance from the same worksheet as shown in Table 6–6.

TABLE 6–6

Computation of Mean and Variance by Short Method with Coding.   Grouped Measurement Data

x_i	f_i	v_i	$f_i v_i$	$f_i v_i^2$
(1)	(2)	(3)	(4)	(5)
102	2	-3	-6	18
117	4	-2	-8	16
132	13	-1	-13	13
147	31	0	0	0
162	17	1	17	17
177	7	2	14	28
192	6	3	18	54
207	2	4	8	32
	82		$+30$	178

$$\bar{x} = x_0 + \frac{\Sigma f_i v_i}{n} c = 147 + 5.49 = 152.49, \text{ or } 152.5 \text{ lbs.}$$

$$s^2 = \left[\frac{\Sigma f_i v_i^2 - \frac{(\Sigma f_i v_i)^2}{n}}{n-1} \right] c^2 = \left[\frac{178 - \frac{(30)^2}{82}}{81} \right] 15 \cdot 15$$

$$= \frac{178 - \frac{900}{82}}{81} 15 \cdot 15 = \frac{167.02}{81} 15 \cdot 15 = \frac{37{,}579.5}{81} = 463.9$$

We find the standard deviation by taking $\sqrt{463.9} = 21.54 = s$.

After selecting one of the midpoints as our arbitrary constant, we readily write down the v_i values of column (3). Column (4) results from multiplying corresponding values in columns (2) and (3). Column (5) follows from the multiplication of corresponding values in columns (3) and (4). For this particular sample of data, the computation would not require the use of a computing machine except perhaps for the division of 37,579.5 by 81.

VARIANCE AND STANDARD DEVIATION OF A FINITE POPULATION

The variance (and thus the standard deviation) of a finite population is defined in two ways. First, we have a definition that corresponds directly to the definition of the sample variance. In mathematical shorthand this definition is:

$$S^2 = \frac{\Sigma(X_i - \mu)^2}{N - 1}$$

where μ is the population mean and the summation extends over all N elements in the population.

Second, we have a definition that would be the same as the one just given except that N appears in the denominator instead of $N - 1$. The formula is:

$$\sigma^2 = \frac{\Sigma(X_i - \mu)^2}{N}$$

where σ is the lower case Greek letter sigma.

There is a good reason for having two definitions of the population variance, but, again, we will have to postpone the explanation until we get to the chapter on statistical estimation.

We have given here only the formulas for finite population variances because the formula for the variance of an indefinitely large population of measurement data requires the notation of the integral calculus.

VARIABILITY IN RELATIVE TERMS; THE COEFFICIENT OF VARIATION

The standard deviation is a measure of absolute variability stated in terms of inches, pounds, yards, dollars, or some other unit. To compare the variability in two different distributions (whether the difference is in the units of measurement or the characteristics measured) however, we need a statistic that is not tied to the units of a particular set of data. Such a statistic is the coefficient of variation (cv), which gives an expression of relative variability. We need learn no new statistics to compute it. The cv is merely the ratio of the standard deviation to the mean, that is, $\text{cv} = \dfrac{s}{\bar{x}}$. Often the cv is expressed as a percentage. Because it is tied to no unit of measurement, we call it an abstract number. If $\text{cv} = .25$ for a given sample, we know that the standard deviation is one-fourth as big as the mean.

The parameter corresponding to the statistic, cv is $\text{CV} = \dfrac{S}{\mu}$.

OTHER STATISTICS AND PARAMETERS

Although there are a number of other statistics and parameters which measure such things as skewness, we are going to conclude our discussion of statistical description at this point. The other descriptive measures we could discuss are of minor importance in business and economic statistics, and they are readily learned if isolated instances of use do occur.

SUMMARY

A measure of variability indicates the extent to which data are scattered from the middle of a set. There are two important such measures, the range and the standard deviation. The square of the standard deviation is known as the variance. The values of the standard deviation and variance have no fixed relationship to the mean for all sets of data. For a sample of ungrouped data, the variance may be computed by any one of the following equivalent formulas:

$$s^2 = \frac{\Sigma(x_i - \bar{x})^2}{n-1} = \frac{\Sigma x_i^2 - n\bar{x}^2}{n-1} = \frac{\Sigma x_i^2 - \dfrac{(\Sigma x_i)^2}{n}}{n-1} = \frac{\Sigma u_i^2 - \dfrac{(\Sigma u_i)^2}{n}}{n-1}$$

where, in the last formula, $u_i = (x_i - x_0)$ and x_0 is any arbitrary constant.

The last formula of those given above results from the principle that subtracting an arbitrary constant from each observation in a set reduces the mean by the amount of the constant but does not alter the value of the variance.

In computing the variance for a frequency distribution of attribute data, the following formula is convenient:

$$s^2 = \frac{\Sigma f_i x_i^2 - \dfrac{(\Sigma f_i x_i)^2}{n}}{n-1}$$

If we bear in mind the principle that dividing each datum in a set by an arbitrary constant causes the mean and standard deviation to be divided by the constant, we may write the following formula for the variance of a distribution of measurement data:

$$s^2 = \left[\frac{\Sigma f_i v_i^2 - \dfrac{(\Sigma f_i v_i)^2}{n}}{n-1} \right] c^2, \text{ where } v_i = \frac{x_i - x_0}{c} = \frac{u_i}{c}$$

The mean and variance of a sample are readily computed from the same worksheet if we use the short methods of computation.

There are two different ways of defining the variance of a finite population:

$$S^2 = \frac{\Sigma(X_i - \mu)^2}{N - 1} \text{ and } \sigma^2 = \frac{\Sigma(X_i - \mu)^2}{N}$$

The variabilities of several distributions may readily be compared if we compute the coefficient of variation for each. The formula is $cv = \dfrac{s}{\bar{x}}$. This statistic, expressing s as a proportion of $\bar{x}$, is called a measure of relative variability.

There are several other descriptive statistics and parameters that can be defined, but the measures of central tendency and variability we have discussed are sufficient for most elementary applications involving business and economic data. The student should become able to compute the sample mean and variance as a matter of routine.

APPENDIX ON RULES OF CODING FOR THE MEAN AND VARIANCE

Part A. Rule: *Subtracting an arbitrary constant from each datum in a set reduces the mean by the amount of the constant but does not change the value of the variance.*

Taking the mean first, we write its formula as follows: $\bar{x} = \dfrac{\Sigma x_i}{n}$. Let x_0 be the arbitrary constant. Since x_0 is subtracted from each value of x_i, we substitute the quantity $(x_i - x_0)$ for x_i in the formula. We have:

$$\frac{\Sigma(x_i - x_0)}{n} = \frac{\Sigma x_i - n x_0}{n} = \frac{\Sigma x_i}{n} - x_0 = \bar{x} - x_0$$

Thus the mean is reduced by the amount of the constant x_0.

Next let us show that the variance is not affected by the subtraction of the constant x_0. We write the formula of the variance as follows:

$$s^2 = \frac{\Sigma(x_i - \bar{x})^2}{n - 1}$$

Substituting $(x_i - x_0)$ for x_i and $(\bar{x} - x_0)$ for $\bar{x}$. We have:

$$s^2 = \frac{\Sigma(x_i - x_0 - (\bar{x} - x_0))^2}{n - 1} = \frac{\Sigma(x_i - x_0 - \bar{x} + x_0)^2}{n - 1}$$

$$= \frac{\Sigma(x_i - \bar{x})^2}{n - 1}, \text{ which is the required result.}$$

PART B. Rule: *Dividing each datum in a set by an arbitrary constant causes the mean and standard deviation to be divided by the constant and causes the variance to be divided by the square of the constant.*

Here we denote the constant by c because this letter is the one we have previously used in the grouped data formula.

Taking first the mean and using the formula for grouped data, we wish to show that $\dfrac{\Sigma f_i(x_i/c)}{n} = \dfrac{\bar{x}}{c}$.

$$\frac{\Sigma f_i(x_i/c)}{n} = \frac{(1/c)\Sigma f_i x_i}{n} = \frac{(1/c)(n\bar{x})}{n} = \frac{1}{c}\bar{x} = \frac{\bar{x}}{c}$$

which is the required result.

Next let us show that the variance is divided by the square of the constant, c. Again using the basic formula for grouped data, $s^2 = \dfrac{\Sigma f_i(x_i - \bar{x})^2}{n-1}$, we wish to show that $\dfrac{\Sigma f_i(x_i/c - \bar{x}/c)^2}{n-1} = \dfrac{s^2}{c^2}$.

We may write the left-hand member of the above expression as follows:

$$\frac{\Sigma f_i[(1/c)(x_i - \bar{x})(1/c)(x_i - \bar{x})]}{n-1}$$

This, in turn, equals

$$\frac{\Sigma f_i(1/c^2)(x_i - \bar{x})^2}{n-1} = \frac{(1/c^2)\Sigma f_i(x_i - \bar{x})^2}{n-1} = \frac{\Sigma f_i(x_i - \bar{x})^2}{c^2(n-1)} = \frac{s^2}{c^2}$$

This result clearly shows why we must multiply by c^2 in our coded computation of the variance for grouped data. In short, $\dfrac{s^2}{c^2} \cdot c^2 = s^2$.

By taking the square root of $\dfrac{s^2}{c^2}$, we show that the standard deviation is divided by the arbitrary constant, c, when each datum in the set has been divided by c.

TERMS TO PONDER

1. Variability or Scatter
2. Range
3. Standard Deviation
4. Variance
5. Absolute Variability
6. Relative Variability
7. Coefficient of Variation

EXERCISES

1. Assuming that the starting salaries are equal (and at a moderate level), would you rather work for (a) a firm in which the mean salary was low but the variability large or (b) a firm in which the mean salary was very high but the variability small? Why?

2. If the mean temperature is 70.5° in Phoenix, Arizona, and 75.2° in Honolulu, Hawaii, in which of these two places would you rather spend a year-long vacation? (We assume that temperature is the only factor you are considering.) Now, suppose you find out that the range of temperatures in Phoenix is 16 to 118 degrees and that the range for Honolulu is 56 to 88 degrees. How would this additional information affect your decision?

3. Jenkins has a B average for his four years in college and almost all his grades are B's. He has no D's or F's. Harris also has a B average, but he has a great many C's and A's as well as 3 D's, but he has no F's. If we were to assign numerical values to letter grades (4 for an A, 3 for a B, 2 for a C, and 1 for a D) and compute the standard deviation for each student, for which one would this statistic be larger? Why?

4. Two typists apply to you for a job. Both of them can type an average (mean) of 50 words per minute on the same types of material. How would a knowledge of variability in the applicants' typing speeds help you in deciding which of the two persons to hire?

5. Find the mean, variance, and coefficient of variation of the following distribution:

Third Quarter Accident Record for a Group of Machinists

Accidents per machinist	No. of machinists
0	294
1	76
2	25
3	9
4	5
5	4
6	2
7	1

6. Suppose the coefficient of variation has been suggested as a measure of industrial concentration. That is, the annual sales of each firm in a given industry are ascertained and the cv of these values is com-

puted for each industry. The industry having the smallest cv is said to have the highest degree of concentration. Drawing upon your knowledge of economics as well as statistics, criticize this use of the cv.

7. *a*. Compute the variance and standard deviation of the ungrouped data given in Exercise 1, p. 86 (Ch. 5).

    b. Compute the coefficient of variation of the distribution given in Exercise 9, p. 87 (Ch. 5) and compare it with the coefficient of variation computed in Exercise 5 of the present chapter.

SELECTED REFERENCES

DIXON, Wilfrid J., and MASSEY, Frank J., Jr., *Introduction to Statistical Analysis,* 2d ed. (New York, McGraw-Hill Book Co., Inc., 1957), Ch. III, Sec. 3–2.

FREUND, John E., and WILLIAMS, Frank J., *Modern Business Statistics* (Englewood Cliffs, N.J., Prentice-Hall, Inc., 1958), Ch. IV, Secs. 4.4–4.8.

McCARTHY, Philip J., *Introduction to Statistical Reasoning* (New York, McGraw-Hill Book Co., Inc., 1957), Ch. V.

7

PROBABILITY

In order that we may gain a clear idea of the principles of sampling and statistical inference, we must understand the concept of a probability distribution. We shall build gradually toward this concept, as several other fundamental ideas must be assimilated along the way.

DEFINITIONS OF PROBABILITY

The development of the theory of probability began in seventeenth-century France, a time when gambling was a favorite recreation among the nobility. Certain problems in the determination of odds were not only interesting but somewhat puzzling to the gamblers, particularly to one Chevalier de Méré. In quest of solutions to these problems de Méré sought the aid of Blaise Pascal, one of the foremost mathematicians of the day. Pascal became interested in the problems of chance, and the correspondence he carried on with his friend, Pierre de Fermat, concerning these problems constitutes the beginning of the mathematical theory of probability.

The early writers in the field formulated what is called the classical "definition" of probability. It may be stated as follows:

If a given trial or experiment can give rise to any one of n equally likely events, and m of these are called successes, then the probability of a success is given by the ratio m/n.

For example, if we toss a coin, two events (heads or tails) are possible, and if the coin is symmetrical and well constructed, we may assume that one outcome is as likely as the other. Thus, *n* equals 2. Now if we call "heads" a success, m equals 1. Therefore, the probability of heads resulting from the toss of a symmetrical coin is $\frac{1}{2}$.

If, instead of tossing a coin, we were to toss a symmetrical die, six outcomes would be possible. If we call the two-spot a success, then the probability of a two-spot turning up is $\frac{1}{6}$. Also, if we were to draw one marble from a bowl containing 50 red marbles and 100 white ones, the probability of getting a red marble would be $\frac{50}{150}$ or $\frac{1}{3}$. (All marbles are assumed to be of the same size and density and thoroughly mixed.) The probability of drawing a white one would be $\frac{2}{3}$.

It is important to be clear on the relationship between the terms *event* and *outcome*. We shall here observe the rule that *an outcome is one of the fundamental results that can happen as a result of a given experiment or trial, and an event consists of one or more outcomes.*

A particularly troublesome difficulty with the classical definition arises because of the phrase "equally likely." It is not only difficult to explain precisely what is meant by the phrase, but also very difficult at times to recognize a set of "equally likely" outcomes even when we feel we know what this means. A simple example involves the toss of two symmetrical coins. The problem is to find the probability of getting a head and a tail. We might reason that the coins could come up (1) both heads, (2) both tails, or (3) a head and a tail. Only one of these three outcomes is a success, so we might say the probability of a head and a tail is $\frac{1}{3}$. However, if we think a moment, we see that there are actually four equally likely outcomes instead of three. They may be indicated as follows: HH, HT, TH, TT.

The combination HT (a head and a tail) can happen in two ways. Thus the correct probability is $\frac{2}{4}$ or $\frac{1}{2}$.

Apparently there are fairly frequent occasions where equally likely events are tacitly assumed. The following seems to be such a case:

You have two chances—one of getting the germ and one of not. And if you get the germ you have two chances—one of getting the disease and one of not. And if you get the disease you have two chances—one of dying and one of not. And if you die—well, you still have two chances.[1]

---

[1] Author unknown. From *Today's Health*, Vol. 34 (March, 1956), p. 29. By permission of the Editorial Board.

If "equally likely" means "equally probable," then the classical "definition" is no definition at all, but only a circular statement wherein we use the idea of probability in the process of "defining" probability. Nevertheless, in a practical sense, the classical "definition" is still useful when we seek to compute the probabilities of various types of successes in games of chance.

Modern approaches to probability do away with the "equally likely" restriction and look upon the possible outcomes of an experiment as a set of undefined "points." Probabilities are then defined as numbers associated with each of these points, such numbers being nonnegative and having a sum equal to 1 for a whole set. These requirements result in a fundamental set of *mutually exclusive* outcomes, that is, a set wherein the occurrence of one outcome precludes the occurrence of the others on the same trial. (From the fundamental set, however, we may form *events* which are not mutually exclusive.)

As we know, an event consists of one or more outcomes. Now this cluster of outcomes is represented by a subset of points, and the probability of the event is given by the sum of the point values in its subset. For example, consider the experiment of drawing one card from a well-shuffled standard deck of 52 cards. The fundamental set of outcomes consists of 52 points. The event, drawing an ace, consists of 4 points, there being four aces in the deck. Now there is no indication, in the modern theory of probability, as to how the point values should be determined. If we have sufficient faith in the adequacy of the shuffling process, we may wish to consider the points equally valued at $\frac{1}{52}$. Then the probability of the event, drawing an ace, would be the sum of the 4 point values associated with aces, or $\frac{4}{52}$.

The same result would follow if we applied the classical definition of probability to this problem. Thus the classical definition, in the modern view, would be treated as a special case wherein equal values were assigned to the points (or outcomes). The classical writers on probability wrote a definition providing for equally valued outcomes and events because of the nature of the experiments they considered and the assumed symmetrical construction of the experimental devices involved (cards, dice, roulette wheels, and so on).

PROBABILITIES AS RELATIVE FREQUENCIES

As stated above, the modern theory of probability does not tell us how to find the point values which should be assigned to a set of fundamental outcomes. Evaluating probabilities is extremely important, however, to the practicing statistician. The *relative frequency* concept of probability indicates a way of making such evaluations. Usually we are interested in evaluating only that one of the outcomes or that group of outcomes which constitutes the event called a "success." Experience shows that after a large number of trials or repetitions of an experiment, the relative frequency or proportion of successes tends to stabilize or become constant at some particular value. It is this value which we shall call the probability of a success. We may frame a rough definition as follows: The probability of a success on one trial is the relative frequency of successes that occurs in the "long run," that is, the limit approached by the ratio, $\dfrac{\text{number of successes}}{\text{number of trials}}$ as the number of trials becomes indefinitely large.

Relative frequencies based not upon the theoretical "long run," but upon an actual finite number of trials are taken as *estimates* of the true probabilities. The student may wish to experiment himself by tossing a coin or a die an extremely large number of times until the frequency ratio tends to stabilize. He should define a success and after each trial compute the ratio, $\dfrac{\text{number of successes}}{\text{number of trials}}$. A few tosses each evening should make for a substantial total by the end of the semester.

The estimated probabilities found in mortality tables are based upon relative frequencies. Suppose, for example, we observe, during the winter of 1959–60, 50,486 persons who have just turned 65. Exactly one year later we observe this group again, but find now that there are exactly 48,460 persons who have survived the year. We then estimate the probability of living one more year (for persons aged 65) as $48,460/50,486 = .95987$. If it were not for estimates of this type, insurance companies would encounter great difficulty in trying to ascertain the correct premiums to charge.

In statistics, the important type of probability experiment or trial is the drawing of a sample of a certain size. We are interested in knowing how samples of a given size would turn out if we repeatedly drew them from a given population. For example, we might be interested in the relative frequency of samples having means lying within a specified range. But these ideas have taken us ahead of our story.

SYMBOLS AND RULES OF PROBABILITY

A probability ratio is denoted by the symbol Pr. The type of event called a success is sometimes indicated briefly in parentheses after the Pr. Thus Pr(heads) means "the probability of getting heads." Pr, in general, we recall, means the relative frequency of successes, whatever a success may be.

The value of Pr ranges from 0 to 1 inclusive. A probability of 0 denotes an impossible event, whereas a probability of 1 indicates an event that is certain to occur. The probability of our eventual death is 1. The probability that the national debt will be repaid tomorrow is 0.[2] But most of the ordinary events of life have probabilities lying between 0 and 1. A possible source of neuroses is the fact that we often cannot assign accurate estimates of probabilities to these occurrences.

The probability of a success not occurring, that is, the probability of failure, is given by $\overline{Pr}$, which equals $1 - Pr$. In tossing one die, with the two-spot being a success, $Pr = \frac{1}{6}$ and $\overline{Pr} = \frac{5}{6}$. That is, five of the sides are not two-spots, if we have a die of the ordinary sort.

The ratio of Pr to $\overline{Pr}$ gives the odds *for* success. The ratio of $\overline{Pr}$ to Pr gives the odds *against* success. In the tossing of a coin, where heads is a success, the odds are $\frac{1}{2}$ to $\frac{1}{2}$ or, as we usually put it, 1 to 1. In the long run, we have one part of success to one part of failure. In drawing a marble from the bowl containing 50 reds and 100 whites, and calling the drawing of a red a success, the odds are 1 to 2 for success or 2 to 1 against success.

Now in any game of chance, if the betting is in accordance with the true odds, the game is called a "fair game." If such is not the case, we have an unfair or "rigged" game. In tossing a symmetrical die with the two-spot being a success, the betting should be, for example, $1 that the two-spot will come up and $5 that it will not.

---

[2] Although it is conceivable that such events could have probabilities differing by extremely small amounts from 0 or 1, we assign 0 to events which for all practical purposes are impossible and 1 to events which for all practical purposes are certain.

In the long run, the two-spot will come up $\frac{1}{6}$ of the time. The person betting for a success will receive $5 on $\frac{1}{6}$ of the tosses, but will have to pay out $1 on $\frac{5}{6}$ of the tosses ($\frac{1}{6} \times \$5 = \frac{5}{6} \times \$1$). Eventually, in theory at least, a fair game will leave the players no richer or poorer than they were at the start. The rule to observe in such cases is to "get out of the game while you're still ahead" . . . provided this is socially and physically possible.

We say that the *mathematical expectation* is zero for each player in a fair game. That is, (amount to be won) $\times$ Pr(winning) $-$ (amount to be lost) $\times$ Pr(losing) $= 0$. In general, for a set of mutually exclusive events E_i, with values (gains or losses) V_i, the mathematical expectation is given by $\sum\limits_{i=1}^{n} V_i \Pr(E_i)$, where n is the number of events in the set. The symbol V_i is assigned positive values for gains and negative values for losses.

TWO THEOREMS ON PROBABILITY

In order to understand the principles underlying an important probability distribution called the binomial distribution, we must assimilate two probability theorems, one called the addition theorem and the other called the multiplication theorem.

The addition theorem for mutually exclusive events may be stated as follows: The probability that *any one* of several mutually exclusive events will occur is equal to the sum of their individual probabilities. For the case of two mutually exclusive events, A and B, we have, Pr(A or B) $=$ Pr(A) $+$ Pr(B). Events are mutually exclusive if the happening of one precludes the happening of the other(s). That is, if one happens, the other(s) cannot happen. In the case of a coin toss, if heads comes up, tails cannot come up on the same toss. In the case of a die, if the one-spot comes up, the 2, 3, 4, 5, or 6 cannot also come up. In drawing 3 marbles simultaneously from the bowl containing 50 reds and 100 whites, if two reds and a white occur, no other combination (for example, three whites) can occur on that draw.

Suppose we are drawing a marble from a bowl containing 50 reds, 100 whites, and 50 blues. What is the probability of getting a red or a white marble? Applying the addition theorem, we have: Pr(R or W) $=$ Pr(R) $+$ Pr(W) $= \frac{1}{4} + \frac{1}{2} = \frac{3}{4}$.

The multiplication theorem for independent events may be stated as follows: The probability that *all* of several independent events will occur is equal to the product of their individual probabilities. For the case of two independent events, C and D, we have $\Pr(C \text{ and } D) = \Pr(C) \cdot \Pr(D)$. Events are independent if the occurrence of one has no effect upon the occurrence of the others. That is, if one event happens, the others may or may not happen. For example, in tossing two dice, the way that the first turns up has no influence on the way that the second turns up.

Suppose that we are tossing two dice. What is the probability that 2 ones will turn up? Applying the multiplication theorem, we have: $\Pr(\text{one and one}) = \Pr(\text{one}) \cdot \Pr(\text{one}) = \frac{1}{6} \cdot \frac{1}{6} = \frac{1}{36}$. In drawing two marbles from the bowl containing 50 reds and 100 whites (and replacing the first marble before drawing the second), what is the probability of getting a red on the first draw and a white on the second? $\Pr(R \text{ and } W) = \Pr(R) \cdot \Pr(W) = \frac{1}{3} \cdot \frac{2}{3} = \frac{2}{9}$.

Incidentally, probabilities for all the possible outcomes that can arise from the toss of two dice are readily found from the following table:

$$
\begin{array}{cccccc}
1,1 & 1,2 & 1,3 & 1,4 & 1,5 & 1,6 \\
2,1 & 2,2 & 2,3 & 2,4 & 2,5 & 2,6 \\
3,1 & 3,2 & 3,3 & 3,4 & 3,5 & 3,6 \\
4,1 & 4,2 & 4,3 & 4,4 & 4,5 & 4,6 \\
5,1 & 5,2 & 5,3 & 5,4 & 5,5 & 5,6 \\
6,1 & 6,2 & 6,3 & 6,4 & 6,5 & 6,6 \\
\end{array}
$$

We may look upon these outcomes as a set of points under the modern concept of probability, each pair of digits being represented by one point.

There are 36 pairs of digits in all. The first digit in any pair indicates the outcome on the first die and the second digit indicates the outcome on the second die. Equal sums are indicated on the diagonals of the square running from the lower left to the upper right. In the longest such diagonal we find six pairs of digits, each pair adding to 7. Thus this subset indicates that the probability of rolling a 7 with two dice is $\frac{6}{36}$ or $\frac{1}{6}$. Similarly, the probability of rolling an 8 is $\frac{5}{36}$.

PROBABILITY DISTRIBUTIONS

A probability distribution is a relative frequency distribution which gives probabilities *for all the various events* that can result from a given type of trial. For example, take the set of events that could arise in selecting one marble from the bowl containing 50 reds and 100 whites. Only two events are possible, a red marble or a white marble. The probability of the former is ⅓ and of the latter, ⅔. If the drawing of a red marble is denoted by 0 and the drawing of a white marble by 1, we may graph the probability distribution as shown in Figure 7–1.

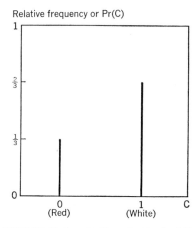

FIGURE 7–1. A Simple Probability Distribution

Now let 0 and 1 be values of the variable C (C for color). A possible general formula for the probability of C would be $Pr(C) = \frac{1}{3}(C + 1)$. If we substitute 0 for C in the formula, $Pr(C) = \frac{1}{3}$, and if we substitute 1 for C, $Pr(C) = \frac{2}{3}$. These results correspond with what the graph shows. All of the probability distributions found in this book can be represented by both graphs and formulas.

THE BINOMIAL DISTRIBUTION: A DISCRETE PROBABILITY DISTRIBUTION

One of the important probability distributions in statistics is the binomial distribution. As we shall see later, it is a type of *sampling distribution.* If we are dealing with sets of n independent events and each of these events consists of two mutually exclusive outcomes, the binomial distribution applies; it gives us the probabilities of all the various ways that the *set* of n events can occur. For example, suppose we have a bowl of marbles with half of the marbles red and half of them white. Suppose further that we are selecting (with replacement) sets of three marbles each from this bowl. In sampling *with replacement,* we select one marble, note its color, and replace it in the bowl before drawing the second marble; we note the color of the second marble and replace it before drawing the third. Three marbles drawn in succession constitute a series or set of three independent events. Now the various combinations [3] of marbles that can occur in a set of three are WWW, RWW, RRW, and RRR. The binomial distribution can give us the probability of getting any one of these four combinations, that is, the probability of drawing 3 white (no red) marbles, the probability of getting 1 red and 2 whites, the probability of getting 2 reds and 1 white, or the probability of 3 reds.

The probabilities of these various outcomes are computed in terms of n, x, P, and Q. Now n equals the number of independent trials in a set; for the above example, $n = 3$. Next, x equals the number of successes in a set. Here we shall define a red marble as a success; x may take on the whole number values from 0 to n inclusive. The letter P is the probability of a success on *one* trial. In the example, $P = \frac{1}{2}$, the probability of getting a red marble on one draw. The letter Q equals $1 - P$, the probability of getting a nonred or white marble on one draw. In the example, $Q = \frac{1}{2}$.

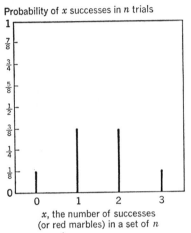

Probability of x successes in n trials

x, the number of successes (or red marbles) in a set of n

FIGURE 7–2. **Binomial Distribution with $P = \frac{1}{2}$ and $n = 3$**

Let us next show the graph of the binomial distribution of our example and then go on to explain how the probabilities were arrived at. The graph is given in Figure 7–2.

Let us rewrite the values of x and underneath each of them indicate the various ways that these values can occur:

0	1	2	3	x, the number of red
WWW	RWW	RRW	RRR	marbles in a set of 3
	WRW	RWR		
	WWR	WRR		

We note that there are three ways in which 1 red marble can occur and also three ways in which 2 red marbles can occur. Zero red marbles can occur in only one way (WWW) and 3 red marbles

[3] See p. 139 for the concept of a combination.

can occur only in one way (RRR). All in all we have eight possible "equally likely" events, each consisting of an arrangement of 3 marbles. Since 0 red marbles (or WWW) can happen in only one way out of 8, the probability for this event is ⅛. Three of the eight sets contain 1 red marble; the probability here is thus ⅜. It is readily seen that the probability of 2 red marbles is also ⅜ and that the probability of 3 red marbles is ⅛.

The various arrangements of 3 marbles each are equally likely because P equals Q. To clarify this statement, we utilize the addition and multiplication theorems. We begin with the multiplication theorem. We know that the probability of getting a red marble on one draw is ½ and that the probability of getting a white marble on one draw is also ½. The outcome of any draw is independent of the outcome of any other draw. Thus WWW represents a result of three independent selections or trials. Applying the multiplication theorem, we find $\Pr(W \text{ and } W \text{ and } W) = \Pr(W) \cdot \Pr(W) \cdot \Pr(W) = ½ \cdot ½ \cdot ½ = ⅛$. Similarly, the probability of RWW is ⅛, the probability of WRW is ⅛, and the probability of WWR is ⅛. But note that RWW, WRW, and WWR are three *mutually exclusive arrangements* (or events) even though each of them contains exactly 1 R and 2 W's. That is, if the three outcomes occur in the order RWW, they cannot at the same time occur in the order WRW or WWR. Thus we combine their probabilities by the addition theorem to find the probability that $x = 1$, that is, the probability that a set of three marbles contains exactly 1 red marble. Applying the addition theorem, we have, $\Pr(RWW \text{ or } WRW \text{ or } WWR) = \Pr(RWW) + \Pr(WRW) + \Pr(WWR) = ⅛ + ⅛ + ⅛ = ⅜$. Thus the probability that $x = 1$ is ⅜. The same type of argument holds in finding the probability that $x = 0$, the probability that $x = 2$, and the probability that $x = 3$.

We can now find a general formula that will give us the probabilities of drawing x red marbles in a set of 3. Instead of restricting P to the value ½, let the proportion of reds in the bowl be *any value P* (between 0 and 1) and let $Q = 1 - P$ or the proportion of white marbles in the bowl. The letter P, we recall, represents the probability of getting a red marble on one draw, and Q is the probability of getting a white marble on one draw. In short, $\Pr(R) = P$, and $\Pr(W) = Q$.

Writing the values of x and the probabilities of these various values in terms of P and Q, we have:

0	1	2	3	x, the number of red marbles out of 3
QQQ	PQQ	PPQ	PPP	
	QPQ	PQP		
	QQP	QPP		

Q^3	$3PQ^2$	$3P^2Q$	P^3	Terms giving the probability of x red marbles out of 3

The probabilities of the various values of x are given in the last row. We could rewrite these terms as follows, so that both P and Q appear in each term and each term has a stated coefficient:

$$(1)P^0Q^3 \qquad (3)P^1Q^2 \qquad (3)P^2Q^1 \qquad (1)P^3Q^0$$

Now note that the exponents of the P's are identical with the values of x. For example, in the term giving us the probability that $x = 0$, the exponent of P is 0. This situation is the rule because of the fact that the probability of any arrangement of a 3-marble combination is found by the multiplication theorem. *The exponent of Q in any term will be 3 minus the exponent of P in that term.* This rule also follows from the application of the multiplication theorem.

THE GENERAL BINOMIAL FORMULA

Now, if n were no longer 3 but any whole number, the exponents of P would correspond to the values of x and the exponents on Q would be $n - x$. Thus the portion of any one of the probability terms exclusive of the coefficient would be equal to P^xQ^{n-x}. Or, we may say that the probability of x successes in a series of n independent trials is given by P^xQ^{n-x} multiplied by a coefficient. Our remaining problem is to find a general formula for this coefficient.

We have noted that the probability of each value of x is computed from a certain combination of P's and Q's. There are n factors in each combination; x of them are P's and $n - x$ of them are Q's. And the number of ways that each combination of P's and Q's can be arranged indicates the number of P^xQ^{n-x} terms that must be added in accordance with the addition theorem so as to get the probability of x. Thus if we had a general formula for the number of ways n things can be arranged when x of them are P's and $n - x$ of them are Q's, we would have a formula for the coefficients we seek. Such a formula is $\binom{n}{x}$, which may be read "n above x."

It is equal to $\dfrac{n!}{x!(n-x)!}$, but for our immediate purposes we need not be concerned with the formula. A detailed explanation of this formula is given in the appendix at the end of this chapter. Here we shall merely call the symbol $\binom{n}{x}$ a binomial coefficient. A bit later we shall show some simple methods of evaluating the coefficient, but at present we want to write out the general formula for the binomial distribution. It is:

$$\Pr(x) = \binom{n}{x} P^x Q^{n-x}$$

This formula gives us the probability of exactly x successes in a series of n independent trials, where n and P are given and P the probability of success on one trial. As x takes on different values $(0, 1, 2, 3, \cdots n)$, the formula gives the required probabilities for the various numbers of successes. Thus we have one formula for a whole distribution of probabilities.

For every different pair of n and P values we have a different binomial distribution. If $P = \frac{1}{2}$, the distribution is symmetrical; if P is less than $\frac{1}{2}$, the distribution is skewed to the right; if P is greater than $\frac{1}{2}$, the distribution is skewed to the left.

Let us apply the formula to a simple problem where P is not equal to $\frac{1}{2}$. If we have a bowl of 150 marbles of which 50 are red and 100 white, and if we draw 5 marbles with replacement, what is the probability that exactly 3 of them will be red? Here we are asking for the probability of 3 successes in 5 independent trials when the probability of success on one trial is $\frac{1}{3}$. The values to be substituted in the formula are as follows:

$$n = 5$$
$$x = 3$$
$$P = \tfrac{1}{3}$$
$$Q = \tfrac{2}{3}$$

Substituting in the formula, $\Pr(x) = \binom{n}{x} P^x Q^{n-x}$, we have

$$\Pr(x = 3) = \binom{5}{3} (\tfrac{1}{3})^3 (\tfrac{2}{3})^{5-3}$$

$$= 10(\tfrac{1}{27})(\tfrac{2}{3})^2$$

$$= 10(\tfrac{1}{27})(\tfrac{4}{9}) = \tfrac{40}{243} = .1646$$

The probability of getting exactly 3 red marbles out of 5 is .1646.

BINOMIAL COEFFICIENTS

Now, the question is: Where did we get the value 10 for $\binom{5}{3}$ in the problem just discussed? We found it in a table called Pascal's triangle of binomial coefficients. A portion of such a triangle is given below:

n\\x	0	1	2	3	4	5
0	1					
1	1	1				
2	1	2	1			
3	1	3	3	1		
4	1	4	6	4	1	
5	1	5	10	10	5	1

If we locate 5 in the n column (left-hand margin of the table) and then move across the row to the right of 5 until we are below the x value 3, we find 10, which is the value of $\binom{5}{3}$.

The student can easily make out his own Pascal's triangle if he notes that any number in the body of the table is equal to the sum of the first number due north and the first number due northwest in the table. Thus, the 10 we have located in the table is equal to 4 (which lies due north of 10) plus 6 (which lies due northwest of 10).

Another way to evaluate $\binom{n}{x}$ is to consider it as a ratio. To form the numerator we start writing $n!$ ("n factorial") but stop after the first x factors have been written. To form the denominator, we merely write $x!$ ("x factorial"). For example, if $n = 5$ and $x = 3$, we have $\binom{n}{x} = \dfrac{5 \cdot 4 \cdot 3}{3 \cdot 2 \cdot 1} = \dfrac{60}{6} = 10$. This method works well except for the case where $x = 0$. In that case, the ratio is equal to 1.

By now the student has perhaps recalled enough of his algebra to remember that $\binom{n}{x} P^x Q^{n-x}$ is the formula for the general term in the binomial expansion, $(Q + P)^n$. Hence the term *binomial distribution*.

The binomial distribution is similar to the frequency distributions of attribute data we have discussed above (Ch. 4). But the binomial distribution is a *theoretical model* and its frequencies are, we should remember, expressed as *relative* frequencies or probabilities.

MEAN AND STANDARD DEVIATION OF THE BINOMIAL DISTRIBUTION

As in the case of any other frequency distribution, the binomial distribution has a mean and standard deviation. The mathematics behind the derivation of the formulas is on too high a level for beginning students, so we will have to accept them without proof. They are as follows: [4]

$\mu = nP$ (Mean of the binomial distribution)

$\sigma = \sqrt{nPQ}$ (Standard deviation of the binomial distribution)

Although we have accepted the formulas on faith, let us at least verify the fact that the mean of the binomial distribution graphed on page 115 (Fig. 7–2) is given by the formula $\mu = nP$. Using the formula for the mean of a distribution having relative frequencies (see p. 66), we compute the mean as follows:

$$\bar{x} = \Sigma \frac{f_i}{n} x_i$$

Since probabilities are relative frequencies, we may write an analogous formula for the mean of the binomial distribution:

$$\mu = \Sigma \; \Pr(x) \cdot x$$

The binomial distribution of Figure 7–2 and the computation of its mean are shown below:

x	$\Pr(x)$	$\Pr(x) \cdot x$
0	$\frac{1}{8}$	0
1	$\frac{3}{8}$	$\frac{3}{8}$
2	$\frac{3}{8}$	$\frac{6}{8}$
3	$\frac{1}{8}$	$\frac{3}{8}$
		$\frac{12}{8}$

$$\mu = \tfrac{12}{8} = \tfrac{3}{2}$$

[4] Both μ and σ are parameters. That is, their values are fixed for each particular binomial distribution but change as we go from one binomial distribution to another.

Using the formula $\mu = nP$, we arrive at the same result, for $\mu = 3 \cdot \frac{1}{2} = \frac{3}{2}$.

The binomial distribution has widespread applications in business and economic statistics. Whenever we are drawing samples from a population for which the bowl of red and white marbles is an appropriate model, the distribution almost always applies. For example, batches of manufactured products are populations consisting of defectives and nondefectives, the persons in the labor force are either employed or unemployed, residential dwelling units are either owner-occupied or not owner-occupied.

The binomial distribution, we recall, is based on the assumption that we are sampling *with* replacement. In most practical sampling problems we sample without replacement, but if the number of elements (N) in the population is fairly large, and NP and NQ are large relative to n, sampling without replacement will not noticeably affect the values of P and Q.

MODIFIED BINOMIAL DISTRIBUTION

Often we wish to know the probabilities of various *proportions* of successes in a series of n trials rather than *numbers* of successes. In other words, we want the values of x in relative terms. This modification is accomplished simply by dividing each value of x in the binomial distribution by n. We know that if each value in a set of data is divided by a constant (such as n) the mean and standard deviation are both divided by that constant. (See appendix to Ch. 6.) Thus, the mean and standard deviation of the modified binomial distribution are as follows:

$$\mu = \frac{nP}{n} = P$$

$$\sigma = \frac{\sqrt{nPQ}}{n} = \sqrt{\frac{PQ}{n}}$$

We shall, in Chapter 9 of this book, find more occasion to use the modified binomial distribution than the original form. Graphically, the modified binomial distribution where $n = 5$ and $P = \frac{1}{3}$ is given in Figure 7–3.

Although our expressing x in relative terms does not alter the values of $\Pr(x)$, we may wish to symbolize the probabilities of the

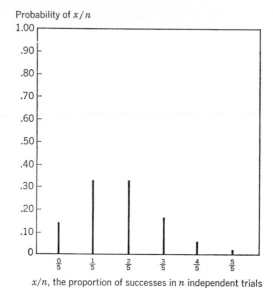

FIGURE 7–3. Modified Binomial Distribution with $n = 5$ and $P = \frac{1}{3}$

modified binomial distribution as $\Pr(x/n)$. Thus $\Pr(x) = \Pr(x/n)$
$= \binom{n}{x} P^x Q^{n-x}$.

THE POISSON DISTRIBUTION

As indicated previously, the binomial distribution is symmetrical only if $P = \frac{1}{2}$; as P becomes less than $\frac{1}{2}$, the distribution becomes skewed to the right (see Fig. 7–3); as P becomes greater than $\frac{1}{2}$, the distribution becomes skewed to the left. Now, if for a given binomial distribution having mean $\mu = nP$ we let n become very large and let P become very small in such a manner that the product nP remains constant, we eventually arrive at the Poisson (pronounced "pwa-soan") distribution.[5] It is a discrete probability distribution having extreme positive skewness. The formula is:

$$\Pr(x) = \frac{e^{-\lambda}\lambda^x}{x!}$$

where e is the constant $2.71828 \cdots$, the base of the Napierian system of logarithms, and λ is both the mean of the distribution

[5] The detailed steps in this transition involve a higher level of mathematical proficiency than we have assumed for the readers of this book.

and the variance. Because of this dual role, the new symbol is more appropriate than either μ or σ. λ is the Greek letter "lambda." $\lambda = nP$.

In practical applications the symbol x of the Poisson distribution may be thought of in the same light as the x of the binomial, that is, x represents the number of successes in n independent trials, but in the case of the Poisson, to repeat, n is very large, while P is very small. That is, the number of trials is very large but the probability of success on one trial is slight.

Although the Poisson distribution has widespread applications in industrial statistics today, its classic application is a rather curious one. The distribution years ago was found to be very closely approximated by the numbers of annual deaths per Prussian Cavalry Corps caused by the kick of a horse. In the formula, $x = 0$ would represent no deaths per corps, $x = 1$ would represent 1 death per corps, and so on.

In modern industrial production, we find that the Poisson distribution is often a good model for the relative frequency distribution of the number of defects per manufactured product or the number of defects per sample of n manufactured products. E. L. Grant cites several examples of distributions for which the Poisson is a good model.[6]

In the analysis of inventory problems, we sometimes assume that the demand for a given good conforms closely to a Poisson distribution. The variable x represents the number of units of a good demanded per unit of time, for example, per month or per week. Substitution of 0 for x in the Poisson formula would give the estimated probability that 0 units would be demanded; substitution of 1 for x would give the probability that 1 unit would be demanded, and so on.

Suppose that we are operating a housewares department in a large department store, and that our inventory system enables us to begin each week with a stock of 4 deluxe-type egg beaters. Suppose further that the demand for the egg beaters is distributed as a Poisson distribution with a mean of 3, that is, $\lambda = 3$. What is the probability that more than 4 egg beaters per week will be demanded, causing us to run out of stock?

To find the answer, we must substitute 0, 1, 2, 3, and 4 in the Poisson formula. For each substitution we get a probability figure.

6 E. L. Grant, *Statistical Quality Control*, 2d ed. (New York, McGraw-Hill Book Co., Inc., 1952), p. 214.

These figures must be added to get the probability that 4 egg beaters *or less* will be demanded. Then this sum must be subtracted from 1 to get the probability that *more than* 4 egg beaters per day will be demanded.

Substituting the x values, 0, 1, 2, 3, 4 in the formula, $\Pr(x) = \dfrac{e^{-\lambda}\lambda^{x}}{x!}$, we have:

x	$\Pr(x)$
0	e^{-3} (By definition, $0! = 1$)
1	$e^{-3}(3)$
2	$e^{-3}(9)/2$
3	$e^{-3}(27)/6$
4	$e^{-3}(81)/24$

Taking $e = 2.71828$, we find that $e^3 = 20.0855$. Thus $e^{-3} = \dfrac{1}{20.0855}$. We may rewrite our computations, then, as follows:

x	$\Pr(x)$
0	$\dfrac{1}{20.0855} = .049787$
1	$\dfrac{3}{20.0855} = .149361$
2	$\dfrac{9}{20.0855(2)} = .224042$
3	$\dfrac{27}{20.0855(6)} = .224042$
4	$\dfrac{81}{20.0855(24)} = .168032$

The sum of the $\Pr(x)$ values is .815264. Subtracting this sum from 1, we have .184736, which is the probability that more than 4 egg beaters per week will be demanded.

Our example is oversimplified, but it should serve to open the door a crack to one important application of the Poisson distribution.

THE NORMAL DISTRIBUTION

Of more fundamental importance in statistics than the Poisson is the normal distribution. It is a continuous probability distribu-

tion which also may be looked upon as a limiting form of the binomial distribution. That is, if $P = \frac{1}{2}$ in the binomial distribution
and n becomes indefinitely large, the result is the normal distribution. Again, the detailed steps in the transition are on too high
a mathematical level for discussion in this book. Let us, however,
become familiar with the normal distribution by describing some
of its prominent characteristics.

In general, we may say that the normal distribution is a par-

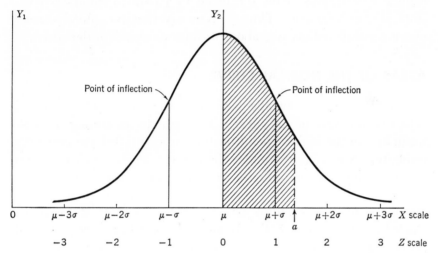

**FIGURE 7–4. Normal Curve Representing a Population (Measurement
Data)**

ticular type of symmetrical relative frequency distribution having
a frequency curve shaped like the cross-section of a bell. The
frequency curve in Figure 7–4 represents a normally distributed
population.

The mean is measured along the X scale of the horizontal axis
from 0 to the point directly under the highest point on the curve.
Points lying whole multiples of the standard deviation from the
mean may be indicated by the symbols $\mu + \sigma$, $\mu - \sigma$, and so forth,
on the X scale. The point on the curve lying directly above $\mu + \sigma$
is a *point of inflection* as is the point on the curve lying directly
above $\mu - \sigma$. A point of inflection is a point at which the direction
of curvature changes. That portion of the curve lying between
the two points of inflection is concave downward, that is, the inside
of the curve is facing downward. Beyond the points of inflection
toward either extreme, the curve is concave upward, that is, the

inside of the curve is facing upward. Points of inflection are always located in these positions (directly above $\mu + \sigma$ and $\mu - \sigma$) on any normal curve.

The extremes (or "tails") of the curve approach closer and closer to the horizontal axis as X becomes extremely large or extremely small.

From the graph, we can see that practically all of the area under the curve lies above the range extending from a point 3 standard deviations below the mean to a point 3 standard deviations above the mean. Thus we may say that the effective range of a normal distribution is about 6 times its standard deviation.

AREAS OF THE NORMAL CURVE

A line drawn perpendicularly from the X axis to the curve is called an *ordinate* of the curve. The ordinate extending from the mean (μ) to the highest point on the curve is called the maximum ordinate. Now the area under the curve lying between the maximum ordinate and an ordinate erected at some other point (for example, at $X = a$: see Fig. 7–4) on the X axis represents the relative frequency of values falling between the mean and a. (See the shaded portion of Fig. 7–4.) In general, the relative frequency (or proportion) of values lying in any given range along the X axis is indicated by the area under the curve standing on top of that range. Such an area, of course, also represents a probability; note, however, that it does *not* represent the probability that X is equal to a particular value; it represents the probability that X *falls within a certain range*. This fact constitutes the important distinguishing characteristic that sets a continuous probability distribution apart from a discrete probability distribution.

The X scale of a normal curve is laid off in units of the particular distribution we wish to represent. The measurements may be in terms of dollars, feet, pounds, miles, or some other unit. Now in order to have a general model that is applicable to *any* particular normal distribution, we convert to a new horizontal scale. This new scale is called the Z scale; the zero point is at the mean of the distribution, and the unit of measure is one standard deviation. The Z scale is laid off directly beneath the X scale in Figure 7–4. Note that by setting $\mu = 0$ we have shifted the vertical axis from Y_1 to Y_2. On the Z scale $+1$ represents a value that is 1 standard deviation bigger than the mean; the number -1.5 represents a value that is $1\frac{1}{2}$ standard deviations less than the mean, and so on. The algebraic formula that transforms the X scale into the Z scale is $Z = \dfrac{X - \mu}{\sigma}$. The numerator, of course, gives us the difference between any value of X and the mean. The division by σ gives us the number of standard deviations contained in this difference. Having converted to the Z scale, we call the curve a *standardized* normal curve; it represents a normal distribution with mean 0 and standard deviation 1.

THE TABLE OF AREAS OF THE STANDARDIZED NORMAL CURVE

Since areas under the normal curve are probabilities or relative frequencies, the total area under the curve is equal to 1. The area between the maximum ordinate and the ordinate at the point where Z equals 1 is .3413. Since the curve is symmetrical, the area from the maximum ordinate to the ordinate at -1 on the Z scale is also .3413. Thus, the proportion of values lying within one standard deviation of the mean (in any normal distribution) is equal to .3413 + .3413 or .6826 (about $\frac{2}{3}$). Similarly, the proportion of values lying within two standard deviations of the mean is .4772 + .4772 or .9544. And the proportion of values lying within three standard deviations of the mean is .9973.

Now suppose we want to know the proportion of values which lie between the mean and a point 1.28 standard deviations above the mean. The answer is readily found in the Table of Areas Under the Normal Curve (Table I, p. 340). This table gives us the area between the ordinate at the mean and an ordinate located Z standard deviations from the mean. Since the curve is symmetrical, the table refers to only half of the curve. We locate our Z value (1.28) in the left-hand and top margins of the table and read off the corresponding area in the body of the table. That is, we first find 1.2 in the left-hand margin and then move across the page to the right until we are directly below .08, which appears in the top margin to give us the second decimal place in Z. The area value in the spot where we have landed is .3997, which is the answer to our problem. About 40% of the values lie between the mean and a value 1.28 standard deviations above the mean. Graphically, the solution to our problem is shown in Figure 7–5.

The student should verify from the table that .3413 is the area

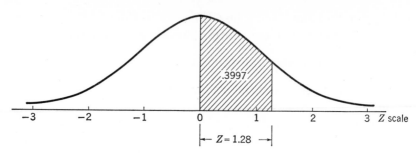

FIGURE 7–5. Standardized Normal Curve. Proportion of Total Area Lying Between 0 and 1.28

value corresponding to a Z value of 1, and that .4772 is the area value corresponding to a Z value of 2.

PROBLEMS INVOLVING USE OF THE AREA TABLE

In order that we may become quite familiar with the table of areas of the normal curve, let us solve several problems requiring its use. All problems involve the accounts receivable balances of the Last Resort Loan Company, which form a normal population having a mean of $76.50 and a standard deviation of $24.50.

Problem 1. Find the proportion of the accounts lying between $54.50 and the mean. First let us diagram the problem (Fig. 7–6).

The shaded portion of Figure 7–6 is the area giving us the required answer. We know immediately that $54.50 is less than the mean, but in order to look up the area in the table we must know how many *standard deviations* it lies from the mean. This number of standard deviations is Z, which we find by substituting in the formula, $Z = \dfrac{X - \mu}{\sigma}$. We find that $Z = \dfrac{54.50 - 76.50}{24.50} = -.898$, or $-.90$. Thus it is $-.90$ of a standard deviation from 76.50 to 54.50.

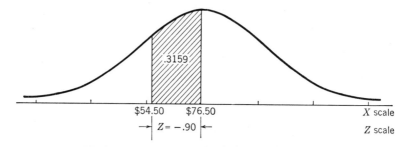

FIGURE 7–6. Use of Area Table: Problem 1

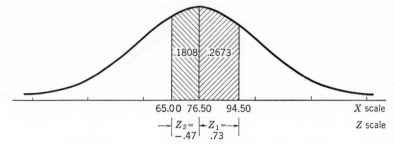

65.00 76.50   94.50   X scale

$\leftarrow|Z_2=|\leftarrow Z_1=\rightarrow|$ Z scale
$\quad -.47| \quad .73$

FIGURE 7–7.   Use of Area Table: Problem 2

Going to the area table, we find that the area between the mean and
$-.90$ on the Z scale is .3159, which is the answer to our problem.

Problem 2. What per cent of the accounts lie between $65.00
and $94.50? Again let us diagram the problem (Fig. 7–7).

Because the table of areas refers to only one-half of the curve
and gives us only areas which are bounded on one side by the maximum ordinate, we will, in this case, have to compute two Z values.
Call them Z_1 and Z_2.

Area

$$Z_1 = \frac{94.50 - 76.50}{24.50} = .73 \qquad\qquad .2673$$

$$Z_2 = \frac{65.00 - 76.50}{24.50} = -.47 \qquad\qquad \underline{.1808}$$

$$.4481 \text{ or } 44.81\%$$

To get our answer, we look up the areas corresponding to each of
the Z values and then add the areas. Figure 7–7 shows at a glance
why we must follow this procedure. But a common error that
students make is to add the Z values with the idea that they will
then have to find only one area figure in the table. This procedure
does not save time if we are interested in getting the correct answer.

Problem 3. What per cent of the accounts lie between $25.00
and $50.00? Drawing a diagram of this problem (Fig. 7–8), we
portray the fact that both of the X values lie below the mean. Here
again we must compute two values of Z.

Area

$$Z_1 = \frac{25.00 - 76.50}{24.50} = \frac{-51.50}{24.50} = -2.10 \qquad\qquad .4821$$

$$Z_2 = \frac{50.00 - 76.50}{24.50} = \frac{-26.50}{24.50} = -1.08 \qquad\qquad \underline{.3599}$$

$$.1222$$

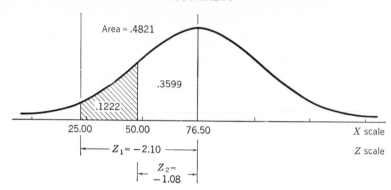

FIGURE 7–8. Use of Area Table: Problem 3

Proceeding from Z_1 in the table, we find the area lying between the mean and 25.00. The area corresponding to Z_2 stretches from the mean to 50.00. We must subtract the second area from the first to get the area between 25.00 and 50.00, which is the shaded portion of Figure 7–8 and equal to .1222.

As a general rule, when the problem involves two X values and we wish to find the area between them, we subtract two areas when both X's are on the same side of the mean and add two areas when the X's are on opposite sides of the mean.

Problem 4. What is the probability that an account selected at random will be less than \$35.00? Drawing a diagram of this problem (Fig. 7–9), we show that \$35.00 is somewhat more than 1 standard deviation below the mean.

In this case the area we seek is on the left-hand extreme of the curve and must be evaluated indirectly. First let us compute the appropriate value of Z. $Z = \dfrac{35.00 - 76.50}{24.50} = -1.69$. Looking this value up in the table, we find the area under the curve between 76.50 and 35.00, which is .4545. But this is not the area we want.

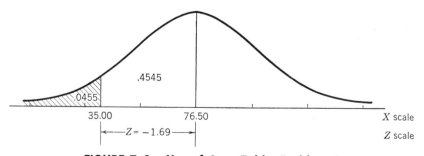

FIGURE 7–9. Use of Area Table: Problem 4

Since half of the area under the curve is below the mean, we find the area below 35.00 (or below -1.69 on the Z scale) by subtracting .4545 from .5000. This procedure gives .0455 as the answer to the problem.

Problem 5. What, approximately, is the smallest account in the largest 10% of the accounts? In this problem we, in effect, reverse the procedure followed in the previous problems, for here an area value is given and we are required to find a certain X value. A diagram of the problem is given below (Fig. 7–10).

The largest 10% of the accounts lies on the extreme right-hand portion of the curve. We go to the table immediately and look up

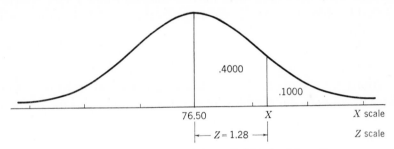

.4000

.1000

76.50 X X scale

$\longleftarrow Z = 1.28 \longrightarrow$ Z scale

FIGURE 7–10. Use of Area Table: Problem 5

an area value to get the corresponding Z. But we do not enter the table with .10, for we recall that the table gives only areas that are bounded on one side by the ordinate at the mean. We enter the table with $.5000 - .1000$ or .4000. Now the closest value in the body of the table to .4000 is .3997, so we take the Z corresponding to that, which is 1.28. The X value we seek separates off the highest 10% of the X values from the rest of the distribution. Thus it is 1.28 standard deviations greater than the mean. In symbols, $X = \mu + 1.28\sigma$. Substituting, we have $X = 76.50 + 1.28(24.50)$ $= 76.50 + 31.36 = 107.86$. We arrive at the same answer, of course, by substituting in $Z = \dfrac{X - \mu}{\sigma}$ and solving for X.

There are other variations on the above types of problems, but the five examples given should enable the student to work his way through any of the modifications.[7]

[7] In the problems given, we have assumed that the X values were measured *exactly* on a continuous scale. Actual observations, of course, would be accurate only to the nearest scale segment, so each observed X value would have to be adjusted by adding or subtracting half a segment before it was substituted in the Z formula. Adjustments of this type are especially important, as we shall see in Chapter 8, in the normal curve approximation to the binomial distribution.

NORMAL AND NONNORMAL POPULATIONS

Many populations of business and economic data conform very closely to the normal curve. For example, if pistons are being produced in an auto parts plant, all pistons will not be of *exactly* the same diameter. The diameters will vary in accordance with the normal curve (with a very small standard deviation, of course). Service lives of various items, for example, telephone poles and vacuum tubes, conform very closely to normal distributions. For large groups of persons of the same age, race, and sex, bodily measurements such as height form normal distributions, a fact which is of considerable importance to manufacturers and distributors of ready-made clothing.

The student should not infer that most population distributions are normal in form. However, in the case of nonnormal distributions we are often able to find mathematical transformations that will convert the distributions to the normal form for purposes of analysis. Such techniques are treated in more advanced statistics courses.

In addition to serving as a theoretical model for a population, the normal curve is also extremely important as a model for certain *sampling distributions,* as we shall see in the next chapter.

SUMMARY

If a given action, trial, or experiment can give rise to any one of several outcomes and if certain specified outcomes constitute a success, then the relative frequency of successes over a very long series of trials is called the probability of a success.

The probability of any given event (a "success") is symbolized by Pr. Often a brief symbolical description of the event follows in parentheses after the Pr. The value of Pr ranges from 0 to 1, 0 indicating an impossible event and 1 indicating an event that is certain.

The probability of failure is denoted by $\bar{P}r$, which is equal to $1 - Pr$. The ratio of Pr to $\bar{P}r$ gives the odds *for* an event. The ratio of $\bar{P}r$ to Pr gives the odds *against* a given event. In a game of chance, if the betting is in proportion to the true odds, the contest is called a fair game.

Two special cases of probability theorems are important for our purposes in this course. The addition theorem for two mutually exclusive events, A and B, may be stated in symbols as follows: $Pr(A \text{ or } B) = Pr(A) + Pr(B)$. The multiplication theorem for two independent events may be given as follows: $Pr (C \text{ and } D) = Pr (C) \cdot Pr(D)$,

A probability distribution is a relative frequency distribution which gives probabilities for all the various events that can result from a given probability experiment. In tossing a coin, we may say that two events are possible, heads or tails. For an unbiased or true coin, the probability distribution for these two events could be graphed as in Figure 7–11.

The binomial distribution is an extremely important type of probability distribution. It is a discrete distribution giving the probabilities of x successes in a series of n independent trials, where the probability (P) of success on one trial is given as well as n. The (discrete) variable x takes on the value 0 and the whole number values from 1 to n. We may develop the formula for the binomial distribution from the two probability theorems discussed above. The n trials may be thought of as a sample of n elements from a population that is divided between two types of elements in the ratio P to Q. Sampling is assumed to be with replacement.

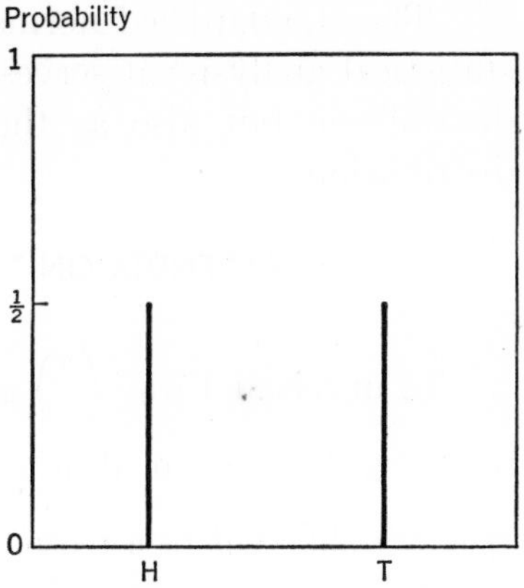

The formula for the binomial distribution is $\Pr(x) = \binom{n}{x} P^x Q^{n-x}$. The mean of the binomial distribution is given by the formula $\mu = nP$, and the standard deviation by $\sigma = \sqrt{nPQ}$.

If the variable x in a binomial distribution is stated in relative terms, that is, if each value of x is divided by n, we have the modified binomial distribution. The mean of this distribution is equal to P and the standard deviation is given by $\sigma = \sqrt{\dfrac{PQ}{n}}$.

FIGURE 7–11. Probability Distribution of Heads and Tails (True Coin)

The Poisson distribution, also a discrete probability distribution, may be derived from the binomial distribution. It has a marked degree of positive skewness. The value of P is very small and n is very large. Distributions of defects per manufactured product or defects per group of products often conform closely to the Poisson distribution.

The normal distribution is a continuous probability distribution. It is represented graphically by a frequency curve which resembles the cross-section of a bell. An area under the curve standing on top of a given interval (on the X axis) represents the probability that the value of X will fall in that interval. Any normal distribution is converted to the standard normal distribution by means of the following transformation:

$$Z = \frac{X - \mu}{\sigma}$$

The standard normal distribution has a mean of zero and a standard deviation equal to one. Areas under the curve between the ordinate at the mean and an ordinate at Z standard deviations from the mean are given in the Table of Areas Under the Normal Curve (p. 340).

The standardized normal distribution is a very useful tool of statistical analysis; it serves not only as a model for a population distribution but also as the model for more than one sampling distribution.

APPENDIX ON THE BINOMIAL COEFFICIENT

To understand why $\binom{n}{x}$ gives us the number of ways n things can be arranged when x of them are alike and of one kind while $(n - x)$ of them are alike but of a second kind, let us consider the formula $\binom{n}{x} = \frac{n!}{x!(n - x)!}$. Take first the numerator of the right member. The symbol $n!$ (n factorial) represents the number of ways that n different things can be arranged in a row. This is so because the first position in the row can be filled in n ways, and after this position is filled, the second can be filled in $(n - 1)$ ways. Each of the n ways of filling the first position can be combined with any one of the $(n - 1)$ ways of filling the second position. Thus we have $n(n - 1)$ ways of filling the first two positions. Similarly there will be $n(n - 1)(n - 2)$ ways of filling the first three positions. Finally we see that there will be $n(n - 1)(n - 2)(n - 3)(n - 4) \cdots 1$ or $n!$ ways of filling the n positions.

It is clear also that the number of ways that x different things can be arranged in a row is $x!$ and the number of ways that $(n - x)$ different things can be arranged is $(n - x)!$.

In arrangements of the n things, the x things are interspersed in different ways among the others, and if the x things were different, there would be $x!$ arrangements of the x things in each of these cases. But since the x things are alike there is only one distinguishable arrangement of the n things for each set of $x!$ ways in which x different things can be arranged. This is the reason we divide $n!$ by $x!$ in the formula. The same kind of reasoning holds in the case of the $(n - x)$ things which are all alike.

To take a simple example, suppose n is equal to 3, and that the set of three things in question consists of poker chips, two of them being red and one being white. On one side of each chip there is a number. One red chip is numbered 1, the other is numbered 2, and the white chip is numbered 3. If we turn the chips so that the numbered sides are showing, we see that there are 3! or 6 ways that they can be arranged, namely:

Numbers showing	*Chips inverted*
①, ②, 3	RRW ⎱ 1
②, ①, 3	RRW ⎰
①, 3, ②	RWR ⎱ 2
②, 3, ①	RWR ⎰
3, ①, ②	WRR ⎱ 3
3, ②, ①	WRR ⎰

We have circled the numbers of the chips which are red. If we now pay attention to the circles and the threes—that is, if we turn the chips over so that we cannot see the numbered sides—we see that the first and second sets are indistinguishable, the third and fourth are indistinguishable, and the fifth and sixth are indistinguishable. Thus there are only three distinguishable arrangements of the set RRW. This number of arrangements is given by $\binom{3}{2} = \dfrac{3!}{2!(3-2)!} = \dfrac{3 \times 2 \times 1}{2 \times 1(1)} = 3.$

TERMS TO PONDER

1. Probability (of Success)
2. Event
3. Relative Frequency
4. Odds
5. Fair Game
6. Mutually Exclusive Events
7. Addition Theorem
8. Independent Events
9. Multiplication Theorem
10. Discrete Probability Distribution
11. Binomial Distribution
12. Sampling with Replacement
13. Binomial Coefficient
14. Modified Binomial Distribution
15. Poisson Distribution
16. Standardized Normal Distribution
17. Z Scale

18. Continuous Probability Distribution
19. Maximum Ordinate
20. Normal Curve Areas

EXERCISES

1. A bowl of marbles contains 100 reds, 50 whites, and 50 blues. All marbles are of the same size and density and thoroughly mixed. One marble is selected. What is the probability that the marble will be blue?
2. In Exercise 1, what is the probability that the marble will be either red or white?
3. Suppose you have a group of 24 marbles, 8 of which are red. Suppose also that you have a second group of marbles totaling 50 and that 12 of these are red. In selecting one marble at random from each group, what is the probability of getting two marbles which are not red?
4. A bin contains 6 defective condensers and 24 nondefective condensers. In selecting 3 condensers one at a time (and replacing each condenser after it is drawn), what is the probability of getting 3 defective condensers?
5. In a dice game (played with two dice), a player loses on the first throw if he rolls a two, a three, or a twelve. What is the probability that a player will lose on the first throw?
6. If 60% of the students on the Maryland campus are lower division students (freshmen or sophomores), what is the probability that 5 students selected at random will include exactly 3 lower division students?
7. State the odds which correspond to each of the following probability figures:
   a. .667. b. .50. c. .95. d. .75. e. .80. f. .85.
8. Find the probability of getting exactly 4 heads in 10 tosses of an unbiased coin.
9. In tossing a symmetrical die 5 times, what is the probability of getting 4 or more threes?
10. In tossing a symmetrical die twice, what is the probability of getting a three or a four on the first toss and anything but three on the second?
11. A normal distribution (population) of sales invoices has a mean of $32.00 and a standard deviation of $8.00. Assume all measurements are exact.
    a. What proportion of the invoices are between $20.00 and $44.00?
    b. What is the smallest invoice in the largest 20% of the invoices?
    c. Find the range of the middle 40% of the invoices.
    d. What is the probability that an invoice selected at random will be less than $20.00?

e. If the total number of invoices is 1500, how many of them lie within $5.00 of the mean?

12. Sam the tailor decides to give up his shop and go into the ready-made clothing business. He plans to have an initial stock of 500 men's suits. If men's suit sizes are normally distributed with a mean of 38.0 and a standard deviation of 2.5, how many suits should he have in stock which are size 40 or larger? (Adjust X by subtracting half a scale segment. That is, use 39.5 instead of 40 for X.)

13. A public utility accountant is collecting data on service lives of telephone poles as an aid in formulating replacement and depreciation policies. If the service lives are normally distributed with a mean of 18.7 and a standard deviation of 5.3 years, what proportion of the poles can be expected to last more than 25.0 years? (Adjust X by adding half a scale segment. That is, use 25.05 instead of 25.0 for X.)

14. In the cafeteria of a large government office building, the frequency distribution of the times at which various numbers of lunches are served is closely approximated by a normal curve with a mean of 0 (12 o'clock noon) and a standard deviation of 20 minutes. If the normal number of lunches served is 6000 per day, how many lunches should the cafeteria be ready to serve between 11:45 and 12:15? (Assume measurements are exact.)

15. A batch (population) of fuses submitted by a vendor on contract contains a proportion, .10, of defectives. If samples of 400 fuses each are drawn repeatedly from this batch (with replacement), what is the mean number of defective fuses that will appear per sample? What is the standard deviation of the number of defective fuses per sample?

16. Jones bets Smith at odds of 2 to 6 (for success) that he (Jones) can roll a seven or an eleven with two honest dice. Smith accepts. Is this a fair game? Why or why not?

SELECTED REFERENCES

FELLER, William, *An Introduction to Probability Theory and Its Applications* (New York, John Wiley and Sons, Inc., 1950), Vol. I, Introd. and Ch. I.

FRYER, H. C., *Elements of Statistics* (New York, John Wiley and Sons, Inc., 1954), Chs. III, IV.

McCARTHY, Philip J., *Introduction to Statistical Reasoning* (New York, McGraw-Hill Book Co., Inc., 1957), Chs. VII, VIII.

WALLIS, W. A., and ROBERTS, H. V., *Statistics: A New Approach* (Glencoe, Ill., The Free Press, 1956), Ch. X.

WILKS, S. S., *Elementary Statistical Analysis* (Princeton, N.J., Princeton University Press, 1952), Chs. IV, V.

8

SAMPLING AND SAMPLING

DISTRIBUTIONS

HAVING DISCUSSED some of the basic concepts of probability, we are now in a position to investigate more thoroughly the concept of a sampling distribution. Sampling distributions are theoretical probability distributions which we derive mathematically but which we may verify approximately by performing sampling experiments. These experiments involve a process of repeated random sampling or an enumeration of all possible different samples of some given size. In the former instance, the experimental population often consists of a box of numbered beads (for measurement data) or beads of various colors (for attribute data). Samples are selected by means of a scoop or paddle having just enough holes to accommodate the required size of sample. Random sampling is closely approximated if the beads are thoroughly mixed before each selection. Other experimental populations may consist of numbered or colored poker chips or numbers laid out in rows and columns on a page. In the latter case, random samples may be selected by means of a table of random digits.

Before describing specific sampling distributions and experiments we shall discuss the nature of simple random sampling and the method used to select such a sample in an actual survey.

SIMPLE RANDOM SAMPLING

As we stated in Chapter 1, a simple random sample is a sample selected in such a manner that each population element has the same probability of getting into the sample. This statement defines clearly enough the process of simple random sampling *with replacement,* for in this case, elements, though selected one by one, are replaced in the population after each selection. Probabilities of selection are equal for all population elements at each and every selection. Sampling with replacement allows an element to be selected more than once in the same sample (if the sample size is greater than 1). Although the binomial distribution is derived on the assumption that sampling is with replacement, we will find that it is still applicable in many practical applications, where we sample without replacement.

Sampling *without* replacement, then, is the procedure actually followed in practice. In this case no element is placed back in the population after having been selected into the sample. We define this process as simple random sampling if after each selection of an element, the elements remaining in the population have equal probabilities of being selected on the next draw. A different way of saying the same thing is to describe this sampling procedure as a selection process whereby each *combination* of n elements has the same probability of being chosen; n is, of course, the number of elements in the sample. A *combination* of elements is a grouping in which we note the identity of the elements but not their arrangement, that is, not the order in which they occur. Thus ABC and BCA are the same combination of 3 elements, but ABE is a different combination of 3 elements. The notion of samples as different combinations of n elements each is particularly important in developing the theory of sampling for the case of finite populations of measurement data.

HOW TO SELECT A SIMPLE RANDOM SAMPLE FROM A FINITE POPULATION

To select a simple random sample, we may use a table of random digits. A page from such a table is shown on page 342 of this book. In order to use such a table, we must have a numbered list of all the elements in the population. This list is sometimes called a "sampling frame." The elements can be in any order whatsoever when we number them from 1 to N.

To take a concrete case, suppose we wish to find out something about summer occupations of students currently registered in the College of Business Administration. In forming the list we could begin with the University Student Directory corrected by up-to-date information on late registrations, withdrawals, transfers to other divisions or colleges in the University, and so on. We would identify those students registered in the College of Business Administration and number them from 1 to N. Suppose that there are 1253 students in the College ($N = 1253$) and that we wish to select a sample consisting of 200 students. The step-by-step procedure is outlined below:

Step 1. We note the number of digits in N. In our example there are 4 such digits. This means we will use 4 adjacent columns of digits in the table.

Step 2. We choose a starting point in the table by opening the table blindly to a page and spotting a random digit; we note this digit and the three digits to the right of it. These four digits are the beginning digits in the four adjacent columns we shall use.

Step 3. We go down the adjacent four columns noting the population element that is identified by each set of four digits. For example, if the first set of digits is 0568, the 568th element on the population list is selected as the first element in the sample. If the next set of four digits is 1193, then the 1193d element in the list is drawn into the sample. If a set of four digits repeats, that is, if it occurs more than once, we skip the repetition(s), for we are sampling without replacement. If a set of four digits gives a number larger than N, we skip it also.

Step 4. We continue through the table as indicated in Step 3 until we have selected n elements. In our example, $n = 200$. Upon arriving at the bottom of the page in our first set of four columns, we start at the top of the page in the next set of four columns to the right.

After selecting the sample of 200 students, we would set out to interview each of them, asking questions about his or her last summer's occupation by following a carefully designed questionnaire.

In sampling granular or semiliquid populations, for example, a carload of wheat or a tin of strawberries, mechanical devices (compartmented metal tubes, covered dippers, and so on) are used to select samples. Though they involve an element of randomness, such samples sometimes are not, strictly speaking, *simple* random samples.

WHERE THE TABLE OF RANDOM DIGITS COMES FROM

Tables of random digits are nowadays generated by mechanical or electronic processes. We might generate our own table by means of the device shown in Figure 8–1. The pointer of the device is mounted so that it spins freely. After spinning the pointer, we wait until it comes to rest and then note the digit to which it is pointing. This digit goes into the table we are constructing. We continue spinning the pointer until we have accumulated several hundred thousand digits.

Because of the symmetrical construction of the device, we reason that, in the long run, each digit will be selected very nearly the

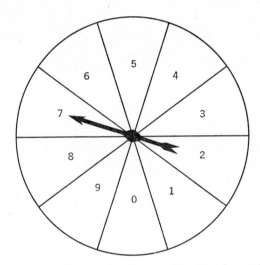

FIGURE 8–1. Device for Generating Random Digits

same proportion of times. It is possible to test the validity of our conclusion, for various mathematical tests of randomness have been devised. For example, a very simple test would be to compute the relative frequency of some digit, say, 3, in successive sets of ten thousand digits each. In each of these successive sets in the table, this relative frequency should be close to $\frac{1}{10}$ if the digits are truly random. Other tests which have been devised are not nearly as simple as this one.

SAMPLING DISTRIBUTIONS

The sampling distribution of a given statistic is the probability distribution of that statistic for some given size of sample, n. In terms of sampling experiments, if we were to select random samples of size n repeatedly (for a very large number of repetitions) from a given population and compute some specified statistic for each of these samples, then the relative frequency distribution of this statistic would be its sampling distribution.

Recall the process of drawing samples consisting of 3 marbles each from a bowl containing 50% reds and 50% whites (Ch. 7, p. 115). Using the theory of probability and without actually drawing any samples, we formed a probability distribution of all the possible ways that samples of 3 marbles each could be drawn. These different ways were:

x:	0	1	2	3
	WWW	RWW	RRW	RRR
		WRW	WRR	
		WWR	RWR	

A statistic x was computed for each of these samples, x being the number of red marbles in each sample. For WWW, $x = 0$, for RWW, $x = 1$, for RRW, $x = 2$, and for RRR, $x = 3$. The relative frequency (probability) of $x = 0$ was $\frac{1}{8}$, for $x = 1$ it was $\frac{3}{8}$, for $x = 2$ it was also $\frac{3}{8}$, and for $x = 3$ it was $\frac{1}{8}$. Since probabilities may be looked upon as relative frequencies, this particular sampling distribution tells us that if we were to select samples of 3 marbles each (with replacement) repeatedly for an extremely large number of times, about $\frac{1}{8}$ of the samples would contain 0 reds, $\frac{3}{8}$ of the samples would contain exactly 1 red, $\frac{3}{8}$ of the samples would contain exactly 2 reds, and $\frac{1}{8}$ of the samples would contain 3 reds.

Now we, of course, are usually going to select only *one* sample in an actual statistical study, but knowledge of how a very large number of equal-sized samples *would* turn out in a hypothetical process of repeated sampling is extremely important in analyzing the one sample that we do take.

To see how knowledge of a sampling distribution can help us in problems involving the drawing of one sample, let us take a simple example.

Suppose we are playing a guessing game wherein a sample of 4 marbles is selected (with replacement) from a bowl containing 50% red marbles and 50% whites. Prior to the selection of the sample we are required to guess the number x of red marbles that will occur in the sample of 4. Now before guessing, it would be a very good idea to consider the sampling distribution of x. We have here a binomial distribution with $P = \frac{1}{2}$ and $n = 4$. By substituting in turn the values 0, 1, 2, 3, 4 for x in the binomial formula, we get the probability of each of these numbers of red marbles occurring in a sample of 4. These probabilities turn out as follows:

$$x: \quad 0 \quad 1 \quad 2 \quad 3 \quad 4$$
$$\Pr(x): \quad \tfrac{1}{16} \quad \tfrac{1}{4} \quad \tfrac{3}{8} \quad \tfrac{1}{4} \quad \tfrac{1}{16}$$

We readily see that $x = 2$ has the greatest probability; therefore, we would be well advised to guess 2 red marbles in this game. Note that 2 is also the mean of the distribution ($\mu = nP$). For any binomial distribution where $P = \tfrac{1}{2}$ and n is an even number, the value of x with the highest probability will be exactly equal to μ.

APPROXIMATING THE BINOMIAL DISTRIBUTION WITH A NORMAL CURVE

In many cases, we find it quite convenient—in the absence of special tables—to approximate the binomial distribution with a normal curve. Suppose, for example, that we are still sampling from a bowl in which half of the marbles are red and half of them are white. But now let the sample consist of 100 marbles. This time, prior to the selection, we are asked to state the odds that the sample will contain less than 45 red marbles. If we were to work this problem by the binomial formula, we would have to make 45 substitutions of x, that is, 0, 1, 2, 3, $\cdots$ 44. Then we would have to add all of the results of the substitutions together to get the probability from which to compute the required odds. As one example, substitution of 20 for x would involve $\binom{100}{20} (\tfrac{1}{2})^{20}(\tfrac{1}{2})^{80}$, which, of itself, is a laborious computation. Computations are made much easier if we use the normal-curve approximation to the binomial distribution. We compute the required probability, that is, from a normal distribution having the same mean and standard deviation as the binomial distribution.

For the distribution in the present problem, $\mu = nP = 100(\tfrac{1}{2})$ $= 50$ and $\sigma = \sqrt{100 \cdot \tfrac{1}{2} \cdot \tfrac{1}{2}} = 10 \cdot \tfrac{1}{2} = 5$. The only important difficulty that we encounter results from the fact that the binomial distribution is discrete, whereas the normal distribution is continuous. We recall that the normal distribution gives us the probabilities that x falls within given intervals or ranges, while the binomial gives us probabilities that x is exactly equal to certain whole numbers.

On the graph of the binomial distribution, probabilities are represented by lengths of lines, but on the normal-curve diagram probabilities are represented by areas. We can, however, employ a simple adjustment that will enable us to represent the binomial probabilities by areas. That is, we can represent the probability of each x value by a bar centered on the x value and having a width of 1 unit. The height of the bar is equal to the length of the line representing the binomial probability. Since the width of the bar is 1, the height and area of the bar are numerically equal, or the probability of x is equal to the area of the bar standing over the range $x \pm \frac{1}{2}$.

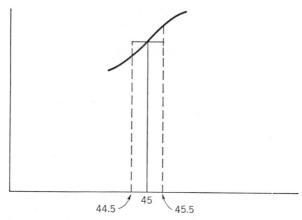

FIGURE 8–2. **Approximating a Binomial Distribution with a Normal Curve ($P = \frac{1}{2}$, $n = 100$, $x = 45$)**

We see in Figure 8–2 that the probability that $x = 45$ is given by a bar standing on top of the range 44.5–45.5, this figure representing a normal curve superimposed upon the binomial distribution with $n = 100$ and $P = \frac{1}{2}$. From the figure, we also see that the curve cuts through the bar in such a manner that the area *under the curve* standing on the range 44.5–45.5 is very nearly equal to the area in the bar.

Thus, the x value, 45, is represented *in the normal curve approximation* by the range 44.5 to 45.5. The probability of x being equal to 45 would be represented by the area between the two dotted ordinates in Figure 8–3.

The probability that x will be *less than* 45 is given by the shaded portion of the curve in Figure 8–3. Evaluating this area is a simple problem in the use of the area table of the normal curve, but we must remember that in finding Z (the number of standard deviations x lies from μ), we must make an adjustment on x by

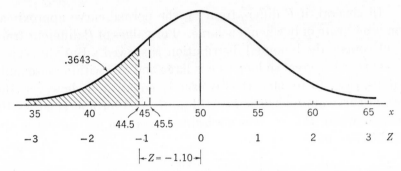

FIGURE 8–3.   Approximating the Binomial Distribution with a Normal Curve

adding ½ or subtracting ½ as indicated by the problem.   The computation is as follows:

$$Z = \frac{x \pm \frac{1}{2} - \mu}{\sigma} = \frac{44.5 - 50}{5} = \frac{-5.5}{5} = -1.10$$

Consulting the table of areas, we find that the area between the ordinate at the mean and the ordinate at a Z of 1.10 is .3643. By subtracting .5000 − .3643, we find the shaded area of Figure 8–3; it is equal to .1357 or about .14.   Fourteen out of 100 is 7 out of 50.   Odds are thus about 7 to 43 or approximately 1 to 6 that a sample of 100 marbles will contain less than 45 reds, when the sampling is from a 50–50 binomial population.

If we had wished to estimate the probability that the sample of 100 would contain *exactly* 45 red marbles, we would have had to compute two Z values so as to evaluate the area between the dotted ordinates in Figure 8–3.   The computations follow:

Areas

$$Z_1 = \frac{44.5 - 50}{5} = -1.10 \qquad .3643$$

$$Z_2 = \frac{45.5 - 50}{5} = -0.90 \qquad .3159$$

$$\qquad\qquad\qquad\qquad\quad .0484 = \text{area between}$$
dotted ordinates
in Figure 8–3

Thus the probability that the sample of 100 marbles would contain exactly 45 red marbles is about .0484, when computed by the normal-curve approximation.   The corresponding probability computed from the binomial formula is .04847.

In general, if P differs from $\frac{1}{2}$, the normal-curve approximation is accurate only when n is large. For values of P different from $\frac{1}{2}$, of course, the binomial distribution is skewed. But this skewness is not very great so long as n is large and P is within reasonable bounds, say, .10 to .90. If P is exactly equal to $\frac{1}{2}$, however, the normal-curve approximation is still quite good for n as small as 10. In cases where $P < \frac{1}{2}$, it is advisable to use the normal-curve approximation only if $nP \geqq 5$.

THE MODIFIED BINOMIAL DISTRIBUTION AS THE SAMPLING DISTRIBUTION OF A PROPORTION, p

The modified binomial distribution is the sampling distribution of x/n, the *proportion* of elements having one of two possible characteristics. In sampling from a bowl of red and white marbles with a 30–70 split, for example, x/n could be .30, .27, .34, or some other proportion of red marbles in a sample. To simplify notation, we set $x/n = p$. (Note that here p is lower case.) Thus we say that the modified binomial distribution is the probability distribution or the sampling distribution of p, the sample proportion. Again, if we were to select *samples* of size n repeatedly from a binomial *population* having elements divided into two classes in the ratio of P to Q, the statistic p (one p per sample) would form a modified binomial distribution with mean P and standard deviation $\sqrt{\dfrac{PQ}{n}}$. (See Ch. 7, p. 121.) Note that the mean of this distribution, $\mu = P$, is also equal to $\Sigma \operatorname{Pr}(p) \cdot p$, the values of $\operatorname{Pr}(p)$ being given by the binomial formula.

Of course, the modified binomial distribution may also be approximated with the normal curve in cases where n is large and P is fairly close to $\frac{1}{2}$. We simply use a normal curve having a mean equal to P and a standard deviation equal to $\sqrt{\dfrac{PQ}{n}}$. In the normal-curve approximation to the regular binomial distribution, x was represented by the range, $x \pm \frac{1}{2}$. Thus in the approximation to the modified binomial distribution, $\dfrac{x}{n}$ or p will be represented by

$$\frac{x \pm \frac{1}{2}}{n} = \frac{x}{n} \pm \frac{1}{2n} = p \pm \frac{1}{2n}$$

The curve is readily standardized by the transformation

$$Z = \frac{p \pm \dfrac{1}{2n} - P}{\sqrt{\dfrac{PQ}{n}}}$$

It is important to remember that the adjustment of x and the adjustment of p are required only when we are using the normal curve to approximate the binomial distribution.

Now—and this is very important—because $\sqrt{\dfrac{PQ}{n}}$ refers to the sampling distribution of p we call it the standard *error* of p and denote it by σ_p instead of σ. We write:

$$\sigma_p = \sqrt{\frac{PQ}{n}}$$

The term *standard error* derives from the fact that a sampling distribution gives probabilities for the various degrees of error that can result from the sampling process. We may think of an "error" as the difference between p and P.

Now we know that the normal curve is a good approximation to the modified binomial distribution; thus normal-curve areas or probabilities apply. Consequently, in a process of repeated sampling, about 68% of the differences $|p - P|$ will be less than σ_p; about 95% of the differences $|p - P|$ will be less than $2\sigma_p$, and so on. Alternatively, we may say that about 68% of all the p values will be within σ_p of P and about 95% of them will be within $2\sigma_p$ of P. σ_p is, of course, a measure of the extent to which the p's are clustered about their mean, P. It is interpreted in much the same manner as a standard deviation. A glance at the formula for σ_p shows that as $\sqrt{n}$ increases, σ_p decreases and the p's become more closely clustered about P.

Let us take a simple problem that we may solve from our knowledge of the sampling distribution of p. Suppose a Kansas newspaper knows that 20% of its subscribers live on farms. What is the probability that a random sample of 400 subscribers will contain more than 24% farm residents? The problem is diagramed in Figure 8–4.

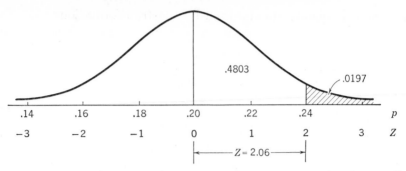

FIGURE 8–4. Problem Involving Normal-Curve Approximation to the Modified Binomial Distribution (Samplng Distributon of p)

The standard error of p is computed from $\sigma_p = \sqrt{\dfrac{PQ}{n}} = \sqrt{\dfrac{.20(.80)}{400}} = \dfrac{.40}{20} = .02$. To find the answer to our problem, we must evaluate the shaded area in Figure 8–4. We must do this indirectly by first getting the area from .20 to .24 and then subtracting that area from .5000. Recalling the required adjustment on p, we have

$$Z = \frac{p \pm \dfrac{1}{2n} - P}{\sigma p} = \frac{.24 + .00125 - .20}{.02} = \frac{.04125}{.02} = 2.06$$

The corresponding area is .4803. And $.5000 - .4803 = .0197$ or about .020. Thus, the probability is about .020 that the sample of 400 subscribers will contain more than 24% farm residents.

THE SAMPLING DISTRIBUTION OF THE MEAN ($\bar{x}$)

We may carry the idea of a sampling distribution over into the area of measurement data to arrive at the sampling distribution of the mean. Again, if we were to select samples of some constant size, n, repeatedly from a given population, and if we were to compute $\bar{x}$ for each of the samples, the relative frequency distribution of the $\bar{x}$'s would be the sampling distribution of the mean. The nature of this particular distribution is given by the *central limit theorem:* For samples drawn from a population with a finite variance, the sampling distribution of the mean approaches a normal curve with mean μ and standard error $\sigma/\sqrt{n}$ as the size of the sample, n, increases.

Thus for large samples, say, $n > 31$, the sampling distribution is closely approximated by a normal distribution having mean μ and standard deviation $\sigma/\sqrt{n}$. This normal distribution is standardized by the transformation

$$Z = \frac{\bar{x} - \mu}{\sigma/\sqrt{n}}$$

That is, this formula transforms a given $\bar{x}$ value into the corresponding Z value.

We know that a *population* of measurement data would have a standard deviation of σ, but, as we have just seen, the sampling dis-

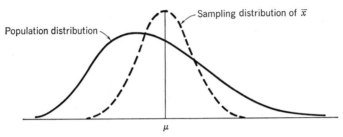

FIGURE 8–5. **Population of Measurement Data and Sampling Distribution of the Mean**

tribution of the mean for samples drawn from that population would have a standard error of $\sigma/\sqrt{n}$. Thus the sample means would have less variability than the original measurements in the population, and—similar to the p's in the modified binomial distribution—the sample means would become more closely clustered about μ as the size of sample increased. Again, a glance at the formula shows that the value of $\sigma/\sqrt{n}$ decreases as $\sqrt{n}$ increases.

The relationship of a population of measurements (X) to the sampling distribution of the mean ($\bar{x}$) generated from that population is shown in Figure 8–5. Note that the population curve in the figure is skewed. The central limit theorem does *not* specify that the population must be distributed symmetrically or in any other fashion.

The standard error of the mean is denoted by the symbol $\sigma_{\bar{x}}$. That is, $\sigma_{\bar{x}} = \sigma/\sqrt{n}$.

Let us now solve a simple problem involving the sampling distribution of the mean. Suppose gross weekly wages of factory laborers in the Zoot Corporation for the week ended July 8, 1957, are distributed with their mean equal to $95.00 and standard deviation equal to $18.00 ($\mu$ = $95.00; σ = $18.00). If a sample of 36 workers is selected, what is the probability that their mean weekly pay on the date in question was $100 or more? This problem is diagramed in Figure 8–6. The curve in the diagram represents the sampling distribution of $\bar{x}$ for samples of size 36.

We compute:

$$Z = \frac{\bar{x} - \mu}{\sigma/\sqrt{n}} = \frac{100.00 - 95.00}{\dfrac{18.00}{6}} = \frac{5.00}{3.00} = 1.67$$

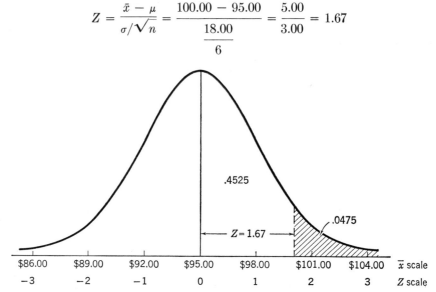

.4525

.0475

Z = 1.67

| $86.00 | $89.00 | $92.00 | $95.00 | $98.00 | $101.00 | $104.00 | $\bar{x}$ scale |

| −3 | −2 | −1 | 0 | 1 | 2 | 3 | Z scale |

FIGURE 8–6. Problem Involving the Sampling Distribution of the Mean

The shaded area of the diagram is found by first getting the area corresponding to a Z of 1.67 and then subtracting that area from .5000. We have .5000 − .4525 = .0475. The probability is .0475 that the sample mean will be equal to or greater than $100.00.

SAMPLING FROM FINITE POPULATIONS

We have so far considered three sampling distributions, all of which may be approximated by the normal distribution when the sample size is large. These sampling distributions are (1) the binomial distribution, (2) the sampling distribution of a proportion p (the modified binomial), and (3) the sampling distribution of the mean. We have given formulas for the means and standard errors of each of these distributions. The latter two distributions will be of most importance for the applications in Chapter 9, so we will confine our discussion in this section to them.

In developing the modified binomial distribution (Ch. 7)(the sampling distribution of p), we assumed that the sampling was done with replacement. Under such circumstances, the size of the population was hardly of any importance. We could, for instance, select a sample of size $n = 100$ with replacement from a 50–50 binomial population consisting of one red marble and one white marble. This procedure is analogous to sampling without replacement from an infinite population. The important thing is that we want to sample from a population in which P is constant or nearly so. Now, in actual practice, we sample without replacement (and usually) from finite populations; under such circumstances P varies as we select the sample, but the value of P still remains very nearly the same if NP and NQ are large relative to n. We shall be concerned here only with applications where NP and NQ are large relative to n and where n is large enough so that the normal-curve approximation applies.

When discussing the sampling distribution of the mean, we did not specify whether the sampling was to be done with replacement or without. Again, it makes no difference when the population is infinite. But, as we have said, in actual practice, we sample without replacement, and almost always in business and economic statistics we are dealing with finite populations. For the case of sampling without replacement from a finite population, the formula for the standard error of the mean becomes:

$$\sigma_{\bar{x}} = \sqrt{\frac{N - n}{N - 1}} \cdot \frac{\sigma}{\sqrt{n}}$$

Also, in sampling without replacement from a *finite population*, the formula for the standard error of a proportion becomes:

$$\sigma_p = \sqrt{\frac{N - n}{N - 1}} \cdot \sqrt{\frac{PQ}{n}}$$

Once the first formula (that for $\sigma_{\bar{x}}$) is developed, the transition to the other (σ_p) is relatively easy. The mathematics involved in the derivation of $\sigma_{\bar{x}}$ is above the level of this book, but it is easy to verify that the formula is correct in the case of a particular finite population. We may use such a population to verify first the fact that the mean of the sampling distribution is equal to the mean of the population.

For these purposes let us take a hypothetical finite population that is small enough so that it will not bog us down in a quagmire of numbers. It will consist of five elements; they could be small lengths of brass wire, each having been measured for breaking strength. The *population* elements are identified by letters and the respective measurements are given in Table 8–1.

TABLE 8–1

Population of Five Lengths of Brass Wire.
Measurement: Breaking Strength

Element	Breaking strength (X) (pounds)
A	2
B	4
C	7
D	8
E	9
	30

$$\mu = \tfrac{30}{5} = 6$$

We see immediately that the population mean, μ, equals 6.

Now let us form the sampling distribution of the mean for samples of size $n = 2$. To do this we must select *all possible* samples (combinations) of two elements each. There are 10 such samples. The probability of selection is thus $\tfrac{1}{10}$ for each combination. The samples are listed and their respective means are computed in Table 8–2. The list of means constitutes the sampling distribution of the mean. In this example there are so few sample means that they need not be grouped into a frequency distribution.

A glance at Tables 8–1 and 8–2 will show the reader that for this sampling distribution, the mean of all the sample means does indeed equal μ, the population mean. This is the first fact that we wished to verify.

The second fact we wish to verify is that the standard error of the mean is equal to $\sqrt{\dfrac{N-n}{N-1}} \cdot \dfrac{\sigma}{\sqrt{n}}$. Now the standard error of the mean is the standard deviation of the sample means. The formula following directly from this definition is $\sigma_{\bar{x}} = \sqrt{\dfrac{\Sigma(\bar{x} - \mu)^2}{N_s}}$,

TABLE 8-2

The Ten Possible Samples of Size $n = 2$ Taken from a Population of Five Brass Wires

Sample elements	Sample measurements	Sample mean ($\bar{x}$)
AB	2, 4	3.0
AC	2, 7	4.5
AD	2, 8	5.0
AE	2, 9	5.5
BC	4, 7	5.5
BD	4, 8	6.0
BE	4, 9	6.5
CD	7, 8	7.5
CE	7, 9	8.0
DE	8, 9	8.5
		60.0

$$\frac{\Sigma \bar{x}}{10} = \frac{60.0}{10} = 6 = \mu$$

where the $\bar{x}$ values are the sample means and N_s is the number of possible samples. In our example, N_s, of course, equals 10.

In short, we wish to show that:

$$\sigma_{\bar{x}} = \sqrt{\frac{N - n}{N - 1}} \cdot \frac{\sigma}{\sqrt{n}} = \sqrt{\frac{\Sigma(\bar{x} - \mu)^2}{N_s}}$$

In order to fill in these formulas we need the value of σ. The computation of σ is shown in Table 8–3.

We see from Table 8–3 that σ is equal to $\sqrt{6.8}$. Substituting this value in the appropriate formula, we may write:

$$\sqrt{\frac{N - n}{N - 1}} \cdot \frac{\sigma}{\sqrt{n}} = \sqrt{\frac{5 - 2}{5 - 1}} \cdot \frac{\sqrt{6.8}}{\sqrt{2}} = \sqrt{\frac{5 - 2}{5 - 1} \cdot \frac{6.8}{2}} = \sqrt{\frac{20.4}{8}} = \sqrt{2.55}$$

Now it remains for us to show that $\sqrt{\dfrac{\Sigma(\bar{x} - \mu)^2}{N_s}}$ also equals $\sqrt{2.55}$. The computation is shown in Table 8–4.

Comparison of the computations of Table 8–3 and Table 8–4 shows that the standard error of the sampling distribution may be computed from either of the two formulas that we set down at the beginning of the discussion. However, note that if we had selected

TABLE 8–3

Computation of σ for the Population of Five Lengths of Brass Wire

X_i	$X_i - \mu$	$(X_i - \mu)^2$
2	-4	16
4	-2	4
7	1	1
8	2	4
9	3	9
		—
		34

$$\sigma = \sqrt{\frac{\Sigma(X_i - \mu)^2}{N}} = \sqrt{\frac{34}{5}} = \sqrt{6.8}$$

TABLE 8–4

Computation of the Standard Error of the Mean. Samples of Size $n = 2$ from Finite Population of Five Brass Wires. $\mu = 6$

Sample mean $(\bar{x})$	$(\bar{x} - \mu)$	$(\bar{x} - \mu)^2$
3.0	-3.0	9.00
4.5	-1.5	2.25
5.0	-1.0	1.00
5.5	-0.5	0.25
5.5	-0.5	0.25
6.0	0	0.00
6.5	0.5	0.25
7.5	1.5	2.25
8.0	2.0	4.00
8.5	2.5	6.25
		——
		25.50

$$\sigma_{\bar{x}} = \sqrt{\frac{\Sigma(\bar{x} - \mu)^2}{N_s}} = \sqrt{\frac{25.50}{10}} = \sqrt{2.55}$$

only *one* sample, all values in $\sqrt{\dfrac{N-n}{N-1}} \cdot \dfrac{\sigma}{\sqrt{n}}$ would be known except σ, and, as we shall see, σ can usually be closely estimated from the sample.

Note also that in our example (see Tables 8–3 and 8–4) $\sigma = \sqrt{6.8}$, whereas $\sigma_{\bar{x}} = \sqrt{2.55}$. Thus we also verify our previous statement that the sampling distribution of the mean has less variability than the population from which the samples are selected.

THE SWITCH TO ATTRIBUTE DATA

Now as we have said, it is a fairly simple matter to get from $\sqrt{\dfrac{N-n}{N-1}} \cdot \dfrac{\sigma}{\sqrt{n}}$ to $\sqrt{\dfrac{N-n}{N-1}} \sqrt{\dfrac{PQ}{n}}$. Of course, the first formula refers to measurement data and the second to attribute data, but there exists a standard device for making the transition. In a binomial population, elements either have a given attribute or they do not. P is the proportion of elements having the given attribute. Now if we assign an element the value 1 when it has the characteristic and assign it the value 0 when it does not, we find that $P = \dfrac{\Sigma X_i}{N}$ $= \mu$; $\Sigma X_i = NP$; and $\Sigma X_i^2 = NP$. Q, of course, equals $1 - P$. Starting with the numerator, the standard formula for σ^2, and making appropriate substitutions of P's and Q's, we make the transition from the first formula to the second by showing that $\sigma = \sqrt{PQ}$.

The required steps are as follows: In the numerator of $\dfrac{\Sigma(X_i-\mu)^2}{N}$, μ is equal to P and X_i will have to be either 0 or 1. It is evident that NP 1's occur, yielding $NP(1-P)^2$ as part of the numerator. Also, NQ 0's occur, yielding $NQ(0-P)^2$ as the remaining part of the numerator. It follows that the summation in the numerator of the formula is equal to $NP(1-P)^2 + NQP^2$. Since $(1-P) = Q$, we have $NPQ^2 + NQP^2$, which equals $NPQ(Q+P)$. But $(Q+P) = 1$. Therefore, $\sigma^2 = \dfrac{NPQ}{N} = PQ$ and $\sigma = \sqrt{PQ}$.

FINITE POPULATION CORRECTION (fpc)

The factor $\sqrt{\dfrac{N-n}{N-1}}$ is known as the finite population correction (fpc),[1] and it does not serve to reduce the standard error much when N is large relative to n, for if such is the case the fpc will be nearly equal to 1. As far as we are concerned in this book, we shall usually assume that the fpc is so close to 1 that it may be neglected. Thus, although we shall assume that our sampling is done without replacement from finite populations, we shall often take the standard error of the mean as $\sigma/\sqrt{n}$ and the standard error of a proportion as $\sqrt{\dfrac{PQ}{n}}$. The formulas we shall frequently use then are:

$$\sigma_{\bar{x}} = \frac{\sigma}{\sqrt{n}} \qquad \text{and} \qquad \sigma_p = \sqrt{\frac{PQ}{n}}$$

ESTIMATING $\sigma_{\bar{x}}$ AND σ_p

Taking a close look at the formulas for $\sigma_{\bar{x}}$ and σ_p, we notice that σ in the former case and PQ in the latter would usually not be known in a statistical study because they must be computed from the population. If we knew enough about a population to compute σ or PQ there would be no sense in taking a sample. Because σ or PQ are usually not known, we *estimate* the appropriate one of them from the sample. That is, we compute s and use it as an estimate of σ, and, for attribute data, we compute pq as an estimate of PQ. If n is large, these estimates are very close to the corresponding parameters. Thus we have arrived at the very important fact that the standard error of the mean may be estimated closely from the information contained in *just one sample*. A like situation exists, as we have seen, in the case of the standard error of the proportion p.

Now, if we estimate a population mean (μ) by drawing a random sample and computing $\bar{x}$, we can without knowing the value of σ make a probability statement about the extent of the sampling error in the estimate. Problems of estimation will be treated in detail in Chapter 9.

[1] See W. G. Cochran, *Sampling Techniques* (New York, John Wiley and Sons, Inc., 1953), p. 17.

SUMMARY

Simple random sampling may be done either with replacement or without replacement. In practical statistical problems, we select samples without replacement. In this process, elements are selected one by one, and those elements remaining in the population after each selection have the same probability of being selected on the next draw. The same idea may be stated in different words: samples are selected in such a manner that each combination of n elements has the same probability of being chosen.

Simple random samples are selected by means of a table of random digits. In such a table each of the ten possible digits (0, 1, 2, 3, 4, 5, 6, 7, 8, 9) has the same relative frequency in the long run. Tables of random numbers are nowadays constructed mechanically or electronically.

In an actual sampling study, we usually select only one sample, but a knowledge of how a very large number of equal sized samples *would* turn out in a process of repeated sampling is very valuable to us in analyzing the one sample that we do take. If we were to select random samples of size n repeatedly (for a very large number of repetitions) from a given population and compute some specified statistic for each of these samples, then the relative frequency distribution of this statistic would be its sampling distribution. When the population is finite, the sampling distribution may be formed by selecting all possible samples of some given size. For our purposes, two sampling distributions in particular will be very important, (1) the sampling distribution of a proportion, p, and (2) the sampling distribution of the mean, $\bar{x}$. We may summarize the important features of these distributions as follows:

Distribution	Finite population		Indefinitely large population	
	Mean	Standard error	Mean	Standard error
Sampling distribution of p	P	$\sigma_p = \sqrt{\dfrac{N-n}{N-1}}\sqrt{\dfrac{PQ}{n}}$	P	$\sigma_p = \sqrt{\dfrac{PQ}{n}}$
Sampling distribution of $\bar{x}$	μ	$\sigma_{\bar{x}} = \sqrt{\dfrac{N-n}{N-1}} \cdot \dfrac{\sigma}{\sqrt{n}}$	μ	$\sigma_{\bar{x}} = \dfrac{\sigma}{\sqrt{n}}$

The factor $\sqrt{\dfrac{N-n}{N-1}}$ is known as the finite population correction (fpc) and is very nearly equal to 1 when N is large relative to n. Both of the sampling distributions referred to above are closely approximated by the normal curve if n is large. Also, NP and NQ should be large relative to n

for the normal curve to apply in the case of the sampling distribution of p.

In actual sampling investigations we almost never know the values of σ or PQ; thus we can hardly evaluate the formulas for $\sigma_{\bar{x}}$ and σ_p by direct substitution. However, we can *estimate* these standard errors from the data in the sample that we select. For the case of indefinitely large populations $\left(\sqrt{\dfrac{N-n}{N-1}} \doteq 1 \right)$, the two standard errors we have considered thus far and their estimates are as follows:

(True) Standard error	*Estimated standard error*
$\sigma_{\bar{x}} = \dfrac{\sigma}{\sqrt{n}}$	$s_{\bar{x}} = \dfrac{s}{\sqrt{n}}$
$\sigma_p = \sqrt{\dfrac{PQ}{n}}$	$s_p = \sqrt{\dfrac{pq}{n}}$

There are, in sum, three particularly important bits of information which the statistician desires to know about any sampling distribution, (1) the form of the distribution, that is, whether it is a normal curve or some other type of curve, (2) the mean of the distribution, and (3) the estimated standard error.

TERMS TO PONDER

1. Simple Random Sample
2. Sampling with Replacement
3. Sampling Without Replacement
4. Random Digits
5. Normal Curve Approximation
6. Sampling Distribution of p
7. Sampling Distribution of x
8. Standard Error of p
9. Standard Error of x
10. Finite Population Correction
11. Estimated Standard Error

EXERCISES

1. The chief inspector at the City Radio Parts Corporation knows that 10% of the condensers being manufactured on line 1 are defective. If 400 condensers are selected at random from line 1, what is the probability that 28 or less will be defective? Use the normal-curve approximation to the binomial distribution.

2. Seventy-five per cent of the dwelling units in Lower Suburbia are owner-occupied. If a random sample of 200 dwelling units is selected, what is the probability that the proportion (p) of owner-occupied dwelling units in the sample will be less than .70? Use the normal-curve approximation to the modified binomial distribution.

3. A finite population consists of seven pieces of plastic fabric. Each piece is tested for resistance to tearing. The measurements are symbolized by X_i.

Element	X_i
A	2
B	3
C	7
D	9
E	8
F	5
G	1

a. Find the population mean.

b. There are 21 possible samples of size $n = 2$ that can be formed from this population. Compute the mean of each of these 21 samples.

c. Find the mean of the 21 sample means. Compare this result with the population mean.

d. Compute the standard deviation (σ) of the population.

e. Compute the standard deviation of the 21 sample means, using

$$\sigma_{\bar{x}} = \sqrt{\frac{\Sigma(\bar{x} - \mu)^2}{N_s}}.$$

f. Compute $\sigma_{\bar{x}} = \sqrt{\frac{N - n}{N - 1}} \cdot \frac{\sigma}{\sqrt{n}}$. Compare this result with the standard deviation of the 21 sample means which was computed in part e.

4. A sample of 12 marbles is drawn (with replacement) from a population consisting of 100 red marbles and 100 whites.

a. Use the binomial formula to find the probability that exactly 5 of the 12 marbles will be red.

b. Use the normal-curve approximation to find the probability that exactly 5 of the 12 marbles will be red.

5. Consider the sampling distribution of the mean generated by selecting random samples of size 49 from a population of accounts receivable balances having a mean of $75.00 and a standard deviation of $10.50. What is the probability that the mean of a sample will lie within $2.00 of the population mean?

6. A random sample of 1000 households in Greentree includes a total of 3342 persons.

   a. Compute the mean number of persons per household for the sample.

   b. If the standard deviation (σ) of the number of persons in a household is 1.32, how confident can one be that the sample mean is not off by more than .10? That is, what is the probability that the sample mean does not differ from the population mean by more than .10?

SELECTED REFERENCES

FREUND, John E., *Modern Elementary Statistics* (Englewood Cliffs, N.J., Prentice-Hall, Inc., 1952), Ch. VIII.

McCARTHY, Philip J., *Introduction to Statistical Reasoning* (New York, McGraw-Hill Book Co., Inc., 1957), Ch. VI.

ROSANDER, A. C., *Elementary Principles of Statistics* (New York, D. Van Nostrand, Inc., 1951), Chs. IX, X.

WALLIS, W. A., and ROBERTS, H. V., *Statistics: A New Approach* (Glencoe, Ill., The Free Press, 1956), Ch. XI.

9

PROBLEMS OF

ESTIMATION

In Chapter 1 we defined statistics as a body of methods for acquiring information in numerical form about populations. One very important type of such information is a sample estimate of a population parameter. The statistic $\bar{x}$ is an estimator of the parameter μ and the statistic p is an estimator of the parameter P.[1] Estimates may be either *point estimates* or *interval estimates*.

POINT ESTIMATES

Point estimates are given in the form of just one number or "point." Thus if we wish to estimate the mean income of all the households in College Park, Maryland, and we select a random sample of 400 households in order to make such an estimate, the sample mean, say, \$5422, may be taken as a point estimate of μ, the unknown population mean. The statement of a point estimate in and of itself gives us no idea of how far off it may be from the parameter being estimated. In the above instance, the statement of the estimate, $\bar{x} = \$5422$, does not tell us anything about the size of the sampling error, $|\bar{x} - \mu|$. However, interval estimates can give us an idea of how large such an error is. We shall get to interval estimates in a moment, but first let us review the point estimates of the two standard errors mentioned at the end of Chapter 8.

---

[1] Strictly speaking, the nonnumerical representation of a statistic used for estimating (for example, $\bar{x}$) is called an estimat*or*, whereas a numerical value substituted for the estimator is called an estimat*e*.

The formulas for $\sigma_{\bar{x}}$ and σ_p give us the true or exact standard errors of $\bar{x}$ and p respectively. But, as we noted previously, these formulas require a knowledge of σ in the one case and P in the other; both σ and P are parameters which would have to be computed from the population. Thus in an actual sampling study, where we select only one sample, we could not compute exact values of the standard errors. However, very good *point estimates* of the standard errors may be computed from the data in the sample, and these are very close estimates if the sample is large. Substituting the appropriate sample statistics, we may form point estimates of $\sigma_{\bar{x}}$ and σ_p as follows:

Estimator	Estimated standard error [2]	
	Finite population	*Indefinitely large population*
p	$s_p = \sqrt{\dfrac{N-n}{N-1}}\sqrt{\dfrac{pq}{n}}$	$s_p = \sqrt{\dfrac{pq}{n}}$
$\bar{x}$	$s_{\bar{x}} = \sqrt{\dfrac{N-n}{N-1}} \cdot \dfrac{s}{\sqrt{n}}$	$s_{\bar{x}} = \dfrac{s}{\sqrt{n}}$

In most of our exercises and examples, we shall, as indicated in Chapter 8, assume that the fpc is so near to 1 that the formulas relating to indefinitely large populations may be employed.

INTERVAL ESTIMATES OR CONFIDENCE INTERVALS

Let us now return to the estimate ($\bar{x} = \$5422$) of average income for households in College Park, which was given in Chapter 1. We said there that the odds were about 19 to 1 (probability of about .95) that this estimate did not differ from the population mean (μ) by more than about $50. We are now in a position to understand how this statement came about.

Since the sample in this case is large (400 households), we may infer from the central limit theorem that the appropriate sampling distribution is a normal distribution with mean μ and standard error $\sigma/\sqrt{n}$. Thus 95.44% of all the sample means would be within 2 standard errors of μ. In other words, if we were to look up the area corresponding to a Z of 2 in the normal-curve area table, we would get .4772, which is exactly half of .9544. The *probability*, then, is

[2] There are logical grounds for using $n-1$ instead of n in the denominator of the formulas for s_p, but since we are using these formulas only for the case of large samples, we have practical grounds for omitting this refinement.

.9544 that the estimator $\bar{x}$ does not differ from (fall above or below) μ by more than two times $\sigma/\sqrt{n}$. It is also true that the interval formed by adding 2 standard errors to $\bar{x}$ and subtracting 2 standard errors from $\bar{x}$ has a probability of .9544 of including μ. This interval is called a 95.44% confidence interval. We may write its formula as $\bar{x} \pm 2 \cdot \sigma/\sqrt{n}$, where the symbol $\pm$ should be read "plus *and* minus." Figure 9–1 will help us to see why such an interval has the probability .9544 of including μ, the population mean.

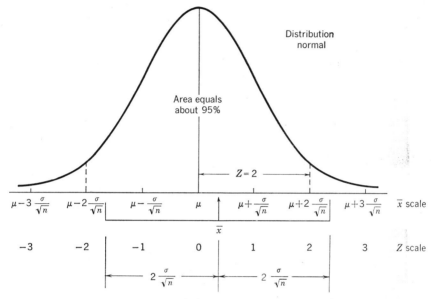

FIGURE 9–1. Interpretation of the 95% Confidence Interval as an Estimate of μ

The sample mean computed for one selected sample is indicated by the arrow pointing to the $\bar{x}$ scale just to the right of μ. The 95.44% confidence interval constructed for this particular sample mean is indicated by the bracket extending out to the right and to the left of $\bar{x}$. Each half of this bracket is 2 standard errors ($2 \cdot \sigma/\sqrt{n}$) long. Now a bracket of this very same length could be constructed for each and every $\bar{x}$ value in the distribution. If $\bar{x}$ were equal to μ, the arrow of the bracket would be opposite μ and the ends of the bracket would be at the points $Z = 2$ and $Z = -2$. If such a mean were larger than μ, the bracket would move to the right. If such a mean were less than μ, the bracket would move to the left. For those sample means lying in the range $\mu \pm 2(\sigma/\sqrt{n})$ the bracket would include ("be hooked around") μ. And 95.44% of all the sample means lie within this range. Thus the probability would be .9544 that the interval $\bar{x} \pm 2 \cdot \sigma/\sqrt{n}$ would include μ.

In general, we may say that a confidence interval is a range determined with reference to a given estimator, this range having a given probability of bracketing or including the estimated parameter. The probability applies prior to the selection of the sample and for this reason is sometimes called a *fiducial* probability.[3] In the case of $\bar{x}$ as an estimator of μ, and where the sampling distribution of $\bar{x}$ is a normal distribution, the confidence interval for μ is formed by adding Z standard errors to $\bar{x}$ (to get the upper limit of the interval) and by subtracting Z standard errors from $\bar{x}$ (to get the lower limit). In symbols, the general confidence interval for estimating μ is given by $\bar{x} \pm Z \cdot \sigma/\sqrt{n}$ (fpc omitted).

Since in practice we would not know the value of σ, we use $s/\sqrt{n}$ as a point estimate of $\sigma/\sqrt{n}$ in the confidence interval formula. When the sample is large, the difference between $s/\sqrt{n}$ and $\sigma/\sqrt{n}$ is not great enough to alter appreciably the probabilities attaching to the confidence interval. In other words, normal-curve areas still apply even though the standard error is estimated from the sample. The formula we use to compute the confidence interval from the sample is thus $\bar{x} \pm Z \dfrac{s}{\sqrt{n}}$ (fpc omitted).

Returning again to the problem with which we began the discussion, we can see how the confidence interval in question was constructed. After selecting the sample of 400 households and ascertaining the income of each household, we computed the sample mean ($5422) and the standard deviation, the latter being $500. Substitution in the confidence interval formula gave us $5422 \pm 2 \cdot 500/\sqrt{400} = \$5422 \pm \$50$. The lower confidence limit is $5372 and the upper limit is $5472. We may write the interval simply as $5372–$5472.

Since the number 2 was substituted for Z in the formula, we have a 95.44% confidence interval. For a central area of exactly 95% on a normal curve, the correct Z value is 1.96. The student may verify this statement by consulting the area table. A Z value of 2 with corresponding probability of .9544 was used in introducing the idea of a confidence interval so that the student could readily apply his knowledge of the normal curve in the explanation.

Some probability values and the corresponding values of Z for commonly used confidence intervals follow on p. 165.

[3] See A. M. Mood, *Introduction to the Theory of Statistics* (New York, McGraw-Hill Book Co., Inc., 1950), p. 222.

Probability	Z
.90	1.65
.95	1.96
.98	2.33
.99	2.58

The reader should verify the values given in this table by looking them up in the normal-curve area table.

For a given probability, a short confidence interval, of course, gives a more precise estimate than a long one. And since, for a given probability, the length of the interval depends upon the standard error of the estimator, standard errors are sometimes called *measures of precision*. A glance at the formulas for $s_{\bar{x}}$ and s_p (p. 162) shows that these estimated standard errors decrease proportionately as the square root of n increases. (See p. 149.) Thus in order to halve $s_{\bar{x}}$ or s_p, we would have to increase the sample to 4 times its former size. And to cut $s_{\bar{x}}$ or s_p to $\frac{1}{3}$ of their former size, we would have to increase the sample to 9 times its former size.

CONFIDENCE INTERVAL ESTIMATION OF A POPULATION MEAN (LARGE SAMPLE)

Now the mechanics of constructing a confidence interval to estimate μ (when n is large) are very simple. After the sample is selected, (1) we compute the mean ($\bar{x}$) and the standard deviation (s); (2) we state the probability we are interested in and find the corresponding Z value, either from the table just given or from the normal-curve area table; (3) finally we fill in the formula, $\bar{x} \pm Z \cdot s/\sqrt{n}$, to get the upper and lower confidence limits. The value of $s/\sqrt{n}$ may be multiplied by the fpc in the case of finite populations.

At this point the student should begin to understand why, as we said earlier, he should be able to compute the sample mean and variance as a matter of routine.

An example involving a confidence interval estimate of a population mean follows.

Suppose that in sharpening its weapons for use in forthcoming collective bargaining sessions, an international clothing workers' union conducts a survey to estimate the average dollar profits (before taxes) of the previous year for the great many small garment-manufacturing firms whose workers are organized by the locals of the international. A list of all the firms is obtained and a sample of 169 of them is selected by using a table of random numbers. The dollar profit is ascertained for each firm in the sample. The mean and standard deviation of these figures are computed. The mean turns out to be \$15,762 and the standard deviation \$4296. A 90% confidence interval is established by the research division of the union to estimate the mean profit of all the firms in the population. The interval is constructed simply by filling in the confidence interval formula: $\bar{x} \pm Z \cdot s / \sqrt{n}$. Substituting the appropriate values, we have:

$$15,762 \pm 1.65 \left(\tfrac{4296}{13}\right) = 15,762 \pm 545 \text{ or } 15,217\text{--}16,307$$

CONFIDENCE INTERVAL ESTIMATION OF A POPULATION TOTAL (LARGE SAMPLE)

Frequently in practical problems involving measurement data, we wish to find an estimate of the total of all observations in the population. For example, an auditor might want to estimate the total dollar volume of 10,000 accounts receivable balances. Such a total may be estimated by simple random sampling. The estimator is $N\bar{x}$, the number of elements in the population times the sample mean. This is a logical estimator, for we know that $N\mu$ would give us ΣX_i, the exact total of all observations in the population.

The sampling distribution of $N\bar{x}$ (for large samples) is a normal distribution and the confidence interval is given by the formula, $N\bar{x} \pm Z \cdot Ns / \sqrt{n}$. The estimated standard error of the population total is thus $Ns / \sqrt{n}$. This may be multiplied by the fpc where appropriate.

Now suppose an auditor selects a simple random sample of 2000 accounts from the 10,000 balances mentioned above in order to estimate their total. Suppose further that the mean of the 2000 accounts ($\bar{x}$) equals \$642 and that the standard deviation is \$53. The estimate of the total is $N\bar{x} = 10,000(642) = 6.42$ million dollars. The 90% confidence interval is computed as follows:

$$N\bar{x} \pm Z \frac{Ns}{\sqrt{n}} = 6.42 \text{ million} \pm 1.65 \frac{10,000(53)}{44.72} = 6.42 \text{ million} \pm \frac{874,500}{44.72}$$

$$= 6.42 \pm .019555 \text{ million, or } 6.42 \pm .020$$

In millions, the confidence limits are 6.40–6.44. The probability is

.90 that the estimate is not off by more than about \$20 thousand. In relative terms this sampling error is $\dfrac{.020}{6.42} = .0031$ or .31%.

CONFIDENCE INTERVAL ESTIMATION OF μ WHEN THE SAMPLE IS SMALL

Although the central limit theorem is usually a sufficient guide for confidence interval estimation of μ when the sample is large, it does not lead to satisfactory results when the sample is small. In the latter case, we build up our analysis on the assumption that the population from which we sample is normally distributed. Under this assumption, the sampling distribution of $\bar{x}$ is a normal distribution with mean μ and standard deviation $\sigma/\sqrt{n}$. It is standardized by the transformation, $Z = \dfrac{\bar{x} - \mu}{\sigma/\sqrt{n}}$. Z is, of course, normally distributed with a mean of 0 and a standard deviation of 1. But we are aware that in most practical situations, we would not know the value of σ, so we would have to estimate it by computing s from the sample that we select. And *if the sample is large*, s is a close enough estimate of σ that the ratio $\dfrac{\bar{x} - \mu}{s/\sqrt{n}}$ is still closely approximated by a normal curve with mean 0 and standard deviation 1. However, as the sample gets smaller, the distribution of this ratio, though remaining symmetrical, becomes flatter and wider than a normal curve having the same mean and variance. This wide, flat distribution is called the "t" distribution, and the ratio $\dfrac{\bar{x} - \mu}{s/\sqrt{n}}$ is called "t." As we have indicated, the areas of this standardized sampling distribution change each time the sample size changes. There is one "t" distribution for samples of size 10, another for samples of size 11, and so on.

The discovery of the "t" distribution is one of the important landmarks in statistical theory. The discoverer was W. S. Gosset, an industrial statistician who worked for a brewery in the British Isles. He published his findings under the name of "Student" in 1908. Thus the distribution is often called Student's "t" distribution.

A sampling experiment which would generate a "t" distribution is as follows. Suppose we have a bowl containing 1000 wooden beads which are all equal in size. Each bead has a number on it, the numbers on all beads together forming a normal distribution with mean μ. Suppose we also have a sampling paddle with which we can scoop out samples (without replacement) of a given size, say, 21. We proceed to scoop out a very large number of such samples. For each sample, we compute the ratio, "t" $= \dfrac{\bar{x} - \mu}{s/\sqrt{n}}$ from the numbers on the sample beads and then return the beads to the bowl. If we selected, say, 500 samples, we would have 500 values of "t" which would be distributed closely in accordance with the table of areas of the "t" distribution as described in the next paragraph.

A table of areas of the "t" distribution appears on page 341. Each horizontal row in the table corresponds to a different sample size. Areas are given along the top margin of the table; they are areas on the tails of the curve. Values of "t" are given in the body of the table. Degrees of freedom (defined as $n - 1$) are given in the left margin. For a sample of 21 elements (degrees of freedom $= 20$), the value of "t" corresponding to a probability of .05 is 2.086. This means that 5% of the "t" values computed in our sampling experiment would have absolute values exceeding 2.086, $2\frac{1}{2}\%$ of them on the upper tail of the curve and $2\frac{1}{2}\%$ on the lower tail. In other words, if we set up an ordinate on the "t" distribution frequency curve at a distance 2.086 above the mean and another at the same distance below the mean, the two equal areas "sliced off" by these ordinates would together equal .05. Thus 95% of the area under the curve would lie between the two ordinates. A "t" of 2.086 is, then, the correct one to use when forming a 95% confidence interval to estimate μ where the sample size is 21. For small samples, in general, the confidence interval formula for estimating μ becomes $\bar{x} \pm$ "t"$\cdot s/\sqrt{n}$.

Since the "t" table provides for only 30 degrees of freedom, we shall define a small sample as one containing 31 elements or less.

To take an example, suppose we have selected a random sample consisting of 9 cans of green beans from the production line of a canning factory. The drained contents of each can are weighed. From this sample we are to estimate the mean weight of the contents of all cans being produced on the production line. We shall use a 90% confidence interval. The appropriate formula is $\bar{x} \pm$ "t"$\cdot s/\sqrt{n}$. Suppose the mean of the sample is found to be 16.06 ounces and the standard deviation .72 ounce. From the table we find that the appropriate value of "t" is 1.860. The standard error is $.72/\sqrt{9} =$ .24. Substituting in the formula, we have $16.06 \pm .45$, that is, $16.06 \pm 1.860(.24)$. The required interval is thus 15.61–16.51.

Because of the variation in s from sample to sample, confidence intervals at a given probability level (computed for equal-sized samples drawn from the same population) will seldom be equal. But still the given probability will hold. If we had 95% confidence intervals, for example, 95% of such intervals, in the long run, would bracket μ, the population mean.

CONFIDENCE INTERVAL FOR ESTIMATING P WHEN THE SAMPLE IS LARGE

Shifting now to attribute data, we can easily construct confidence intervals for estimating P, the proportion of elements of one given kind in a binomial population. We know that the sampling distribution of p is approximated by a normal distribution with mean P and standard error $\sigma_p = \sqrt{\dfrac{PQ}{n}}$ (fpc omitted) and that we may estimate this standard error by $s_p = \sqrt{\dfrac{pq}{n}}$. The formula for the confidence interval is analogous to that applying in the case of the mean when the sample is large. We have: $p \pm Z \sqrt{\dfrac{pq}{n}}$.

As an example, we may take the case mentioned in connection with the table of random digits. In that case, we selected a simple random sample of 200 students from those enrolled in the College of Business Administration. Suppose we wished to estimate the proportion of students in the whole college who worked for pay or profit 10 days or less during the past summer. A 98% confidence interval is to be used. Suppose further that of the 200 students in the sample, 60 worked 10 days or less. Then $p = \frac{60}{200} = .30$. The appropriate value of Z for the 98% confidence interval is 2.33. Substituting in the formula, we have as the required result: .30 $\pm$

$2.33 \sqrt{\dfrac{.30(.70)}{200}} = .30 \pm 2.33(.0324) \doteq .30 \pm .08$. The 98% confidence interval is thus .22–.38. The interval has a probability of .98 of including the true proportion of Business Administration students who worked 10 days or less for pay or profit during the summer.

The Bureau of the Census conducts a sample survey during a specified week in each month to estimate the size of the labor force, the number of employed persons, and the number of unemployed persons, among other things. A probability sample of about 35,000 households is used, and although the sample design and the estimators are much more complex than those we study in elementary statistics, it is interesting to note some of the recent estimates and the degrees of precision attached to each.

The survey conducted in May, 1959, gave the U.S. civilian labor force as 69.405 million persons and the number of unemployed as 3.389 million. The standard error of the former estimate was 250 thousand persons and of the latter 100 thousand. Thus the 95% confidence interval for the latter estimate would be about $3.389 \pm 2(.100)$ in millions. The lower confidence limit is 3.189 million and the upper limit is 3.589 million.

RATIO DELAYS

Industrial engineers are often interested in estimating the ratio of idle time to total working time for a given worker, group of workers, or piece of equipment. Such ratios are called *ratio delays;* the appropriate statistic for estimating them is p, the sample proportion. In making the estimates, we think of the working day as divided into minutes beginning, say, with 8:00 in the morning and ending at 5:00 in the afternoon, the lunch hour and regularly scheduled rest periods excepted. After the desired sample size (n) is determined, n of the designated minutes are selected at random from the working day and instantaneous observations are made at each of these times. An observation consists of noting whether the worker is productively employed or not at the designated instant of time. The ratio delay is then computed as follows:

$$p = \frac{\text{Number of observations showing nonproductive time}}{\text{Total number of observations } (n)}$$

Prior to sampling, of course, a list of worker activities must be drawn up indicating which activities are productive and which ones are not. For machinists, the list of nonproductive activities (delays) might include oiling a machine, waiting for foreman, tools, stock, or supplies, changing cutting tool, or cleaning the equipment.

Suppose, for example, that a ratio delay study is being made of 5 workmen in the Ajax Machine Shop. Ten consecutive working days are divided off into minutes and 80 minutes are selected at random from each day for each workman studied. There is, then, a total of 4000, that is, $10 \times 80 \times 5$ minutes at which observations are to be made by the time-study men.

At the conclusion of the study, suppose it is found that there were 350 delays in the 4000 observations. Thus the ratio delay would be estimated as $p = {}^{350}\!/_{4000} = .0875$ or 8.75%.

A detailed breakdown of the various types of delays, let us say, showed that most of them were due to waiting for foreman, inspectors, tools, or supplies. Suppose that exactly 90 delays were of this type. That is, ${}^{90}\!/_{350}$ or about 26% of the total nonproductive time was this type of waiting time. This result would indicate that steps should be taken to reduce this type of delay by improving the scheduling and internal transportation activities of the plant.

Confidence intervals may, of course, be established in connection with the ratio delay estimate.

THE PROBLEM OF SAMPLE SIZE

In simple random sampling the one important problem of sample design is determining the sample size. The answer to the question, "How large a sample should I take?" is "It all depends." That is, it all depends upon (1) how much money you have to spend on the sampling study and (2) how much precision you desire in the estimates. As one would suppose, the more precision you want, the more it is going to cost you. We shall assume here that cost goes up in proportion to sample size.

To develop a formula for determining sample size, let us consider the confidence interval for estimating a population mean (fpc omitted). The formula for such an interval is $\bar{x} \pm Z \cdot s/\sqrt{n}$. Let us rewrite this formula to get $\bar{x} \pm Z \cdot \hat{\sigma}/\sqrt{n}$, where $\hat{\sigma}$ ("sigma hat") is a general expression for an estimate of σ. This estimate may come from past studies of similar data or a preliminary sample. In the formula, the product $Z \cdot \hat{\sigma}/\sqrt{n}$ gives us an amount of error that has a certain probability of not being exceeded. This probability depends upon the value of Z. Now suppose that in estimating μ we wish the probability to be A that we are not off by more than d in our estimate. That is, $\Pr\{|\bar{x} - \mu| \leq d\} = A$. The $A\%$ confidence interval tells us that the probability is A that an error of $Z \cdot \hat{\sigma}/\sqrt{n}$ will not be exceeded. Since we want the probability to be A that an error of d is not exceeded, d must be equal to $Z \cdot \hat{\sigma}/\sqrt{n}$. Solving the equation $d = Z \cdot \hat{\sigma}/\sqrt{n}$ for n, we have $n = \left(\dfrac{Z\hat{\sigma}}{d}\right)^2$, the formula for sample size when the fpc is omitted and the sampling distribution of the estimator is a normal distribution.

The discerning student will note that the same result is achieved if we substitute d for $(\bar{x} - \mu)$ and $\hat{\sigma}$ for s in the transformation,

$$Z \doteq \frac{\bar{x} - \mu}{s/\sqrt{n}}.$$

To illustrate the use of the formula, let us take the following problem:

A survey is being designed to estimate the mean annual income of households in the village of Blue Forest. Simple random sampling is to be used. If the variance of household incomes is known to be approximately $160,000, how large a sample must be selected in order for the probability to be .98 that the estimate is within $75 of the population mean?

The formula is $n = \left(\dfrac{Z\hat{\sigma}}{d}\right)^2$.

The Z value corresponding to a probability of .98 is 2.33.

Since $\hat{\sigma}^2 = \$160,000$, $\hat{\sigma} = \$400$; d is given as $75. We have:

$$n = \left(\frac{2.33(400)}{75}\right)^2$$

$$= \left(\frac{932}{75}\right)^2 = (12.4)^2 \doteq 154$$

If we use the finite population correction, we must solve the equation $d = Z \sqrt{\dfrac{N - n}{N - 1}} \cdot \dfrac{\hat{\sigma}}{\sqrt{n}}$ for n in order to get the appropriate sample size formula. The result is:

$$n = \frac{NZ^2\hat{\sigma}^2}{d^2(N - 1) + Z^2\hat{\sigma}^2}$$

In determining sample size for an estimate of P, a population proportion, an estimate of $\sqrt{PQ}$ is substituted for $\hat{\sigma}$ in the appropriate sample size formula. (See Ch. 8, p. 155.)

SAMPLING ERRORS AND NONSAMPLING ERRORS

The purpose of studying probability and developing the concept of a probability distribution was to gain some insight into the nature, estimation, and control of sampling errors. In estimating a mean μ, we know that the sampling error may be defined as the difference $\bar{x} - \mu$. The probability distribution of these differences for samples of a given size is the sampling distribution of the mean. The sampling error arises, of course, because we examine the data in just one sample instead of taking a census of the population.

Now nonsampling errors are essentially errors of measurement or count. They are particularly troublesome in the sampling of human populations. Sometimes it is difficult even to define precisely what we are measuring or counting. Take the variable "income" for example. What is "income"? We might say that it is all money earned by a person during a calendar year. The use of the term *money* immediately excludes nonmoney income, and the use of the term *earned* requires us to distinguish between earned and unearned income. Gifts, inheritances, winnings, and stealings would be excluded, perhaps, from earned income as would income from pensions, investments, or trust funds. The exclusion of nonmoney incomes may cause a serious defect in our definition, for in the case of persons living on farms, nonmoney incomes are likely to be quite substantial.

In spite of all the difficulties, suppose we are able to frame a satisfactory definition of "income." Our problems are not at an end, for we are still faced with the fact that persons are often reluctant to talk about their incomes. If we mail questionnaires out to them, they may not send them back. If we interview people personally, they may refuse to answer or give erroneous answers, whether this be the result of design or ignorance. Responses may differ depending upon what the respondent thinks the survey results are to be used for. Some persons seem to have available two income figures, one relating to taxpaying and one relating to bragging. Of course, the former is smaller and it is the one quoted when there is any thought that the interviewer is even remotely connected with the tax collector. Strange to say, some persons have little or no idea what their incomes are.

In the face of these added difficulties, we might decide not to ask persons about their incomes but to sample tax returns instead. In this case, our definition of income becomes "income that must be reported as required by the tax laws," and as a result, we miss those small incomes of persons who do not have to file tax returns. Additional difficulties arise out of the fact that some persons pay taxes on a fiscal year basis and others pay on a calendar year basis.

Though the problems of definition, nonresponse, and intentionally misleading response can cause serious difficulties, more primitive aspects of the communications problem still must be faced. The wording of a question, the sequence in which questions are asked, and even the tone of voice of the questioner can influence responses.

Incidentally, some nonresponse is due to the fact that persons have been conditioned against "survey takers." The conditioning is provided by the modern door-to-door salesman who, in order to get his foot inside the door, states that he is taking a survey.

In the sampling of human populations, the problems of non-sampling errors may seem so large that some samplers will claim sampling errors are extremely small in comparison. Such persons may decide to concentrate on minimizing nonsampling errors and disregard probability sampling techniques altogether. However, in a good many cases measurement is quite precise and our prime concern is with the sampling error. It would seem that in all cases, we should seek to minimize both types of error and neglect neither in deference to the other.

EXPECTED VALUES AND BIAS

The expected value of an estimator is the mean of the estimator taken over all possible samples of a given size. For the sampling distribution used as an illustration in Chapter 8, page 152, we found that the mean of all the sample means was equal to μ, the population mean. In general, in the absence of nonsampling errors the expected value of $\bar{x}$ is μ. In symbols, $E(\bar{x}) = \mu$, where $E(\bar{x})$ is read, "the expected value of the sample mean."

Assuming there are no nonsampling errors, if the expected value of an estimator is equal to the parameter being estimated, we say that the estimator is unbiased. Thus $\bar{x}$ is an unbiased estimator of μ. In general, we prefer estimators which have this quality. When an unbiased estimator has a symmetrical sampling distribution, the probability of an overestimate is equal to the probability of an underestimate. But in the case of a biased estimator with a symmetrical sampling distribution, these probabilities would not be equal. If the expected value is greater than the parameter being estimated, the bias is positive; in the reverse case, bias is negative. The quantity $(\bar{x} + 3)$, for example, would be a positively biased estimator of μ. Nonsampling errors such as mistakes in observation or unequal probabilities of selection frequently cause biases in other-wise unbiased estimators.

At this point we are in a position to understand why we divide by $n - 1$ in computing the sample variance. (Refer to Ch. 6, p.

90.) We recall that the formula for the sample variance is $s^2 = \dfrac{\Sigma(x_i - \bar{x})^2}{n - 1}$ and that the population variance is defined for a finite population in two ways, namely (1) $S^2 = \dfrac{\Sigma(X_i - \mu)^2}{N - 1}$ and (2) $\sigma^2 = \dfrac{\Sigma(X_i - \mu)^2}{N}$.

Now if we consider s^2 as an estimator of S^2, and we are sampling without replacement from a finite population, s^2 is an unbiased estimator of S^2. If we did not divide by $n - 1$ in computing s^2, it would be a biased estimator of S^2.

Further, s^2 (with $n - 1$ in the denominator) is also an unbiased estimator of σ^2 when we are sampling *with* replacement from a finite population, or when we are sampling (with or without replacement) from an indefinitely large population.

Strange to say, although s^2 is an unbiased estimator of S^2, s is *not* an unbiased estimator of S. Neither is s an unbiased estimator of σ. Furthermore, although $s_{\bar{x}}^2$ is an unbiased estimator of $\sigma_{\bar{x}}^2$, $s_{\bar{x}}$ is not an unbiased estimator of $\sigma_{\bar{x}}$. However, this bias is slight, and in practice we often neglect it.

Incidentally, the formula for $\sigma_{\bar{x}}$ (which we wrote as $\sqrt{\dfrac{N - n}{N - 1}} \cdot \dfrac{\sigma}{\sqrt{n}}$ for a finite population) may be written as $\sqrt{\dfrac{N - n}{N}} \cdot \dfrac{S}{\sqrt{n}}$. The equivalence of these two forms is readily seen if the student recognizes that $S = \sqrt{\dfrac{N}{N - 1}} \, \sigma$.

SUMMARY

Sample estimates of parameters may be either (1) point estimates or (2) interval estimates. Point estimates are stated in terms of one number only, whereas interval estimates are stated in the form of a range. Point estimates of standard errors are used in the construction of interval estimates or confidence intervals. Such intervals are an expression of the precision of a given estimate. In general, we may say that a confidence interval is a range determined with reference to a given estimator, this range having a given probability of bracketing or including the estimated parameter.

When the sample is large, the confidence interval for estimating the population mean is given by the formula $\bar{x} \pm Z \cdot s/\sqrt{n}$ (fpc omitted). The value of the standardized variable Z depends upon the probability attaching to the confidence interval and may be evaluated from the table of areas of the normal curve.

When the sample is small ($n \leqq 31$), the confidence interval for estimating the population mean is given by the formula $\bar{x} \pm$ "t"$\cdot s/\sqrt{n}$. The standardized variable "t" is not normally distributed, and special tables are needed for finding the appropriate values to substitute for "t" in the confidence interval formula. The "t" distribution approaches the normal distribution as the sample size increases, and for samples of $n > 31$, the difference between the two distributions may, in most cases, be neglected. The "t" distribution was discovered in the early part of this century by W. S. Gosset.

When the sample is large, the confidence interval for estimating the proportion P of a binomial population is given by the formula

$$p \pm Z \sqrt{\frac{pq}{n}} \text{ (fpc omitted).}$$

Also, when the sample is large, the total of all observations in the population may be estimated by the confidence interval: $N\bar{x} \pm Z \cdot \dfrac{Ns}{\sqrt{n}}$ (fpc omitted).

The size of sample to take depends upon the degree of precision desired in the estimates. The higher the degree of precision, the greater the sample size and cost. From the idea of a confidence interval we develop the following formula for determining sample size when seeking to estimate a population mean:

$$n = \left(\frac{Z\hat{\sigma}}{d}\right)^2$$

where Z is determined by the probability associated with the desired confidence interval, $\hat{\sigma}$ is an estimate of the population standard deviation, and d is the sampling error specified as half the length of the desired confidence interval.

In estimating P, an estimate of $\sqrt{PQ}$ is substituted for $\hat{\sigma}$ in the above formula to get the desired sample size.

The expected value of an estimator is the mean of that estimator over all possible samples of size n. The expected value of the mean is symbolized by $E(\bar{x})$. Assuming there are no nonsampling errors, if the expected value of the estimator is equal to the parameter being estimated, the estimator is said to be unbiased. The sample mean is an unbiased estimator of the population mean. That is, $E(\bar{x}) = \mu$.

In computing the sample variance, s^2, we divide by $n - 1$ so that this statistic will be an unbiased estimator of S^2 when we are sampling without replacement from a finite population. In sampling *with* replacement from a finite population, s^2 is an unbiased estimator of σ^2. However, s is *not* an unbiased estimator of either S or σ.

Sampling errors result from the fact that a sample of elements is studied rather than all the elements in the population. This situation causes the value of a given estimator to vary from sample to sample.

On the other hand, nonsampling errors are essentially errors in measuring and/or counting. They are particularly important in sampling of human populations and may arise from ambiguous or unworkable definitions, nonresponse, intentionally misleading responses, or unintentionally misleading responses (due to poorly constructed questionnaires or unskilled interviewers).

In some surveys, nonsampling errors may be of greater magnitude than sampling errors, but the attempt to minimize both should never be abandoned.

TERMS TO PONDER

1. Estimator
2. Point Estimate
3. True Standard Error
4. Estimated Standard Error
5. Confidence Interval
6. Student's "t" Distribution
7. Ratio Delay
8. Expected Value
9. Bias
10. Sampling Error
11. Nonsampling Error

EXERCISES

1. Using the table of random numbers (Table III, p. 342), select a simple random sample of 50 elements from the population of customer account balances of the Last Resort Loan Company, December 31, 1958. (See following page.)

   a. For this sample of 50 elements, compute $\bar{x}$, s^2, and $\sqrt{\dfrac{N-n}{N-1}} \cdot \dfrac{s}{\sqrt{n}}$.

   b. Compute μ, the population mean, and compare the result with $\bar{x}$.

   c. Construct a 95% confidence interval for estimating μ.

   d. Using the data in the sample, estimate the total of all accounts outstanding on December 31, 1958. Compare this estimate with the true total of all accounts.

Population: Customer Account Balances Receivable
of the Last Resort Loan Co., December 31, 1958

133	56	84	73	59	66	61	66	82	138	86	75	26	82	74	
77	44	50	72	76	90	85	20	16	33	26	99	82	75	20	
91	98	52	86	77	41	14	30	16	31	65	99	82	59	32	
16	28	73	29	79	80	135	46	84	56	123	22	79	59	90	
82	20	65	60	61	158	53	105	56	89	20	80	87	35	41	
111	55	60	64	20	48	62	16	98	46	99	62	88	121	122	
39	47	52	149	67	87	98	165	41	132	32	12	80	23	71	
53	17	74	51	21	93	33	32	72	55	28	83	35	66	164	
60	15	88	42	65	70	65	70	65	13	21	150	93	38	82	
89	46	36	42	97	93	87	33	55	86	78	55	54	45	80	
64	85	39	157	42	75	95	41	13	24	99	41	135	88	65	
50	122	53	53	56	54	94	39	12	86	71	141	53	107	65	
64	69	20	34	53	73	68	90	31	21	28	41	63	16	12	
29	80	145	40	19	20	37	84	16	25	54	21	18	35	82	
67	65	23	45	131	30	128	151	63	18	44	96	13	32	87	
45	85	33	54	96	22	63	72	125	99	73	60	88	125	84	
56	22	85	54	74	68	21	95	67	81	88	51	12	35	26	
74	34	61	17	30	32	82	33	56	28	39	27	58	62	77	
72	85	75	56	23	34	84	84	63	22	72	28	41	38	14	
75	93	20	25	85	19	96	106	31	30	86	26	90	30	51	

2. Using the sample selected in Exercise 1, construct a 98% confidence interval for estimating μ. (Omit the fpc.)

3. The following numbers represent a simple random sample of plastic knobs, each knob having been measured for breaking strength. The figures are given in pounds. Use a 95% confidence interval to estimate the mean breaking strength of the population from which the sample was drawn.

$$8 \quad 9 \quad 6 \quad 10 \quad 7 \quad 7 \quad 5 \quad 5 \quad 9$$

4. A batch of new automobile exhaust valves is sampled so that an estimate of the proportion of defective valves can be made. Suppose a simple random sample of 400 valves is selected and 40 of these are found to be defective. Compute a 90% confidence interval to estimate the true proportion of defective valves.

5. Suppose that in evaluating its physical properties, an electric utility company must designate circuit breakers as belonging to class A or class B, the latter group representing older types that are evaluated at a lower figure than those of class A. Out of a random sample of 485 circuit breakers, 170 fall into class B. Find 98% confidence limits for estimating the true proportion of class B circuit breakers.

6. In conducting an audit of a company's books, we wish to estimate the mean balance of a population consisting of accounts payable. If

the population variance is known to be about $2500, how many accounts must we select in order that our sample mean will not differ from the true mean by more than $10 with a probability of .95?

7. A company having very important defense contracts with the federal government wishes to keep absenteeism at a minimum and therefore seeks to estimate how many of its employees would be willing to take Asian "flu" shots if the company furnished them free of charge. A sample of 100 workers is selected at random. Eighty of these persons are willing to take the shots. Form a point estimate of the proportion of workers who are willing to take the shots. Use this result and the fact that there are, in all, 985 workers in the company to estimate the *number* of workers who will take the shots. The latter estimate would assist the company physician in ordering the proper amount of vaccine.

8. Suppose we have selected a simple random sample of 144 vacuum tubes from a given production run. From this sample we have estimated the true mean length of tube life as 1782 hours. If the sample standard deviation is 108 hours, what is the probability that our estimate is not more than 15 hours different from the true mean?

9. The following numbers represent family sizes (in number of persons per family) for a simple random sample taken from a population of 500 *families*.

2	3	2	5	6	3	3	4
7	3	5	3	3	2	4	5
6	5	4	4	3	2	2	4
3	4	2	3	3	6	3	3

Form a point estimate of the total number of *persons* in the population.

10. An office manager conducts a ratio delay study of several secretaries. A total of 788 instances of delay are found in a sample of 3500 observations. Compute 95% confidence limits for this ratio delay.

11. A real-estate syndicate is interested in estimating the current vacancy rate for apartments in Washington, D.C., that is, the proportion of all apartment units which are vacant. A simple random sample consisting of 3180 apartment units is selected. Three hundred and fifty of these are found to be vacant. Construct a 95% confidence interval to estimate the true proportion of vacant apartments.

12. A market survey of Middletown households is to be carried out by simple random sampling, one of the objects being the estimation of the proportion of households planning to buy "compact cars" in 1960. A preliminary survey shows that this proportion is about .15. How many households must be selected in order for the probability to be

about .95 that the estimate is within 2 percentage points of the true proportion?

SELECTED REFERENCES

FREUND, John E., and WILLIAMS, Frank J., *Modern Business Statistics* (Englewood Cliffs, N.J., Prentice-Hall, Inc., 1958), Ch. IX.

HANSEN, M. H., HURWITZ, W. N., and MADOW, W. G., *Sample Survey Methods and Theory* (New York, John Wiley and Sons, Inc., 1953), Vol. I, Ch. IV.

HIRSCH, Werner Z., *Introduction to Modern Statistics* (New York, The Macmillan Co., 1957), Chs. VIII, X.

10

TESTING HYPOTHESES

In Chapter 9 we found that important information about a statistical population often takes the form of estimates of one or more parameters. We construct estimates, of course, because of the need for answers to such questions as "what is the value of the population mean?" or "How big is the population standard deviation?"

In testing hypotheses, however, our methods arise from the need for answers to such questions as "Is the population mean equal to some certain hypothetical value?" or "Is the population mean greater than some hypothetical value?"

In testing hypotheses, we make choices between various alternatives. Thus such tests may be considered a part of statistical decision-making. However, the latter subject covers a rather large area and is by no means confined to the elementary testing of hypotheses. Decision-making includes the testing of hypotheses and much more.

In making a test, we must first of all make a clear statement of the hypothesis. We then note the manner in which an appropriate *test statistic* would be distributed if the hypothesis were true. We may call this the hypothesized sampling distribution. The test statistic gives a relationship between the hypothesis and sample observations made for purposes of the test. Next, we designate certain *critical values* of the test statistic. These values delimit the range of sampling variation over which we agree to accept the hypothesis as plausible and that range over which we agree to reject the hypothesis, this latter being called the *critical region*. The probability associated with the critical region is called a *level of significance* and, of course, represents the probability of rejecting the hypothesis when it is actually true. We next compute a value of the test statistic from sample observations. If this value falls in the critical region, we reject the hypothesis in favor of some apparent alternative hypothesis. On the other hand, if the computed value does not fall in the critical region, we "accept" the hypothesis as plausible, that is, we admit that it *could* be true but recognize that our test has in no way *proved* that it is true.

TESTING A HYPOTHESIS CONCERNING A POPULATION MEAN (LARGE SAMPLE)

To illustrate, suppose that an electronics firm has succeeded in producing a new type of TV picture tube called "Silverglim." On the basis of past experience and knowledge of the specifications under which the tube is to be produced, the engineers of the company formulate the hypothesis that Silverglim tubes will have a mean service life of 1200 hours. This hypothesis is, of course, equivalent to the statement that the population of all tubes produced according to Silverglim specifications will last, on the average, 1200 hours under conditions of actual use.

To test this hypothesis, suppose we select a random sample of the new TV picture tubes and life-test each one of them. We then compute the sample mean length of life and compare it with the hypothetical population mean (μ_0) of 1200 hours. If the difference between the two means is small, we (1) accept the hypothesis *as plausible,* and if the difference is large, we (2) reject the hypothesis.

Suppose that the sample size is 100 tubes, that the sample mean is found to be 1155 hours and the standard deviation, 150 hours. The estimated standard error of the mean is $s/\sqrt{n} = {}^{150}\!/_{10} = 15$ hours. The difference between $\bar{x}$ and μ_0 is $1155 - 1200 = -45$ hours. We determine how many standard errors there are in -45 hours by computing the test statistic $Z \doteq \dfrac{\bar{x} - \mu_0}{s/\sqrt{n}} = -\dfrac{45}{15} = -3.$ Thus the sample mean lies about 3 standard errors below the hypothetical population mean, a distance sufficient to cause us to reject the hypothesis that Silverglim tubes have a mean service life of 1200 hours.

As stated earlier, in making the choice between the two alternatives, that is, accepting the hypothesis *as plausible* or rejecting it, we utilize the concept of a *hypothesized sampling distribution.* For this illustrative problem, we know that if the population mean were actually equal to 1200 hours, then means of random samples (of constant size n) selected from that population would be distributed normally with a mean of 1200 hours and a standard error of $\sigma/\sqrt{n}$, provided n were large.   About $\frac{2}{3}$ (68.26%) of the sample means would lie within 2 standard errors of the population mean, 95% of them would lie within 1.96 standard errors of the population mean, and so on.   Again, if the *population* mean actually were 1200 hours, then the probability would be small that a *sample* mean would lie a "great" distance (on the Z scale) from 1200.   (We know from our knowledge of the normal curve, for example, that only 5% of the sample means would lie beyond 1.96 standard errors from the population mean.)   Thus if the mean of the sample actually selected did lie a "great" distance away from the hypothetical population mean, we would, because of the small probability of such a result, reject the hypothesis.

In our illustration, it so happens we rejected the hypothesis that $\mu = 1200$ because we reasoned as follows: If the true mean actually is 1200 hours, then a test statistic $\left(\dfrac{\bar{x} - \mu}{s/\sqrt{n}}\right)$ value of more than $|1.96|$ is highly improbable.   But such a highly improbable result $\left(\dfrac{\bar{x} - \mu}{s\sqrt{n}} = -3\right)$ *did* happen.   Therefore, the true mean is very probably not equal to 1200 hours.

On the other hand, if the mean of the selected sample had been close to the hypothetical value, we would have accepted the hypothesis as plausible, that is, we would have been willing to admit that the hypothesis could be true, *although we would not have had conclusive proof of its truth;* sampling from populations with means *near* 1200 could easily give rise to $\bar{x}$ values close to 1200.

The question that persists in our minds at this point is "Where do we draw the line between acceptance and rejection?" or "How many standard errors must the sample mean lie from the hypothetical population mean in order for us to reject the hypothesis?"   As in the case of the problem of sample size, the answer is, "It all depends."   That is, it all depends on the risk we are willing to take of rejecting a hypothesis when it is actually true.

In our illustration, we decided to take 1.96 standard errors as the maximum "acceptable" difference between $\bar{x}$ and μ_0, or $|1.96|$ as the maximum acceptable value of the test statistic.   That is, we decided to reject the hypothesis if the sample mean was more than 1.96

standard errors distant from 1200 hours, and to accept the hypothesis as plausible if the sample mean was within 1.96 standard errors of 1200.

Now, if the population mean was *in fact* equal to 1200 hours, the probability would be, as we have said, .05 that a sample mean (based upon a large number of independent random observations) would lie more than 1.96 standard errors distant from 1200. And if we rejected the hypothesis in all cases where the mean was more than 1.96 standard errors from 1200, we would, in the long run, be rejecting the hypothesis wrongly 5% of the time.

Rejecting a hypothesis when it is actually true is called a *Type I Error*. On the other hand, accepting a hypothesis as plausible when it is actually false is a *Type II Error*.

We have noted that the range of sampling variation over which we agree to reject a hypothesis is called the *critical region* and is associated with a certain probability area on the hypothesized sampling distribution. This probability is called the level of significance and represents the probability of committing a *Type I Error*. In the illustration, the critical region lies outside the range 1200 ± 1.96 standard errors or outside the range, 0 ± 1.96 on the Z scale, the values ± 1.96 being the *critical values* of the test statistic $\dfrac{\bar{x} - \mu}{s/\sqrt{n}}$. This critical region is shown graphically in Figure 10–2.

A level of significance having a particular probability is not unique. For example the critical region for a 5% level of significance could be represented on the hypothesized sampling distribution in a great many ways. But it so happens that a critical region with associated area divided equally between the two tails of the distribution is appropriate for the test of the hypothesis that $\mu = \mu_0$. As we shall see, location of the critical region on one tail of the curve is appropriate for other hypotheses such as $\mu \leq \mu_0$ and $\mu \geq \mu_0$. A critical region equally divided between the two tails of the curve is said to result in a two-tailed test. A critical region which is continuous and on one extreme of the curve or the other is said to involve a one-tailed test.

Figure 10–1 shows three ways of choosing a 5% critical region on a hypothesized sampling distribution which is normal in form. Figure 10–1(a) is appropriate for the test of the hypothesis that $\mu = \mu_0$. Figure 10–1(b) is appropriate for the test of the hypothesis that $\mu \geq \mu_0$. Figure 10–1(c) is appropriate for the test of the hypothesis that $\mu \leq \mu_0$.

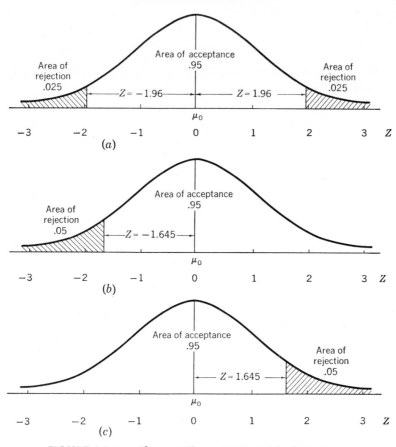

FIGURE 10–1. Three Different 5% Critical Regions

PROCEDURE FOR TESTING A HYPOTHESIS CONCERNING A POPULATION MEAN (LARGE SAMPLE)

The steps involved in the process of testing a hypothesis relevant to a mean (when the sample is large) are quite simple. We may summarize them as follows:

1. State the hypothesis, for example, $\mu = \mu_0$, or as in the illustrative problem, $\mu = 1200$ hours.
2. Choose a level of significance and locate the critical region on the hypothesized sampling distribution.
3. Note the *critical value* of the test statistic, that is, the maximum acceptable difference between $\bar{x}$ and μ_0 on the Z scale. In the illustrative problem, $Z = \pm 1.96$.

4. Find the approximate *computed value* of Z from the sample data.
$Z \doteq \dfrac{\bar{x} - \mu_0}{s/\sqrt{n}}$. For the illustrative problem, computed $Z \doteq -3$.

5. Compare the critical value of Z with the computed value of Z. If these values have opposite signs, accept the hypothesis as plausible. If they have the same sign, compare their absolute values. If the absolute value of the computed Z is greater than that of the critical Z, reject the hypothesis; otherwise accept the hypothesis as plausible.

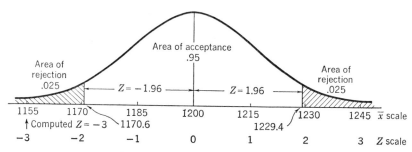

FIGURE 10–2.   Test of Hypothesis That $\mu = 1200$ Hours (Silverglim TV Tubes)

It is very important that we choose our level of significance *before* we make any computations from the sample observations, for once we know the computed value of the test statistic, we can always choose a level of significance that will lead to rejection of the hypothesis, that is, cause this value to be significant.

Problems of testing hypotheses are easier for most students if they are diagramed. The diagram of the TV picture tube problem is given in Figure 10–2.

Although in our list of steps for testing hypotheses concerning the mean we have operated on the Z scale, it is, of course, possible to solve such problems by operating on the $\bar{x}$ scale. Transforming the critical Z values of the Silverglim problem (± 1.96) to the $\bar{x}$ scale, we have 1170.6 and 1229.4, that is, $1200 \pm 1.96 \dfrac{150}{\sqrt{100}}$. (See Fig. 10–2.) Since the sample mean (1155) falls outside of the range 1170.6–1229.4, we reject the hypothesis and conclude that the population mean is probably different from 1200.

In this particular type of test, that is, two-tailed, a confidence interval could be used to test the hypothesis. That is, we could compute $\bar{x} \pm 1.96 \, s/\sqrt{n}$ (where the level of significance was .05 or 5%)

and note whether μ_0 fell within the interval. If it did not, we would reject the hypothesis. Otherwise we would accept the hypothesis as plausible. The confidence interval technique does not work satisfactorily in the case of one-tailed tests.

ONE-TAILED TESTS CONCERNING A SINGLE MEAN (LARGE SAMPLE)

Suppose that in the TV picture tube example, the hypothesis had been that the tube would last *at least* 1200 hours. "At least 1200 hours," of course, means "equal to or more than 1200 hours." In this case we construct our sampling distribution under the hypothetical condition that $\mu = 1200$ and then locate the critical region and area of rejection as in Figure 10–3; that is, the entire region is

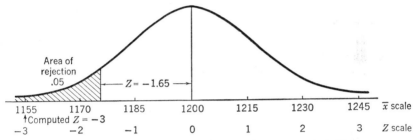

FIGURE 10–3.   Test of Hypothesis That $\mu \geqq$ 1200 Hours (Silverglim TV Tubes)

placed on the lower tail of the curve, for we desire to reject the hypothesis only when the sample mean ($\bar{x}$) is significantly *less than* 1200 hours. Let us again use a 5% level of significance.

Going through the five-step procedure, we have the following:

1. State hypothesis: $\mu \geqq$ 1200 hours.
2. Choose level of significance: 5% with 5% critical region on the lower tail of the hypothesized sampling distribution.
3. Note critical value of Z: -1.65.
4. Find approximate computed value of Z: $Z \doteq \dfrac{1155 - 1200}{15} = -3.$
5. Compare critical value of Z with computed value of Z. Both have same sign and latter is larger in absolute value. Reject hypothesis and conclude that the mean is probably less than 1200 hours.

If the sample mean had been equal to or greater than 1200 hours, we would, of course, have immediately accepted the hypothesis as plausible, and there would have been no need for going through the five-step procedure.

Let us next consider a problem where it is appropriate to place the region of rejection on the upper tail of the hypothesized sampling distribution.

In manufacturing liver sausage, a meat packing company seeks to maintain a mean fat content of no more than .25 or 25% by weight. A certain amount of fat is desirable so that the meat can be easily spread on bread, but too much fat results in an undesirable taste.

If a random sample of 49 8-ounce liver sausages has a mean fat content of .270 and a standard deviation of .077, state and test the appropriate hypothesis. In this case let the level of significance be 2%.

Following our five-step outline, we have:

1. State hypothesis: $\mu \leq .25$.
2. Choose level of significance: 2% with the 2% region of rejection on the upper tail.
3. Note critical value of Z: $+2.33$.
4. Find computed value of the test statistic: $Z \doteq \dfrac{.270 - .25}{.077/7} = \dfrac{.020}{.011}$
   $\doteq 1.82$.
5. Compare critical and computed values of Z. Both have the same sign. The absolute value of the computed Z (1.82) is less than the absolute value of the critical Z, so we accept the hypothesis that $\mu \leq .25$ as plausible at the 2% level of significance.

The student should draw the appropriate diagram of this problem.

TESTS CONCERNING THE MEAN WHEN THE SAMPLE IS SMALL

As we learned when considering problems of estimation, the appropriate sampling distribution of the mean to use when the sample is small ($n \leq 3_1$) is the "t" distribution. The ratio "t", we recall, is defined as $\dfrac{\bar{x} - \mu}{s/\sqrt{n}}$, wherein, it is important to note, both $\bar{x}$ and s are subject to sampling variation. We should also note the important underlying assumption that the population is normal.

The five-step procedure for testing a hypothesis is the same in this case as for the large-sample case, except that here we find a critical value and a computed value of the test statistic "t" rather than a critical value and an approximate computed value of Z.

To take an illustrative problem, a new type of ceramic insulator for use on high-voltage electrical lines has been developed. Among other things, the resistance to crushing force is an important characteristic of such insulators. Engineers establish the hypothesis that the mean force that can be withstood by the insulators is *at least* 260 pounds. In order to test this hypothesis, a sample of 5 of the new insulators is selected at random and each one is mechanically squeezed until it begins to crack. The maximum amount of stress (in pounds) that each insulator is able to bear is recorded. Suppose the data are as follows:

$$251 \quad 238 \quad 269 \quad 245 \quad 250$$

Before going through our five-step testing procedure, we must compute the sample mean and standard deviation. The computations are readily accomplished if we code our data by subtracting 250 from each of them. (See appendix at end of Ch. 6.) Let us symbolize the coded data by $u_i = x_i - 250$. We have:

x_i	u_i	u_i^2
251	1	1
238	-12	144
269	19	361
245	-5	25
250	0	0
	$\Sigma u_i = 3$	$\Sigma u_i^2 = 531$

$$\bar{x} = 250 + \tfrac{3}{5} = 250.6$$

$$s^2 = \frac{531 - \dfrac{(3)^2}{5}}{5 - 1} = \frac{531 - 1.8}{4} = \frac{529.2}{4} = 132.3$$

$$s = \sqrt{132.3}$$

$$s/\sqrt{n} = \frac{\sqrt{132.3}}{\sqrt{5}} = \sqrt{26.46} \doteq 5.14$$

Having made the necessary preliminary calculations, we can go through the five-step procedure for testing the hypothesis.

1. State hypothesis: $\mu \geq 260$ lbs.
2. Choose level of significance: 5% with the 5% region of rejection on the lower tail.
3. Note critical value of "t": -2.132.
4. Find computed value of "t": "t" $= \dfrac{\bar{x} - \mu_0}{s/\sqrt{n}} = \dfrac{250.6 - 260}{5.13} = \dfrac{-9.4}{5.14}$
   $\doteq -1.83$.
5. Compare values of the critical "t" and the computed "t." They have the same sign and the absolute value of the computed "t" is greater. Accept hypothesis as plausible.

A diagram of this problem is given in Figure 10–4.

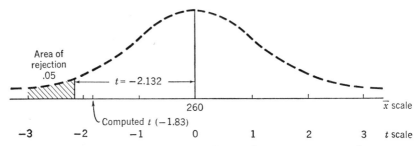

FIGURE 10–4. Test of Hypothesis That $\mu \geq 260$ Pounds (Ceramic Insulators)

It is important to note that in finding the critical value of "t" from the "t" table, we looked in the column headed .10 rather than the column headed .05. Recall that if ordinates are erected at $+$"t" and $-$"t" from the center of the horizontal axis, these ordinates "chop off" two equal areas which *together* equal the probability value given at the head of the column. Thus, for a one-tailed test (where we take "t" in one direction only) we find our critical "t" value in that column having a heading which is twice the probability of our level of significance. For two-tailed tests, we utilize that column which has a heading equal to the probability denoting our level of significance. (See Table II, p. 341.) In either case, we must, of course, take account of the appropriate degrees of freedom ($n - 1$).

PROBLEMS IN CONSTRUCTING A TEST

We have, so far, considered essentially three hypotheses concerning a population mean. They are (1) $\mu = \mu_0$, (2) $\mu \geq \mu_0$, (3) $\mu \leq \mu_0$. There are, of course, many other hypotheses that can be tested, but the three given are stated in such a manner that the alternative hypothesis in each case is suggested and the appropriate location of the region of rejection indicated. In general, once the level of significance is chosen, the construction of the test consists of locating the region of rejection on the hypothesized sampling distribution curve. The idea is to locate this region so that the probability of rejecting the hypothesis will be large when the hypothesis is false and small when it is true. Or looking across the fence the other way, the idea is to locate the region so that the probability of accepting the hypothesis will be large when the hypothesis is true and small when it is false. Ideally, we should like to *minimize* the probability of a Type I error and of a Type II error.

There is only one value of μ for which hypothesis (1) is true but a great many possible alternative values of μ for which the hypothesis is false. In the case of hypotheses (2) and (3) there are a great many alternative values of μ for which they are true as well as a great many for which they are false. By establishing the criterion of rejection on the $\bar{x}$ scale of the hypothesized sampling distribution and letting μ take on various alternative values, we may compute the probability of rejecting the hypothesis for each alternative value. We shall do this for all three hypotheses. An examination of the results will then verify the fact that we have used the most appropriate locations for the regions of rejection in our previous tests of the hypotheses.

For purposes of discussion, let us suppose that the sample drawn in making our tests consists of 64 elements and that the population standard deviation σ is known to be 16. The standard error of the mean will then equal 2, that is, $\sigma/\sqrt{n} = \frac{16}{8} = 2$. Furthermore, let us suppose that the level of significance for all three tests is .10 or 10% and that the hypothetical value of μ is 20.

POWER FUNCTION OF A TWO-TAILED TEST
(HYPOTHESIS: $\mu = \mu_0$)

We wish to ascertain the probabilities of rejecting the hypothesis ($\mu = \mu_0$) at the 10% level of significance when μ has various alternative values. We shall get one probability figure for each of these alternative values of μ. As indicated above, we shall for purposes of the discussion locate our critical values on the $\bar{x}$ scale. For the chosen 10% level of significance, the critical values are approximately $\mu_0 \pm 1.65 \sigma/\sqrt{n} = 20 \pm 1.65(2) = 20 \pm 3.3$ or 16.7 and 23.3. We know, then, that we are to reject the hypothesis for sample means which are greater than 23.3 and sample means which are less than 16.7.

Let our first alternative value of μ be 20. That is, we assume first of all that the hypothesis is true. We know, already, that in this case the probability of rejecting the hypothesis is .10 and the probability of accepting it is .90. The value .10, then, is the probability of committing a Type I error.

Next let us suppose that μ is actually equal, in turn, to 14, 18, 22, and 26. These figures represent in our illustration four values

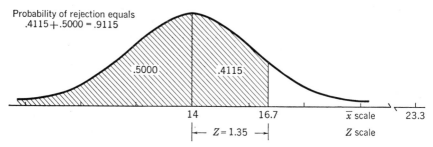

FIGURE 10–5. Probability of Rejecting Hypothesis That $\mu = 20$ When μ Is Actually Equal to 14

of μ for which the hypothesis is false. We wish to find for each of these values the probability of rejecting the hypothesis under the conditions we have established. These conditions, again, are that we reject the hypothesis for sample means less than 16.7 and for sample means greater than 23.3.

The hypothesized sampling distribution of the mean with μ assumed equal to 14 is diagramed in Figure 10–5.

The shaded area of the curve in Figure 10–5 represents the probability of rejecting the hypothesis when $\mu = 14$. This area is readily evaluated if we compute the number of standard errors that 16.7 lies from 14 and then note the total area lying to the left of the ordinate at 16.7, this area being .9115. Since 23.3 lies 4.65 standard errors from 14, the probability that a sample mean would be larger than 23.3 is virtually 0.

Next, suppose that μ is actually equal to 18. This situation is shown in Figure 10–6, the probability of rejection being .2618.

The probability of rejection will also be .2618 if we assume that μ is actually equal to 22. This is so because 22 lies the same

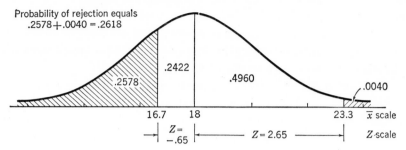

FIGURE 10–6. Probability of Rejecting Hypothesis That $\mu = 20$ When μ Is Actually Equal to 18

distance above 20 as 18 does below 20. We shall, however, show how this probability value is computed in Figure 10–7.

It is also the case that if μ were actually 26, the probability of rejecting the hypothesis that $\mu = 20$ would be .9115, as was the case for an assumed μ of 14. At this point, then, we have, if we include the case where $\mu = 20$, five alternative values of μ and the corresponding probabilities of rejecting the hypothesis. We may summarize these figures as follows:

Alternative values of μ	*Probability of rejecting hypothesis that $\mu = 20$*
14	.9115
18	.2618
20	.1000
22	.2618
26	.9115

To get a spatial picture of the relationship between these two columns of numbers, let us graph them, with the values of μ on the horizontal axis and the probability figures on the vertical axis.

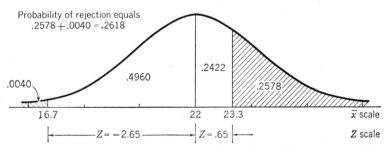

FIGURE 10–7. Probability of Rejecting Hypothesis That $\mu = 20$ When μ Is Actually Equal to 22

Note that here probabilities are represented by ordinates, not areas. This graph, with the appropriate smoothed curve drawn through the plotted points, is shown in Figure 10–8. The curve is said to represent the *power function* of the test.

We see at a glance from Figure 10–8 that under our criteria the probabilities of rejection increase rather rapidly as the actual value of μ differs from 20 in either direction. This verifies the fact that the two-tailed test is appropriate for the hypothesis that $\mu = \mu_0$,

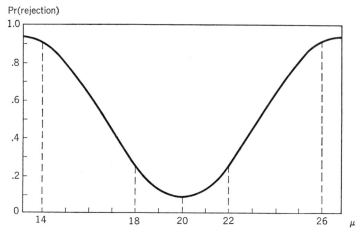

FIGURE 10–8.   Power Function of a Two-tailed Test.   Hypothesis: $\mu = 20$,
$$\sigma_{\bar{x}} = 2$$

where it is desirable for values of μ both above and below μ_0 to cause rejection of the hypothesis.

If we were to extend the ordinates of the curve in Figure 10–8 to the top of the graph, then the portions of these ordinates lying above the curve would represent probabilities of accepting the hypothesis. A graph of these probabilities would result if we turned Figure 10–8 upside down and reversed the order of the numbers on the vertical scale. This bell-shaped curve would be called the *operating characteristic curve* of the test at the given level of significance.

POWER FUNCTION OF A ONE-TAILED TEST
(HYPOTHESIS: $\mu \geqq \mu_0$)

In making a one-tailed test of the hypothesis that $\mu \geqq 20$ at the 10% level of significance, the region of rejection is located on the lower tail of the sampling distribution curve. This region is "sliced off" by the ordinate erected at -1.28 on the Z scale. The value on the $\bar{x}$ scale which corresponds to a Z value of -1.28 is $20 - 1.28$ $\sigma/\sqrt{n} = 20 - 1.28(2) = 20 - 2.56 = 17.44$.   Thus in testing the hypothesis, we agree to reject it for sample means lying below 17.44 and accept it as plausible for sample means which are equal to or more than this value.

We know, of course, that if μ is actually equal to 20, the probability of rejecting the hypothesis is .10 and the probability of ac-

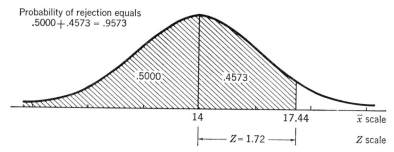

Probability of rejection equals
.5000+.4573 = .9573

.5000   .4573

14   17.44 $\bar{x}$ scale

$Z = 1.72$ Z scale

FIGURE 10–9. Probability of Rejecting Hypothesis That $\mu \geqq 20$ When μ Is Actually Equal to 14

cepting the hypothesis is .90.   Let us now determine what the probabilities of rejection would be if μ were equal to the following values: 14, 16, 18, and 22. We shall begin with 14 and take the others one by one.

The computation of the probability of rejecting the hypothesis ($\mu \geq 20$) when μ is actually equal to 14 is shown graphically in Figure 10–9. This probability is .9573, as indicated by the shaded area of the figure.

The Z value is found, of course, by computing:

$$Z = \frac{17.44 - 14}{2} = \frac{3.44}{2} = 1.72$$

Proceeding in a similar fashion, we find that the probability of rejection is .7642 when μ is actually equal to 16. This result is shown graphically in Figure 10–10, the probability of rejection being indicated by the shaded area under the curve.

We shall, without showing the computations, indicate the probabilities of rejection corresponding to alternative μ values of 18 and 22. The probabilities are .3897 and .0113 respectively. The student should satisfy himself that these results are correct.

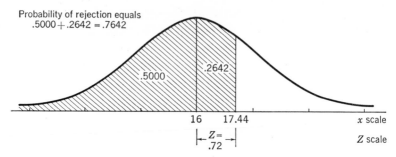

Probability of rejection equals
.5000 + .2642 = .7642

.5000

.2642

16   17.44   x scale

$\left|\leftarrow \begin{array}{c} Z= \\ .72 \end{array} \rightarrow\right|$ Z scale

FIGURE 10–10. Probability of Rejecting Hypothesis That $\mu \geqq 20$ When μ Is Actually Equal to 16

In summary, we have the following alternative values of μ and the corresponding probabilities of rejecting the hypothesis that $\mu \geqq 20$.

Alternative values of μ	Probability of rejecting hypothesis that $\mu \geqq 20$
14	.9573
16	.7642
18	.3897
20	.1000
22	.0113

Again, graphing these results, we have a picture of the power function as shown in Figure 10–11.

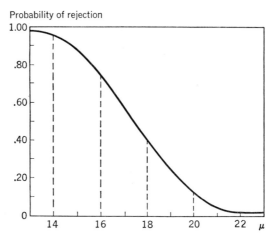

Probability of rejection

FIGURE 10–11. Power Function of a One-tailed Test. Hypothesis: $\mu \geqq 20$, $\sigma_{\bar{x}} = 2$

Figure 10–11 shows clearly why we locate the region of rejection on the lower tail of the curve for the hypothesis $\mu \geqq \mu_0$, for the probability of rejection increases rather rapidly as alternative values of the population mean decrease. For an alternative μ value only moderately larger than the hypothetical value, the probability of rejection is quite close to 0. In this regard note the probability value of .0113, which corresponds to a μ value of 22.

If we were to use a two-tailed test (at a given level of confidence) for the hypothesis that $\mu \geqq \mu_0$, the probabilities of rejection would increase for values of μ larger than μ_0, so that the hypothesis would be rejected frequently when it was actually true, for it would be true in any case where μ was greater than μ_0. Because of this situation, we say that a one-tailed test with the region of rejection located on the lower tail of the curve gives us a more powerful test of the hypothesis $\mu \geqq \mu_0$ than the two-tailed test. In general, the most powerful test is the one providing the greatest probability of rejection when the hypothesis is false and the smallest probability of rejection when the hypothesis is true.

POWER FUNCTION OF A ONE-TAILED TEST
(HYPOTHESIS: $\mu \leqq \mu_0$)

For the test of the hypothesis that $\mu \leqq \mu_0$, let us use a region of rejection located on the upper tail, the lower bound of the region being the ordinate at $20 + 1.28\ \sigma/\sqrt{n}$ on the $\bar{x}$ scale. This critical value is 22.56. Thus the hypothesis is to be rejected in cases where the sample mean is greater than 22.56.

Now if we assume alternative values of 18, 22, 24, and 26 for μ, the corresponding probabilities of rejecting the hypothesis are as follows:

Alternative values of μ	Probability of rejecting hypothesis that $\mu \leqq 20$
18	.0113
20	.1000
22	.1103
24	.7642
26	.9573

The graph of these figures is shown in Figure 10–12.

Comparison of Figure 10–12 with Figures 10–8 and 10–11 shows us immediately why it is appropriate to locate the region of

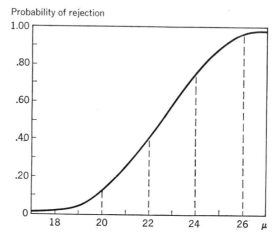

FIGURE 10–12.   Power Function of a One-tailed Test.   Hypothesis:
$$\mu \leqq 20, \; \sigma_{\bar{x}} = 2$$

rejection entirely on the upper tail of the hypothesized sampling distribution curve. Had we located it symmetrically on the two extreme portions of the curve, the probability of rejection would have increased as the alternative values of μ fell below 20. But such values are in conformity with our hypothesis, so we certainly do not wish to reject the hypothesis for such population means.

Similarly, if we located the region of rejection entirely on the *lower* tail, as in Figure 10–11 (appropriate for the hypothesis $\mu \geqq \mu_0$), the probability of rejection would increase for decreasing values of μ.

Of the three alternatives considered, therefore, location of the region of rejection entirely on the upper extreme portion of the hypothesized sampling distribution curve gives the most powerful test of the hypothesis $\mu \leqq \mu_0$. For the alternative values of μ which make the hypothesis false, the probability of rejection increases rapidly as the values differ more widely from μ_0. Also the probability of rejection diminishes rapidly as the alternative values of μ become smaller than μ_0.

The operating characteristic curve (see p. 194) corresponding to the power function for a one-tailed test would be shaped like an "S" for a region of rejection on the lower tail and like a reverse "S" for a region of rejection on the upper tail. Recall that Pr(acceptance) $= 1 - $ Pr(rejection) for each alternative value of μ.

USE OF THE BINOMIAL DISTRIBUTION IN TESTING HYPOTHESES

As we know from our discussions in Chapters 7 and 8, the binomial distribution is often the appropriate model for a sampling distribution when the population is split into two qualitative categories such as defective and nondefective. Important applications of the model arise in attempting to classify persons as to whether or not they possess an unusual quality such as an extremely fine sense of taste.

In determining whether certain foods or beverages conform to established standards of taste or flavor, business firms often employ taste panels, that is, groups of persons who possess such sensitive palates that they can discriminate between the desired flavor and the unwanted flavor in a product. In selecting persons to serve on such a panel, it is, of course, very important to determine whether they can, in fact, consistently discriminate between the desired taste and other flavors.

Let us show how the binomial model may be utilized in determining whether or not a person is a good enough taster to serve on a panel. Suppose that J. H. C. Smith represents himself as an expert coffee taster and it is up to us to decide whether or not he can consistently pick out Bitterbean coffee from other blends. We decide to give him 10 independent trials, each trial consisting of the tasting of three outwardly identical cups of coffee, only one of which is Bitterbean. On each trial, the correct identification of Bitterbean is defined as a success, while an incorrect identification is a failure. And on each trial, the probability of success is $\frac{1}{3}$ and the probability of failure is $\frac{2}{3}$ for a person who cannot tell the difference between Bitterbean and other blends of coffee. Thus we have here a binomial probability distribution with n equal to 10, P equal to $\frac{1}{3}$, and Q equal to $\frac{2}{3}$.

Suppose that we decide to place Mr. Smith on our taste panel if he can correctly identify Bitterbean coffee in at least 7 trials out of 10. Now if Mr. Smith *cannot,* in fact, tell the difference between Bitterbean and other blends of coffee, what is the probability that he will guess correctly in 7 or more trials (out of 10) and thus be erroneously placed on our taste panel?

To get the required answer, we must use the binomial formula to compute the probability of 7 successes out of 10, of 8 successes out of 10, 9 successes out of 10, and 10 successes out of 10, and then we must add these four results.

The computations are as follows:

$$\Pr(x = 7) = \binom{10}{7} (\tfrac{1}{3})^7 (\tfrac{2}{3})^3 = \frac{10 \cdot 9 \cdot 8 \cdot 7 \cdot 6 \cdot 5 \cdot 4}{7 \cdot 6 \cdot 5 \cdot 4 \cdot 3 \cdot 2 \cdot 1} \frac{8}{59,049} = \frac{120 \cdot 8}{59,049} = \frac{960}{59,049}$$

$$\Pr(x = 8) = \binom{10}{8} (\tfrac{1}{3})^8 (\tfrac{2}{3})^2 = \frac{10 \cdot 9 \cdot 8 \cdot 7 \cdot 6 \cdot 5 \cdot 4 \cdot 3}{8 \cdot 7 \cdot 6 \cdot 5 \cdot 4 \cdot 3 \cdot 2 \cdot 1} \frac{4}{59,049}$$

$$= \frac{45 \cdot 4}{59,049} = \frac{180}{59,049}$$

$$\Pr(x = 9) = \binom{10}{9} (\tfrac{1}{3})^9 (\tfrac{2}{3})^1 = 10 \frac{1}{19,683} (\tfrac{2}{3}) = \frac{20}{59,049}$$

$$\Pr(x = 10) = \binom{10}{10} (\tfrac{1}{3})^{10} (\tfrac{2}{3})^0 = (\tfrac{1}{3})^{10} = \frac{1}{59,049}$$

Adding these four results, we have the probability of 7 or more successes out of 10 for a person who can't tell Bitterbean coffee from other blends:

$$\frac{960 + 180 + 20 + 1}{59,049} = \frac{1161}{59,049} = .01966 \doteq .02$$

Thus the probability of Smith identifying correctly in 7 trials or more when he cannot, in fact, discriminate is about .02. To put it another way, this figure .02 represents the probability of committing a Type I error, that is, the probability of rejecting the hypothesis that Smith cannot discriminate when it is actually true.

J. P. Crockston, being unaware that whisky tasters are not allowed to swallow the whisky after tasting it, applies for a job on the taste panel of a Kentucky distillery. The company is interested in determining whether or not Crockston can consistently identify their famous Old Scorch blend (aged in charcoal). Twenty apparently identical pairs of whisky taste samples are presented to Crockston, each pair consisting of a glass of Old Scorch and a glass of some other blend. Crockston will be placed on the taste panel if he can correctly identify Old Scorch in 15 or more of the twenty trials. If he cannot, in fact, discriminate between Old Scorch and other blends, what is the probability that he will pass the test and get the job?

Here again we have a binomial model, but since $P = \frac{1}{2}$, we

may, even though n is only 20, use the normal-curve approximation. Essentially, the problem is to find the probability of getting
15 or more successes in 20 independent trials when the probability
of success on each trial is $\frac{1}{2}$. To use the normal-curve approximation, we must compute the mean and standard deviation of the
relevant binomial distribution. We have:

$$\mu = nP = 20 \times \tfrac{1}{2} = 10$$

and

$$\sigma = \sqrt{nPQ} = \sqrt{20 \cdot \tfrac{1}{2} \cdot \tfrac{1}{2}} = \sqrt{5} \doteq 2.24$$

Next we must find the area under the normal curve which lies
to the right of the ordinate at 14.5. We must locate 14.5, therefore,
on the Z scale. The value 14.5 results from computing $x - \frac{1}{2}$, that
is, $15 - .5$, the adjustment required in the normal-curve approximation. The computation of Z is:

$$Z = \frac{x - \tfrac{1}{2} - \mu}{\sigma} = \frac{14.5 - 10}{2.24} = \frac{4.5}{2.24} \doteq 2.01$$

The appropriate area is $.5000 - .4778$ or $.0222$, which represents
the approximate probability that Crockston will correctly identify
Old Scorch in 15 or more trials out of 20 when he actually cannot
discriminate between it and other blends.

In this case, the hypothesis is, of course, that Crockston cannot
discriminate, the alternative hypothesis is that he can, and the level
of significance is about .02. A diagram of the problem is given in
Figure 10–13.

If a table of binomial probabilities were available to us, we
could read the required probability figure directly from the table.
For a binomial distribution with $P = \frac{1}{2}$ and $n = 20$, the probability
of 15 or more successes is .0207, which compares fairly well with

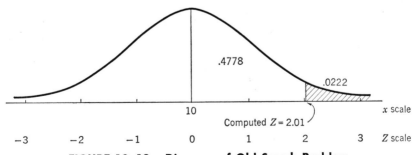

FIGURE 10–13. Diagram of Old Scorch Problem

the normal-curve result (.0222) as computed for the Old Scorch problem.

TEST OF A HYPOTHESIS CONCERNING A POPULATION PROPORTION

The normal-curve approximation to the (modified) binomial distribution may be used to test hypotheses concerning a population proportion, provided that $nP \geq 5$ when P is less than or equal to $\frac{1}{2}$.

To take an example, suppose that production engineers in an automobile parts plant have stated the hypothesis that a new order of 10,000 valve-seat inserts contains 6% or less defectives. We are asked to test this hypothesis using a 5% level of significance and a random sample of size $n = 150$. We select the sample and find that 13 inserts are defective.

Here the hypothesized sampling distribution is an approximately normal distribution of p, the sample proportion, with the mean of the p's being P, the population proportion. As we learned in Chapter 8, in this normal-curve approximation, p is represented by the range $p \pm \dfrac{1}{2n}$. In computing Z, we will here take the upper limit of this range to represent p. The standard error of p, we recall, is given by $\sigma_p = \sqrt{\dfrac{PQ}{n}}$.

The five-step procedure utilized in testing hypotheses concerning the mean may be adapted to tests concerning P. The steps are as follows:

1. State hypothesis: $P \leq .06$.
2. Choose level of significance: 5% with 5% critical region on the upper tail.
3. Note critical value of Z: 1.65.
4. Find computed value of Z:

$$Z = \frac{p + 1/2n - P}{\sqrt{\dfrac{PQ}{n}}} = \frac{\frac{13}{150} + \frac{1}{300} - .06}{\sqrt{\dfrac{.06(.94)}{150}}}$$

$$= \frac{.090 - .060}{\sqrt{\dfrac{.0564}{154}}} = \frac{.030}{\sqrt{.000376}} = \frac{.030}{.0194} \doteq 1.55$$

(Note that the hypothetical upper limit (.06) of P is the appropriate value to substitute in the Z formula.)

5. Compare critical Z and computed Z: Both are positive and the latter (1.55) is less than the former (1.65), so we accept the hypothesis as plausible.

It is possible to use the binomial distribution in its unmodified form to make this test. We simply test the hypothesis that nP is equal to or less than $.06(150)$ or 9. The critical value of Z remains 1.65. The test statistic is $Z = \dfrac{x \pm \frac{1}{2} - \mu}{\sigma}$. In the sample, $x = 13$, but because of the normal-curve approximation, we substitute $13 + \frac{1}{2}$ when computing Z. This computation is as follows:

$$Z = \frac{x + \frac{1}{2} - \mu}{\sigma} = \frac{13.5 - 9}{\sqrt{150(.06)(.94)}} = \frac{4.5}{\sqrt{9(.94)}} = \frac{4.5}{2.909} \doteq 1.55$$

Since 1.55 is less than 1.65, we accept the hypothesis as plausible, just as before.

We can, of course, use similar methods to test the hypothesis that $P = P_0$ and the hypothesis that $P \geqq P_0$, the former case involving a two-tailed test.

THE BINOMIAL DISTRIBUTION IN ACCEPTANCE SAMPLING

Every day millions of dollars' worth of products are bought by private industry and the various levels of government, many of these goods being subject to sampling inspection before they are either accepted or rejected by the purchaser. If goods are subject to sampling inspection, the items in a given purchase order are divided into batches or lots, which may be considered as populations. A sample is selected from each lot and on the basis of the sample data, the whole lot is either accepted or rejected.

The purchaser is often interested in the proportion of defective products in the lot and in that case, the binomial distribution is frequently the appropriate model for the sampling distribution.

To take an example, suppose that we are working as statisticians for the federal government and that we are instructed to devise an *acceptance sampling plan* for an order of special-type electrical fuses which are being submitted by the vendor in lots of 10,000 fuses each. We are told that if lots contain 6% or less defectives, quality will be considered satisfactory and that it is permissible to accept lots containing 6% defectives 95% of the time. Under these conditions, the acceptable quality level (AQL) is said to be .06 or 6%. We are directed to select a sample of 200 fuses from each lot in determining whether to accept the lot or reject it.

Our procedure will be essentially the same as testing the hypothesis that the population proportion is 6% or less. We are operating at a 5% level of significance, for we have been told that the probability of accepting the hypothesis should be .95, that is $(1 - .05)$, when the percentage of defectives in the lot is actually .06, that is, when the hypothesis is true.

Under these conditions, we can find, by using the normal-curve approximation, the criteria for accepting or rejecting a lot.

The first step is to find the mean of a binomial distribution having $P = .06$ and $n = 200$; $\mu = nP = 200(.06) = 12$.

Next we find the standard deviation. $\sigma = \sqrt{nPQ} = \sqrt{12(.94)}$ $= \sqrt{11.28} \doteq 3.36$.

The ordinate which slices off the highest 5% (or the lowest 95%) of area on the normal curve is located at $\mu + 1.65\sigma$, which for our example equals $12 + 1.65(3.36) \doteq 12 + 5.54 = 17.54$. We recall that in approximating the binomial distribution by a normal curve, a given value of x in the binomial is represented by the range $x \pm \frac{1}{2}$ on the normal curve. Thus 17.54 is nearly equal to the upper bound of the range which represents 17, that is, nearly equal to 17.5. Now, since acceptance sampling plans are devised so that whole numbers may be used as *acceptance numbers* and *rejection numbers*, let us take 17 as our acceptance number. That is to say, any lot that contains 17 or fewer defectives will be accepted, whereas any lot that contains 18 or more defectives will be rejected. The rejection number, then, is 18.

If possible, we would, under the specified conditions, like to devise a plan having an operating characteristic curve as pictured in Figure 10–14.

In this ideal case, the probability is 1 that all lots containing 6% or *less* defectives would be accepted, while the probability is 0 that those containing *more than* 6% defectives would be accepted. However, we can only devise OC curves which are approximations to the ideal curve, if we use a sample which is smaller in size than the lot.

Let us, therefore, examine the actual OC curve of the sampling plan we are using. Utilizing the normal-curve approximation to the binomial distribution, with $n = 200$ and letting P (the lot fraction defective or population proportion) take on the alternative

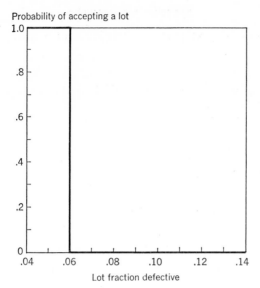

Probability of accepting a lot

Lot fraction defective

FIGURE 10–14. Ideal OC Curve for a Quality Level of 6% Defective or Less

values .05, .06, .07, and so on up to .14, we can find the various probabilities of accepting lots containing such fractions of defectives.

To show the method of computation, let us work through the steps for $P = .05$, that is, let us find the probability of accepting a lot that contains 5% defectives. (Refer to Fig. 10–15.)

Remember, we accept the lot if the sample contains 17 defectives or less. We must first compute the mean and standard deviation of the appropriate binomial distribution. We have:

$$\mu = nP = .05(200) = 10$$

and

$$\sigma = \sqrt{nPQ} = \sqrt{10(.95)} = \sqrt{9.5} \doteq 3.082$$

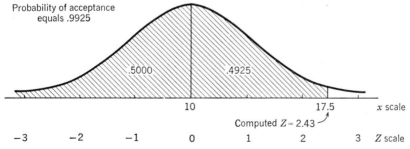

Probability of acceptance equals .9925

.5000   .4925

10   17.5   x scale

Computed $Z = 2.43$

−3   −2   −1   0   1   2   3   Z scale

FIGURE 10–15. Probability of Accepting a Lot Containing 5% Defectives (Acceptance Number 17, Rejection Number 18; $n = 200$)

Thus for a binomial distribution having a mean of 10 and a standard deviation of 3.082 (and with $n = 200$) we wish to find the probability that x has a value of 17 or less. In the normal-curve approximation, we take the upper limit of 17 as 17.5 and compute the approximate value of Z as follows:

$$Z \doteq \frac{x + \frac{1}{2} - \mu}{\sigma} \doteq \frac{17.5 - 10}{3.082} \doteq \frac{7.5}{3.082} \doteq 2.43$$

As illustrated in Figure 10–15, the area under the curve lying to the left of the ordinate at 17.5 is $.5000 + .4925 = .9925$.

If we were to apply similar procedures to the case where the lot fraction defective was .07, the probability of acceptance would be .8340. The probabilities would fall off steadily as the lot fraction defective increased, until for a lot fraction defective of .14, the probability of acceptance would be .0162. This phenomenon is shown graphically by the operating characteristic curve of Figure 10–16. We see at a glance that our sampling plan OC curve is only an approximation to the ideal OC curve of Figure 10–14. However, the slope of an OC curve can be made somewhat steeper if the sample size is increased and the acceptance number is decreased.

It is important to bear in mind that the probabilities shown in Figure 10–16 are only approximate, for they were computed by

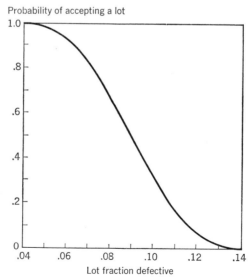

FIGURE 10–16. OC Curve for an Acceptance Sampling Plan (AQL = .06, n = 200, Acceptance Number = 17, Rejection Number = 18)

means of the normal-curve approximation to the binomial distribution. If high-speed computing facilities were available, we could compute the correct probabilities directly from the binomial formula, or in the case of plans where P was extremely small and n very large, we could find the probabilities from the formula of the Poisson distribution. In cases where the lot size is small, the probabilities of the OC curves must be computed from the *hypergeometric* distribution, which arises under the same conditions as the binomial model, except that sampling is assumed to be *without* replacement.

TYPES OF SAMPLING PLANS

The acceptance sampling plan for which we have constructed the operating characteristic curve is an example of a single sampling plan. Other plans, such as double sampling or multiple sampling, provide for the selection of more than one sample in the process of reaching a decision of acceptance or rejection. In such plans, three choices are available after the selection of any sample prior to the last one. That is, we have the choice of rejection, acceptance, or of drawing another sample, the choice being indicated by the number of defectives which turn up. In the case of the last sample, of course, the choice is solely between acceptance and rejection. For example, a double sampling plan devised by the Statistical Research Group [1] provides for a first sample of 100 items with an acceptance number of 11 and a rejection number of 31. This means that if the first sample contains 11 or less defectives, we accept the lot; if this sample contains 31 or more defectives, we reject the lot; and if this sample contains between 11 and 31 defectives, we draw the second sample, consisting of 200 items. The acceptance number for the second sample is 30 and the rejection number is 31, no provision being made for further sampling. We should note that the figures 30 and 31 refer to the number of defectives in the first sample plus those found in the second.

Acceptance sampling plans are classified not only by the number of samples to be drawn but by size of sample, Acceptable Quality Level (AQL), and Lot Tolerance Fraction Defective (LTFD). As noted previously, the AQL is an indication of acceptable or "satisfactory" quality stated in terms of lot fraction defective. The LTFD is a characterization of "unsatisfactory" quality expressed

[1] Statistical Research Group, Columbia University, *Sampling Inspection* (New York, McGraw-Hill Book Co., Inc., 1948), p. 319.

in terms of lot fraction defective. Many acceptance sampling plans are designed so that lots conforming to the AQL will have a probability of about .95 of being accepted, while at the same time lots having a quality designated by the LTFD will have a probability of about .10 of being accepted.

Once the AQL and the related probability of acceptance as well as the LTFD and its corresponding probability of acceptance are stated, an appropriate single sampling plan may be devised. That is, the requisite size of sample may be determined.

In the example for which we determined the OC curve, the AQL (6% defective) was given, together with its associated probability of acceptance (about 95%). The sample size was given also ($n = 200$). It was then possible to construct the OC curve. From this curve (Fig. 10–16) we find that a lot containing between 11 and 12% defectives would have a probability of .10 of being accepted. The plan, then, has an LTFD of between 11 and 12%.

Rather than devise our own sampling plans, we can almost always find ready-made plans that will serve our purposes.[2]

We should note also that our brief discussion has treated the application of acceptance sampling plans to only one type of attribute data. Attribute plans are used also in cases where it is possible for an item to possess several defects. An application of this kind is the acceptance sampling procedure used by the Army in the purchase of jeeps.[3] In this plan, lot quality is described in terms of the average number of defects per product.

Plans involving the use of measurement are available also. In this case, measurements are used in establishing criteria for the acceptance or rejection of lots.[4]

SUMMARY

Important information about a population may be found by using the technique of testing hypotheses. In such cases, we frequently seek to ascertain whether a parameter is equal to, greater than, or less than

[2] Such plans are found in the reference of footnote 1, in H. F. Dodge and H. G. Romig, *Sampling Inspection Tables—Single and Double Sampling* (New York, John Wiley and Sons, Inc., 1944), and Department of Defense, *Military Standard 105 A: Sampling Procedures and Tables for Inspection by Attributes* (Washington, D.C., U.S. Government Printing Office, 1950).

[3] B. L. Hansen, "Acceptance Plan for Automotive Vehicles," *Industrial Quality Control,* Vol. 14 (December, 1957), p. 18.

[4] In this connection, see Department of Defense, *Military Standard 414, Sampling Procedures and Tables for Inspection by Variables for Percent Defective* (Washington, D.C., U.S. Government Printing Office, 1957).

some hypothetical value. The procedure, in general, is to state the hypothetical value of the parameter and note the hypothesized sampling distribution of an appropriate test statistic. The test statistic is computed and its relationship to certain critical values determines whether the hypothesis is to be rejected or accepted as plausible.

In making the test, we seek to minimize the chance of making errors of Type I and Type II. The former type of error is the rejection of a hypothesis which is actually true, while the latter is the acceptance as plausible of a hypothesis which is actually false.

After deciding upon a specific criterion for rejecting a hypothesis, that is, choosing a level of significance and locating the region of rejection (critical region), we can formulate the power function of a test. This function relates various alternative values of the parameter in question to the probabilities of rejecting the hypothesis. Since we wish the probability of rejection to be large for those values of the parameter which do not conform to the hypothesis (and small for those values which do conform), we verify the fact that a two-tailed test is appropriate for the hypothesis that $\mu = \mu_0$, that a one-tailed test (upper tail region of rejection) is appropriate for the test of $\mu \leq \mu_0$, and that a one-tailed test (lower tail region of rejection) is appropriate for the test of $\mu \geq \mu_0$.

The complements of the power function probabilities form a distribution known as the operating characteristic function of a test. The OC curve, that is to say, relates the probabilities of accepting the hypothesis to various alternative parameter values.

The binomial distribution is an appropriate model for the hypothesized sampling distribution in certain elementary tests, including those appropriate to the selection of persons to serve on taste panels.

The binomial distribution is also important as a basis for the construction of certain acceptance sampling plans. In the case of a single sampling plan for attribute data, one sample is drawn from a batch (or lot) of products, and on the basis of the number of defective items in the sample, the entire lot is either accepted or rejected. Acceptance sampling plans are classified according to the Acceptable Quality Level (AQL), the Lot Tolerance Fraction Defective (LTFD), and the sample size. Essentially, this acceptance sampling technique is the testing of hypotheses concerning population proportions. In addition to single sampling plans, there are double sampling plans and multiple sampling plans.

APPENDIX ON A TEST CONCERNING THE VARIANCE

In Chapter 6 (p. 96) we demonstrated the computation of a sample variance, taking as our data the tar contents (in milligrams) of ten cigarettes. The sample variance equaled 10 milligrams. The question raised at that time was that if 9 milligrams or less is considered a satisfactory population variance, is the sample variance of 10 large enough to cause us to reject the hypothesis that $\sigma^2 \leq 9$?

Let us test this hypothesis at a 5% level of significance. One sampling distribution appropriate to this test is called chi-square (χ^2). As applied to this particular type of test, the chi-square distribution is the probability distribution of the ratio $\dfrac{\Sigma(x_i - \bar{x})^2}{\sigma^2}$ or $\dfrac{(n-1)s^2}{\sigma^2}$, under certain assumptions. The distribution is positively skew with χ^2 becoming indefinitely large in a positive direction but having a minimum value of 0. The appropriate number of degrees of freedom is $n - 1$.

To test our hypothesis, we compute $\chi^2 = \dfrac{(n-1)s^2}{\sigma_0^2}$, where σ_0^2 is the hypothesized value of the population variance. Then we note if this value is large enough to extend into the critical region on the upper tail of the curve. When the sample size is 10, the lower bound of our 5% critical region is the ordinate at a χ^2 value of 16.919.[5] In other words, for samples of ten elements (drawn from a normal population), a χ^2 value of 16.919 would be exceeded only 5% of the time. For our illustration, then, 16.919 is the critical value of χ^2. We find the computed χ^2 for our example as follows:

$$\chi^2 = \frac{(n-1)s^2}{\sigma_0^2} = \frac{9(10)}{9} = 10$$

Since the computed χ^2 is smaller than the critical χ^2, that is, since the computed χ^2 is not large enough to extend into the critical region, we accept the hypothesis as plausible. Had the computed χ^2 value exceeded the critical χ^2, we would, of course, have rejected the hypothesis and concluded that σ^2 was probably greater than 9.

TERMS TO PONDER

1. Hypothesized Sampling Distribution
2. Type I Error
3. Type II Error
4. Two-tailed Test
5. One-tailed Test
6. Power Function
7. Operating Characteristic Curve
8. Acceptance Sampling
9. Acceptable Quality Level (AQL)
10. Lot Tolerance Fraction Defective (LTFD)

[5] See Table IV of R. A. Fisher and Frank Yates, *Statistical Tables for Biological, Agricultural and Medical Research*, 5th ed. (New York, Hafner, 1957), p. 45. This table is reprinted in the useful little book, *Tables for Statisticians* by Herbert Arkin and Raymond R. Colton (College Outline Series, New York, Barnes and Noble, 1950), p. 121.

EXERCISES

1. A person claims he can distinguish brand L cigarettes from brand C. If 30 pairs of cigarettes are submitted to this person, each pair containing an L and a C, what is the probability that he will make 20 or more correct choices when he is, in fact, unable to tell the difference between an L and a C? (Use the normal-curve approximation to the binomial distribution.)

2. A statistician employed by a consumer testing organization is checking weights of 16-ounce boxes of Pone brand corn flakes. A random sample of 9 boxes is selected and the contents of each box is weighed. The observed weights are as follows:

$$15.2 \quad 16.1 \quad 14.9 \quad 15.5 \quad 15.0$$
$$16.3 \quad 14.6 \quad 13.9 \quad 15.4$$

At the 5% level of significance, test the hypothesis that the mean of the population is 16.0 ounces or more.

3. An order of 10,000 shell casings is submitted to the federal government for acceptance. A random sample of 256 casings is selected and 24 of these are found to be defective. At the 5% level of significance, test the hypothesis that the proportion of defectives in the order is 6% or less.

4. In the field of acceptance sampling by attributes, a single sampling plan has an Acceptable Quality Level of .04 with associated probability of .95. The sample size is 400.

   a. Find the acceptance number and the rejection number for the plan.

   b. Letting the various alternative values of P (population fraction defective) be .02, .04, .06, .08, .12, find the operating characteristic curve of the plan.

5. a. An industrial statistician is testing the hypothesis that a certain type of electric bulb has a mean service life of at least 1500 hours. To test this hypothesis 100 bulbs are life-tested. The sample mean is 1403 and the sample variance is 349 hours. At the 2% level of significance, would you reject this hypothesis or accept it as plausible?

   b. Sketch the power function of the test.

SELECTED REFERENCES

DUNCAN, Acheson J., *Industrial Statistics and Quality Control* (Homewood, Ill., Richard D. Irwin, Inc., 1953), Ch. VII.

FREUND, John E., and WILLIAMS, Frank J., *Modern Business Statistics* (Englewood Cliffs, N.J., Prentice-Hall, Inc., 1958), Ch. X.

HIRSCH, Werner Z., *Introduction to Modern Statistics* (New York, The Macmillan Co., 1957), Chs. XI, XII.

11

STATISTICAL

QUALITY CONTROL

STATISTICAL QUALITY CONTROL is a body of subject matter having roots extending into both statistical estimation and the testing of hypotheses. It is one of the most rapidly growing areas of statistical application and certainly no student of modern industrial processes can afford to ignore it.

Early developments in the field are associated with the name of Dr. Walter A. Shewhart, a physicist at the Bell Telephone Laboratories, who wrote the pioneering work, *Economic Control of Quality of Manufactured Product,* which was published in 1931 by D. Van Nostrand Co., Inc. In this book, Dr. Shewhart not only laid down the basic principles of statistical quality control but also showed how they could be verified by the performance of sampling experiments.

Essentially, statistical quality control provides for the maintenance of a continuing statistical record of an industrial production process and the making of decisions on the basis of that record so as to bring the process under "control" and thus maintain a consistent level of quality in the product. When a process is "in control" an observed characteristic differs from product to product or a relevant statistic varies from sample to sample only as a result of chance variation. When the process is "out of control," an "assignable cause" is said to be operating to cause greater variation from sample to sample than could reasonably be expected on the basis of chance alone.

The continuing statistical record is called a *control chart* and is based on a series of samples, usually of constant size, which are selected from time to time. Quality may be specified in terms of either measurement or attribute data. In the former case, the sample means may be recorded on one control chart and the sample ranges or standard deviations on another. In the latter case, the sample proportions or numbers of defects per unit may be recorded.

NOTATION OF QUALITY CONTROL

Before we go further in examining the principles underlying statistical quality control charts, we must shift our mental gears so as to adapt our thinking to quality control notation. First of all, we should note that statistics are denoted by Roman letters (either capital or lower case) or lower case Greek letters and that parameters are denoted by attaching primes (′) to the symbols of the corresponding statistics. Thus $\overline{X}$ denotes a sample mean, whereas $\overline{X}'$ denotes a population mean; p represents a sample proportion, whereas p' denotes a population proportion. A bar is used to denote the mean of a given statistic over several samples. For example, $\overline{\overline{X}}$ represents the mean of several $\overline{X}$ values, $\bar{\sigma}$ represents the mean of several sample standard deviations, and $\overline{R}$ denotes the mean of several sample ranges.

Second, it is important to note that in the field of quality control, the sample standard deviation is defined according to the following formula:

$$\sigma = \sqrt{\frac{\Sigma(X - \overline{X})^2}{n}}$$

where X represents the individual observations, $\overline{X}$ is the sample mean, and n is the number of elements in the sample.

CONTROL CHARTS FOR MEASUREMENT DATA

Let us take an illustration that will enable us to show how control charts are constructed and interpreted. We shall begin with control charts for measurement data. Suppose that the Proud Oil and Refining Company is using statistical techniques to control the operation of filling 1-quart cans with motor oil. With the oil at a temperature of 70°, the filling machine is set to fill each can with 1.870 pounds of oil. Now, because of small variations in oil temperature, machine settings, and other factors, it is virtually impossible to put *exactly* 1.870 pounds of oil in each can. But the company would like to maintain an *average* (mean) weight of about 1.870 and keep the variation within the limits indicated in the specifications. Company engineers have set tentative specifications on individual measurements at 1.870 ± .050 pounds. That is, weights of oil in *individual* cans are expected to remain within the limits of 1.820 and 1.920 pounds. Before determining whether or not specifications are being met, we must construct certain basic control charts.

For purposes of constructing the charts, samples consisting of four cans each are selected at random and the content of each can is weighed on an accurate balance. The mean, standard deviation, and range ($\overline{X}$, σ, and R) of the observations in each sample are computed. These statistics enable us to construct the appropriate control charts for determining whether or not the filling process is "in control." The means, standard deviations, and ranges for 25 samples (four cans each) are, let us say, as shown in Table 11–1.[1]

The control chart for sample means (called an "X-bar chart") is shown in Figure 11–1. On this chart, the center line is drawn at 1.871 pounds, which is the value of $\overline{\overline{X}}$, the mean of the 25 sample means. $\overline{\overline{X}}$ is, of course, an estimate of $\overline{X}'$. The plotted points represent the sample means, the different samples being identified by the sequence of numbers laid off along the horizontal axis. We can interpret the chart as representing points along the $\overline{X}$-axis of a sampling distribution of the mean, which has been turned through a 90° angle and which we are looking down upon from above, the $\overline{X}$-axis (vertical dimension of the control chart) being repeated at intervals so as to give effect to the passage of time and to allow space for distinguishing one sample point from another. In short, we may imagine a sampling distribution graph similar to that drawn at sample number 9 positioned at each of the sample points, with the plane of the curve perpendicular to the page.

The central limit theorem tells us that, regardless of the population distribution, means of samples should be distributed approximately as a normal curve with a mean of μ and a standard error equal to $\sigma'/\sqrt{n}$ (quality control notation) provided the sample is sufficiently large. If, however, the population is normally distributed, the sample means will be normally distributed for *any* size of sample, the standard error remaining $\sigma'/\sqrt{n}$.

---

[1] In actual practice, we would almost never compute values of both σ and R. We would use one or the other. R is preferable for small samples and σ for samples of perhaps 15 items or more. Values of both statistics are shown here so that two different methods of constructing control limits on the same chart can be compared.

TABLE 11-1

Oil Can Example
Data on 25 Samples of Size $n = 4$

Sample no.	$\overline{X}$	σ	R
1	1.867	.0075	.024
2	1.879	.0153	.038
3	1.869	.0094	.015
4	1.864	.0124	.034
5	1.870	.0033	.007
6	1.865	.0094	.032
7	1.859	.0133	.021
8	1.880	.0155	.039
9	1.863	.0087	.018
10	1.875	.0064	.014
11	1.878	.0103	.022
12	1.864	.0092	.017
13	1.877	.0089	.025
14	1.870	.0032	.010
15	1.890	.0131	.037
16	1.869	.0100	.033
17	1.872	.0064	.021
18	1.868	.0062	.018
19	1.864	.0121	.036
20	1.870	.0079	.024
21	1.889	.0136	.032
22	1.867	.0068	.030
23	1.862	.0100	.035
24	1.854	.0035	.008
25	1.887	.0096	.010
	46.772	.2320	.600

$$\overline{\overline{X}} = \frac{46.772}{25} = 1.871$$

$$\bar{\sigma} = \frac{.2320}{25} = .009280$$

$$\overline{R} = \frac{.600}{25} = .0240$$

$\overline{X}$ Chart

Center line $= \overline{\overline{X}} = 1.871$

$\text{UCL} = \overline{\overline{X}} + A_1\bar{\sigma}$

$\quad = 1.871 + 1.880(.009280)$

$\quad = 1.871 + .0174 \doteq 1.888$

$\text{LCL} = \overline{\overline{X}} - A_1\bar{\sigma} = 1.871 - .0174 \doteq 1.854$

$\text{UCL} = \overline{\overline{X}} + A_2\overline{R} = 1.871 + .729(.0240)$

$\quad = 1.871 + .0175 \doteq 1.888$

$\text{LCL} = \overline{\overline{X}} - A_2\overline{R} = 1.871 - .0175 \doteq 1.854$

σ Chart

Center line $= \bar{\sigma} = .009280$

$\text{UCL} = B_4\bar{\sigma} = 2.266(.009280) \doteq .0210$

$\text{LCL} = B_3\bar{\sigma} = 0(.009280) = 0$

R Chart

Center line $= \overline{R} \doteq .0240$

$\text{UCL} = D_4\overline{R} = 2.282(.0240) \doteq .0548$

$\text{LCL} = D_3\overline{R} = 0(.0240) = 0$

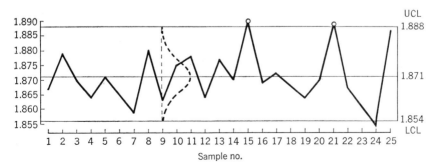

FIGURE 11-1. $\overline{X}$ Chart. Contents of 1-Quart Cans of Motor Oil (Pounds at 70°: $n = 4$, $\overline{\overline{X}} = 1.871$)

215

On the $\bar{X}$ chart (see Fig. 11–1) the upper control limit (UCL) is drawn at a distance of 3 standard errors above the center line and the lower control limit (LCL) is drawn at a distance of 3 standard errors below the center line. The width of the band between the two control limits represents the scope allowed for chance variation. Variation of sample means about $\bar{X}$ within these limits is said to arise from "chance causes," and to indicate that the process is "in control." But a point or points outside of the limits represent an unusual amount of variability which is said to arise from "assignable causes." We know from our study of the sampling distribution of the mean that if the population mean is actually equal to a specified value, then the probability that a sample mean will lie more than 3 standard errors from the specified value is about .0027. Thus if a sample mean is found to lie outside of the control limits (such as the mean of sample 15 in Fig. 11–1), an unusual factor must be operating to cause it to be so "far out," for if the process were in control, a sample mean would lie outside the control limits with a probability of only 27 in 10,000. To put it another way, if we look for an assignable cause each time a point lies outside the control limits, the search is needless only 27 times out of 10,000.

The mean of sample 15 (Fig. 11–1) could very well indicate that the filling machine was out of adjustment, that a sharp drop in oil temperature had occurred, that the oil had become contaminated by a denser fluid, and so on. Having found assignable causes to account for the means of samples 15 and 21, we would correct the deficiencies and eliminate these values in computing a value of $\bar{X}$ to serve as a center line for future use. This new value of $\bar{X}$ would be 1.869 pounds.

CONTROL CHART FACTORS AND THE $\bar{X}$ CHART

In order to locate the control limits on the $\bar{X}$ chart, we must, of course, estimate $\sigma'/\sqrt{n}$, the standard error of the mean. We may use a factor known as c_2 in making this estimate. This factor is the ratio of the expected value of the sample standard deviation to the population standard deviation. A normally distributed population is assumed. In short, $c_2 = \dfrac{E(\sigma)}{\sigma'}$. If we have computed σ for each of several samples and have then found $\bar{\sigma}$, the mean of the sample sigmas, we may estimate σ' by computing $\dfrac{1}{c_2}\,\bar{\sigma}$ or $\dfrac{\sigma'}{E(\sigma)}\,\bar{\sigma}$. (It should be noted that although $E(\bar{X}) = \bar{X}'$, $E(\sigma) \neq \sigma'$.) Since $\bar{\sigma}$ is likely to be very nearly equal to $E(\sigma)$, these two quantities will almost cancel in the computation, giving us a very good estimate of σ'. Then to find the UCL, we divide the estimate of σ' by $\sqrt{n}$, multiply the result by 3, and add this number to the center line value. We subtract this number from the center line value to get the LCL.

Values of c_2 have been tabulated for samples of various sizes as shown in Table IV on page 343. For samples of size $n = 4$, c_2 equals .7979. From Table 11–1, we find that $\bar{\sigma}$ equals .009280 for the oil can filling example. Our estimate of σ', then, is $\dfrac{\bar{\sigma}}{c_2} = \dfrac{.009280}{.7979}$

$= .01163$. From this result, we find $\sigma'/\sqrt{n} = \dfrac{.01163}{\sqrt{4}} = .00581$ and

that $3\dfrac{\sigma'}{\sqrt{n}} = 3(.00581) \doteq .0174$. Thus $1.871 + .0174$ gives us our

upper control limit of 1.888 pounds (after rounding) and $1.871 -$ .0174 yields the lower control limit of 1.854. These are the limits appearing in Figure 11–1.

We may combine c_2, $\sqrt{n}$, and 3 to form one factor which may be multiplied by $\bar{\sigma}$ in order to get the amount that must be added to and subtracted from $\bar{X}$ to find the upper and lower control limits.

This factor is $\dfrac{3}{c_2\sqrt{n}}$ and is known as A_1. The factor A_1 has been

tabulated for samples of various sizes so that control limits may be computed with ease and speed. Its value for samples of size 4 is 1.88, as shown in Table IV on page 343. We see immediately that $A_1\bar{\sigma} = 1.88(.009280) = .0174$.

Another, and perhaps more common, method of finding the control limits of the $\bar{X}$ chart is to use the mean range $(\bar{R})$ and either the factor d_2 or the factor A_2. The factor d_2 is equal to the expected value of the sample range divided by the population standard deviation. In short, $d_2 = \dfrac{E(R)}{\sigma'}$. If we divide $\bar{R}$, the mean of several

sample ranges, by d_2, we have $\dfrac{\bar{R}}{d_2} = \dfrac{\sigma'}{E(R)}\bar{R}$. Here $\bar{R}$ and $E(R)$ will

nearly cancel, again giving us a good estimate of σ'. We may now readily compute $3\dfrac{\sigma'}{\sqrt{n}}$.

The multiplier A_2 is formed by taking $\dfrac{3}{d_2\sqrt{n}}$. Multiplying $\bar{R}$

by A_2 gives us the amount that should be added to $\bar{X}$ and subtracted from it in order to get the upper and lower control limits respectively. The factor A_2 has been tabulated for various different values of n, as shown in Table IV on page 343. For the oil can example, $A_2 = .729$ and $\bar{R} = .0204$. Thus $A_2(\bar{R}) \doteq .0175$, which is very close to the value we found by computing $A_1\bar{\sigma}$.

TOLERANCE LIMITS

Having set control limits of $\bar{\bar{X}} \pm 3(\sigma'/\sqrt{n})$ for sample means we note that the corresponding variation in individual observations (samples of 1 element each) would be $\bar{\bar{X}} \pm 3\sigma'$. These latter are called *tolerance limits*. In the oil can example, the *control limits* for sample means were 1.888 and 1.854. The corresponding tolerance limits are $1.871 \pm 3(.01163)$ or $1.871 \pm .0349$, that is, 1.836 and 1.906. Thus, if the process is in control, with $\bar{X}$ equal to 1.871, individual cans of oil will contain between 1.836 and 1.906 pounds of oil 99.73% of the time $(1 - .0027 = .9973)$. We see that the tolerance limits on this process are well within the specifications 1.820–1.920 which were stated on page 214.

TWO GENERAL CASES IN QUALITY CONTROL

In the construction of control charts, two general cases arise, (1) the case where we are analyzing past data to see if the process is in control and to estimate the standards that the process is capable of maintaining, and (2) the case where standard parameter values (for example, $\bar{X}'$, σ', or p') have been established. In the former case, emphasis is on statistical estimation. In the latter case, emphasis is on testing the hypothesis that the established standards are being adhered to. Standards should not be set unless enough data have accumulated on the process to show that it is in control and unless tolerance limits lie within the specifications for individual measurements.

Formulas for finding center lines and control limits on measurement data charts are grouped according to these two cases, that is, "analysis of past data" and "standards given," in the table of control chart factors (Table IV) on page 343.

THE σ CHART AND THE R CHART

For normally distributed observations, the standard deviation and the range are independent of the mean. Therefore, we need either an R chart or a σ chart in order to determine whether the variability of a process is in control. We shall first give a brief explanation of how the σ chart is constructed and then proceed to the R chart, which is more widely used in practice, not only because R is easier to compute than σ, but also because R is a reliable measure of variability when the sample is small.

When n is large, the sampling distribution of the standard deviation is closely approximated by a normal curve with a mean of σ' and a standard error of $\sigma'/\sqrt{2n}$. We write $\sigma_\sigma = \dfrac{\sigma'}{\sqrt{2n}}$ when n is large. When the sample is small, the mean of this sampling distribution is no longer close to σ'. Also, in order to get the proper value of σ_σ, we must multiply $\sigma'/\sqrt{2n}$ by a factor which becomes larger than 1 and increases as the sample size decreases. Control limits on the σ chart are located by adding $3\sigma_\sigma$ to the center line value (to get the UCL) and subtracting $3\sigma_\sigma$ from the center line value (to get the LCL).

If the value of σ' is known or if a standard value has been established, the center line on the σ chart is located by computing $c_2\sigma'$, which gives the value of $E(\sigma)$. Instead of computing $3\sigma_\sigma$ separately and then adding it to and subtracting it from $c_2\sigma'$ to get the two control limits, we may find each limit by one simple multiplication operation if we have a table of B factors. UCL $= B_2\sigma'$ and LCL $= B_1\sigma'$.

The two ways of getting the upper control limit may be set equal to each other as follows: $c_2\sigma' + 3\sigma_\sigma = B_2\sigma'$. Solving this equation for B_2, we find that $B_2 = c_2 + \dfrac{3\sigma_\sigma}{\sigma'}$. B_1 may be evaluated by a similar process, that is, by solving $c_2\sigma' - 3\sigma_\sigma = B_1\sigma'$ for B_1.

If the σ chart is based upon an observed value of $\bar{\sigma}$, as in the oil can filling example, then the center line is taken simply as $\bar{\sigma}$ and the B_3 and B_4 factors are used to find the lower and upper control limits respectively. That is, LCL $= B_3\bar{\sigma}$ and UCL $= B_4\bar{\sigma}$.

In this case, the two ways of denoting the upper control limit give us the equation, $\bar{\sigma} + 3\sigma_\sigma = B_4\bar{\sigma}$. Solving for B_4, we arrive at $B_4 = 1 + \dfrac{3\sigma_\sigma}{\bar{\sigma}}$. However, in constructing tables of B_4, we do not know particular values of $\bar{\sigma}$. We therefore use $E(\sigma)$ instead. $E(\sigma)$, we recall, is the expected value of the sample standard deviation, or the mean of the sample standard deviations over an indefinitely large number of samples of equal size. Our formula for B_4 becomes

$$B_4 = 1 + \frac{3\sigma_\sigma}{E(\sigma)}.$$

Although the σ chart is usually used in cases where n is considerably larger than 4, the σ chart for the oil can example is given in Figure 11–2. The center line is taken as $\bar{\sigma}$; the upper control limit is given by $B_4\bar{\sigma}$ and the lower control limit, by $B_3\bar{\sigma}$. UCL = 2.266(.009280) = .02103 $\doteq$ .0210.   LCL = 0(.009280) = 0.   On this chart, all points are seen to be "in control."

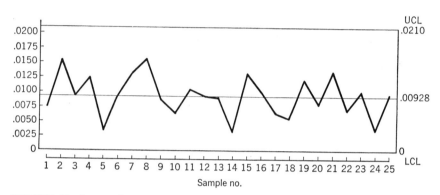

FIGURE 11–2. σ **Chart. Contents of 1-Quart Cans of Motor Oil (Pounds at 70°: $n = 4$, $\bar{\sigma} = .009280$)**

If one or more points had been out of control and if an assignable cause had been found in each case, then, as in the case of the $\overline{X}$ chart, these out-of-control points would have been omitted in computing a new value of $\bar{\sigma}$ to be used in establishing a revised center line and control limits for future use.

Incidentally, we should note that on a σ chart the probability of a point falling above the upper limit is not exactly the same as the probability of a point falling below the lower limit. This situation arises from the fact that the sampling distribution of σ is asymmetrical, especially so when the sample size is small.

In constructing the R chart, we find the center line by computing $d_2\sigma'$ if σ' is known or specified. The product $d_2\sigma'$, of course, gives the value of $E(R)$, the expected value of the sample range (see p. 217 for definition of d_2). The lower control limit is found by computing $D_1\sigma'$ and the upper control limit is found by computing $D_2\sigma'$. By definition, $D_1\sigma' = E(R) - 3\sigma_R$ and $D_2\sigma' = E(R) + 3\sigma_R$, where σ_R is the standard error of the range. These equations may be solved to get explicit expressions for D_1 and D_2. For example, $D_2 = \dfrac{E(R)}{\sigma'} + \dfrac{3\sigma_R}{\sigma'}$. The values of $\dfrac{E(R)}{\sigma'}$ and $\dfrac{\sigma_R}{\sigma'}$ in the right member of this equation have been tabulated for samples of various sizes drawn from a normal population.[2]

In cases such as the oil can filling example, where we are analyzing past data and have not specified a standard value of σ', we use $\bar{R}$ as the center line on our chart. (See Fig. 11–2.)   The LCL is found by computing $D_3\bar{R}$ and the UCL is found by computing $D_4\bar{R}$.

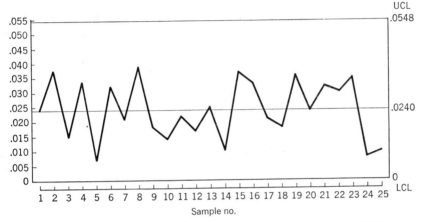

FIGURE 11–3.   R Chart.   Contents of 1-Quart Cans of Motor Oil (Pounds at 70°: $n = 4$, $\bar{R} = .0240$)

In Figure 11–3, we see that the UCL equals .0548 and the LCL equals zero.   As in the case of the σ chart, all points on the R chart are "in control."   The formulas for D_3 and D_4 may be written as follows: $D_4 = 1 + \dfrac{3\sigma_R}{E(R)}$ and $D_3 = 1 - \dfrac{3\sigma_R}{E(R)}$.   These formulas may be evaluated by means of the $\dfrac{E(R)}{\sigma'}$ and $\dfrac{\sigma_R}{\sigma'}$ values from Pearson's table.   Values of D_3 and D_4 are given in the table of control chart factors (Table IV) on page 343.

CONTROL CHARTS FOR ATTRIBUTE DATA

For cases where a product or part may be classified as either defective or acceptable, statistical quality control provides the p chart.

[2] The tabulation was made by E. S. Pearson.   His table, originally appearing in *Biometrika*, is reproduced in Bernard Ostle, *Statistics in Research* (Ames, Iowa State College Press, 1954), Appendix 10, pp. 460–61.

On this chart we record the proportion p of defective items in each sample. The model for the sampling distribution of p is, of course, the modified binomial distribution. If a standard value of p' is given, control limits are found from the formula $p' \pm 3 \sqrt{\dfrac{p'(1 - p')}{n}}$, that is, control limits are again located at 3 standard errors above and below the mean of the sampling distribution. On the other hand, if we wish to analyze the performance of a process without reference to a given standard, we find our control limits from the formula, $\overline{p} \pm 3 \sqrt{\dfrac{\overline{p}(1 - \overline{p})}{n}}$, where $\overline{p}$ is the average proportion of defectives taken over several samples.

To take an example of the latter case, that is, where we are analyzing the performance of a given process, let us consider the production of aluminum disks. These items are produced for sale to fabricators, who form them into skillets, lids, and many other products and utensils. There are, in general, three types of defects that a disk can possess, namely, scratches, wrinkles, and blisters. If, upon inspection, a disk is found to have one or more of these defects, it is classified as defective.

Suppose now that samples of 400 disks each are selected at random at various time intervals and from the data on the first 20 samples, a p chart is constructed. The data are, let us say, as in Table 11–2.

From the data in Table 11–2, we readily find the control limits by means of the formula,

$$\bar{p} \pm 3 \sqrt{\frac{\bar{p}(1 - \bar{p})}{n}}$$

Substituting, we have:

$$\frac{1.0125}{20} \pm 3 \sqrt{\frac{.0506(.9494)}{400}} = .0506 \pm 3 \sqrt{.0001200991}$$

$$= .0506 \pm 3(.01095898) = .0506 \pm .0329$$

$$\text{LCL} = .0177 \qquad\qquad \text{UCL} = .0835$$

The p chart drawn with these limits is shown in Figure 11–4. We see at a glance that all values of p are in control. If a great many points had been out of control, it might have been desirable to construct three different p charts for the aluminum disks, one for

TABLE 11–2

Data for Construction of p Chart
(400 Aluminum Disks in Each Sample)

Sample no.	No. of defectives	p
1	21	.0525
2	12	.0300
3	17	.0425
4	21	.0525
5	26	.0650
6	18	.0450
7	21	.0525
8	21	.0525
9	20	.0500
10	21	.0525
11	20	.0500
12	30	.0750
13	20	.0500
14	13	.0325
15	33	.0825
16	20	.0500
17	15	.0375
18	23	.0575
19	15	.0375
20	18	.0450
	405	1.0125

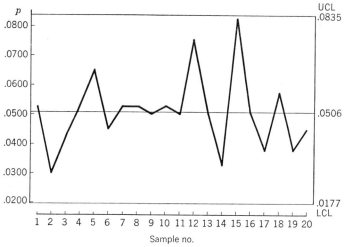

FIGURE 11–4. *p* Chart. Defects in Aluminum Disks ($\bar{p}$ = .0506)

scratches, one for blisters, and one for wrinkles. With the three charts at hand, we could find out if there were about the same number of defects of all types or whether only certain types of defects were causing points to go out of control.

As would also be the case for the $\bar{X}$ chart, if several successive points form a run on one side of the center line, the proper inference is that the process level has changed; thus a new center line and control limits should be computed.

It is important to note that on a p chart the lower control limit is not superfluous. Nor does such a limit represent an attempt to keep quality from becoming too good. Points out of control below the lower limit may indicate such assignable causes as lax inspection, nonrandom samples, hidden defective work, and so on.

THE c CHART

The second major type of attribute data chart is the c chart. The letter c denotes the number of defects per product or per group of products, where a very large number of products are exposed to the hazard of acquiring a defect but the probability of an individual defect occurring is very small. The product may be an automobile carburetor, a yard of fabric, a roll of newsprint, a television set, a tin can, a beer bottle, or any one of an almost endless list of items. In the case of the c chart, the sample size is, in effect, equal to 1. If single items are inspected, then c is the number of defects per item. If a group of items is the unit of inspection, for example, a group consisting of 5 carburetors each, then c is the number of defects per group. The nature of the defects that can occur must, of course, be specified clearly and the defects must be readily identifiable by the inspectors if the c chart is to be used successfully.

The Poisson distribution is the appropriate model for indicating the probabilities of occurrence of various numbers of defects. In other words, the Poisson model is used to represent the probability distribution of c. The symbol $\bar{c}$, which represents the average number of defects over several items or inspection units, is taken as an estimate of λ, the mean and variance of the Poisson distribution. Thus $\sqrt{\bar{c}}$ is an estimate of the standard deviation of the distribution. It is customary in American practice to find control limits from the formula $\bar{c} \pm 3\sqrt{\bar{c}}$, even though the probability of a point falling above the upper limit is not the same as the probability of a point falling below the lower limit.

To take an example, suppose we are inspecting units which consist of three auto ignition distributors each. A distributor may possess such defects as a loose shaft, a nonsymmetrical cam, a cracked housing, or a bent plate. The data for 24 inspection units are given in Table 11–3.

TABLE 11–3

Defects in Ignition Distributors

Inspection unit (3 carburetors)	No. of defects per inspection unit	Inspection unit (3 carburetors)	No. of defects per inspection unit
1	3	13	2
2	0	14	3
3	4	15	6
4	1	16	9
5	6	17	2
6	8	18	4
7	3	19	7
8	2	20	1
9	1	21	1
10	4	22	6
11	0	23	2
12	1	24	2
		total	78

$$\bar{c} = \frac{78}{24} = 3.25$$

$$\bar{c} \pm 3\sqrt{\bar{c}} = 3.25 \pm 3(1.803)$$

$$= 3.25 \pm 5.409$$

$$\text{UCL} = 8.659, \text{ or } 8.66$$

$$\text{LCL} = 0$$

From the computations shown in connection with the table, we see that the mean number of defects per inspection unit is 3.25 and that the UCL is 8.66. We take the LCL as 0, for negative values cannot occur on the Poisson distribution. The c values of Table 11–3 are plotted in Figure 11–5.

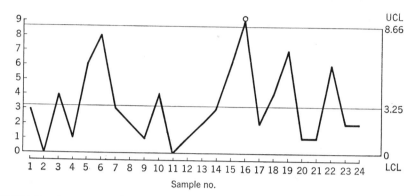

FIGURE 11–5.   c Chart.   Defects in Ignition Distributors (Unit = 3 Distributors, $\bar{c}$ = 3.25)

CLASSIFICATION AND WEIGHTING OF DEFECTS

If certain types of defects are known to have more serious effects upon the quality of a product than others, the defects may be grouped into classes such as critical, major, and minor. Each defect in the critical category could be assigned a demerit of, say, 50 points, each major defect 25 demerit points, and each minor defect 1 demerit point. Critical defects could be those that would prevent the product from functioning at all, major defects could be those that would prevent the product from functioning at top efficiency or which would cause it to stop functioning after a relatively short period of time. Minor defects could be such things as defects of finish and appearance, which would not impair the proper functioning of the product.

By processes of weighting, it is possible to find the demerit point values to be plotted on the control chart, the center line, and the control limits.[3]

SUMMARY

Both of the major techniques of statistical inference—estimating and testing hypotheses—are important in the field of statistical quality control. Essentially, statistical quality control provides for the maintenance of a continuing statistical record of an industrial production process and the making of decisions on the basis of that record so as to bring the process under "control" and maintain a consistent level of quality in the product. The continuing statistical record is called a control chart, this chart having

[3] See the brief discussion in Irving W. Burr, *Engineering Statistics and Quality Control* (New York, McGraw-Hill Book Co., Inc., 1953), p. 241.

a center line, an upper control limit, and a lower control limit. If quality is expressed in terms of a measurable characteristic, an $\overline{X}$ chart and either a σ chart or an R chart will be constructed. Means of successive samples are plotted on the $\overline{X}$ chart, standard deviations on the σ chart, and sample ranges on the R chart. In American practice, control limits are located 3 standard errors above the center line and 3 standard errors below the center line. The center line is located at the expected value of the statistic plotted or at the estimated expected value of that statistic. A normally distributed population of measurements is assumed.

Factors facilitating the construction of measurement data control charts are c_2, d_2, A, A_1, A_2, B_1, B_2, B_3, B_4, D_1, D_2, D_3, D_4. The c_2 and d_2 factors are useful for finding center lines and for understanding the other factors. The A factors relate to the $\overline{X}$ chart, the B factors to the σ chart, and the D factors to the R chart.

There are, in general, two types of attribute data control charts, the p chart and the c chart. On the former chart, we plot the proportion of defective items found in successive samples. On the latter, we plot the numbers of defects per inspection unit. The modified binomial distribution is the basic model for the p chart. The center line on the p chart is located at p' (standards given) or at $\bar{p}$ (analysis of past data), whereas the respective locations are at c' and $\bar{c}$ on the c chart. As in the case of measurement data charts, control limits are located 3 standard errors above and below the center line.

Two general cases arise in statistical quality control: (1) the case where standards are given or specified, and (2) the case where we are analyzing past data or "seeing what the process can do." It is advisable that standards not be set until there is good reason to believe that the process is in control and that specifications are being met.

TERMS TO PONDER

1. Control Charts for Measurement Data
2. Control Chart Factors
3. Chance Variation
4. Assignable Cause
5. Upper Control Limit (UCL)
6. Lower Control Limit (LCL)
7. Center Line
8. Control Charts for Attribute Data

EXERCISES

1. The following data represent electrical resistance measurements made on new rheostats at a standard setting. Data are tabulated for a series of 20 samples, each sample consisting of 5 rheostats.

Data on 20 Samples of 5 Rheostats Each

Sample no.	Observations in sample				
1	10.8	11.8	11.2	10.0	11.2
2	10.0	8.0	10.2	10.4	10.2
3	11.2	11.8	11.6	10.8	9.0
4	10.8	10.4	9.2	10.0	10.0
5	10.4	11.6	8.4	9.2	10.0
6	9.6	10.0	9.4	10.0	9.3
7	8.6	8.8	9.2	8.8	10.4
8	9.3	9.2	8.8	9.2	9.0
9	8.0	11.2	9.0	10.0	10.0
10	10.0	10.8	11.2	10.4	9.4
11	9.6	9.0	9.4	10.4	8.0
12	10.0	10.2	8.8	9.2	10.2
13	11.2	9.2	9.6	11.2	10.8
14	10.8	10.0	8.4	10.8	9.2
15	10.4	10.0	11.6	10.6	9.4
16	9.7	9.6	9.9	10.1	9.2
17	9.8	9.9	11.2	9.9	8.8
18	8.2	10.9	11.2	12.2	11.9
19	11.7	11.8	9.9	9.1	9.0
20	9.3	10.4	9.4	11.6	8.2

a. Compute $\bar{X}$ and R for each sample. Then find center lines and control limits for the $\bar{X}$ and R charts.

b. Draw the $\bar{X}$ and R charts.

c. Using $\bar{R}$ and d_2, estimate the population standard deviation and then estimate the tolerance limits of the process. Are the tolerance limits within specifications of 10.0 ± 1.5?

2. Following are given the numbers of defective bushings found in 25 samples of 200 bushings each.

Sample no.	Number of defectives	Sample no.	Number of defectives
1	22	14	22
2	25	15	33
3	13	16	10
4	16	17	26
5	26	18	21
6	21	19	19
7	22	20	25
8	24	21	23
9	25	22	21
10	19	23	24
11	15	24	19
12	20	25	14
13	23		

  a. Construct a p chart for these data, locating the center line and control limits properly.

  b. Is the lower confidence limit of any importance on this type of chart? If so, what type of assignable cause could give rise to a point that is out of control below the lower limit?

3. Look up the reference of footnote 2 in the library and verify that D_1, D_2, D_3, and D_4 can be evaluated from the table referred to.

4. From the table of control chart factors on page 343, and your knowledge of the $\overline{X}$ chart, write the formula that defines the factor A.

5. Define each of the following factors:

  a. A_1.

  b. c_2.

  c. d_2.

  d. B_1.

  e. B_4.

6. Suppose that the control charts for a given process indicate that the process is in control but that the specifications are not being met. Would you classify this problem under statistics or engineering? Why?

SELECTED REFERENCES

Burr, Irving W., *Engineering Statistics and Quality Control* (New York, McGraw-Hill Book Co., Inc., 1953), Chs. V, VI, IX.

Duncan, Acheson J., *Quality Control and Industrial Statistics*, rev. ed. (Homewood, Ill., Richard D. Irwin, Inc., 1959), Part IV.

Grant, Eugene L., *Statistical Quality Control*, 2d ed. (New York, McGraw-Hill Book Co., Inc., 1952), Parts II, III.

12

LINEAR REGRESSION

AND CORRELATION

IN EXAMINING VARIOUS METHODS of acquiring information about populations, we have thus far concerned ourselves with observations made on only one characteristic of the elements under study. We have considered such things as family incomes, balances of accounts receivable, and service lives of electronic tubes.

In some cases, however, the process of estimation is facilitated and various important hypotheses may be tested if observations are made on more than one characteristic. Let us take a couple of simple examples. A truck fleet operator may be interested in observing (1) mileage and (2) total maintenance expenditures for each of the trucks in a sample under study. An economist studying family consumption patterns may observe annual income and annual food expenditures for each of several families. If it is found that the two characteristics (or variables) are related rather closely in some consistent fashion, a knowledge of values of one characteristic may aid us in making estimates of values of the other. Pursuing the second example, suppose we found that family food expenditures were very nearly a constant proportion p of total income. Then letting F stand for food expenditures and Y for total income, we could indicate the relationship between the variables F and Y by writing $F = pY$. If we were willing to assume that this relationship held through time, then from a knowledge of Y for a given family, we could estimate food expenditures for that same family by computing pY.

We also may formulate and test various hypotheses concerning the form of the relationship between the variables and the degree of association between them.

TYPE OF RELATIONSHIP

In this chapter we shall confine ourselves to the study of linear relationships between two variables. Further, we shall be concerned only with the case of ungrouped data.

Because we have decided to consider only linear relationships, one of the important preliminary problems facing anyone attempting a regression analysis has been solved for us. This problem is the determination of the type of the relationship between the variables. When we speak of a *linear* relationship between *two* variables, we mean that the equation or function defining the relationship can be represented by a straight line.

A set of hypothetical data which may be described rather well by a straight line is given in Table 12–1. The observations relate

TABLE 12–1

**Observations on a Sample Consisting of
Twelve Modern Novels**

x_i (no. of pages)	y_i (price)
190	2.00
240	2.90
240	2.20
280	3.00
320	3.80
370	3.20
400	4.20
400	3.70
460	4.20
480	4.80
520	4.60
560	5.30

to a sample of modern novels. For each book, the x_i observation is the number of pages it contains and y_i is the retail price. The price figures are given in constant dollars, having been adjusted by an index of publishing costs.

In Figure 12–1, we have plotted the pairs of x_i and y_i values on a *scatter diagram*, x_i being measured along the horizontal axis and

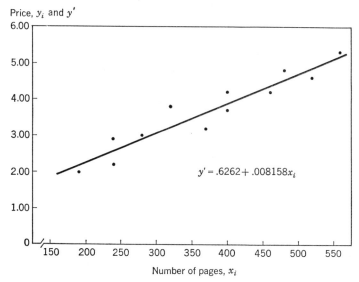

FIGURE 12–1. Scatter Diagram with Least Squares Line. Size and Price of Twelve Modern Novels

y_i along the vertical axis. We easily verify the fact that the point representing the first book is found by moving 190 units parallel to the horizontal axis and 2.00 units parallel to the vertical axis. Plotting the data on such a diagram is of considerable help in determining the form of the relationship between two variables. A straight line has been fitted to the data by a method we shall explore in a moment. This line is said to represent the regression of y on x.

The publisher is interested in these data as an aid in setting prices on new novels. Fairly early in the publishing process, the publisher knows just how many pages the book will contain. The relationship between number of pages and price enables him to use his knowledge of book size to help estimate or "predict" the price to be charged for the book.

METHOD OF FITTING THE LINE

Once the form of the relationship between x and y has been decided upon—a straight line in the example at hand—we are faced with the problem of deciding what method to use in fitting the line to the observations. The method chosen will provide us with one specific straight line out of the infinite number of such lines that could conceivably be fitted to the data.

The standard equation of a straight line may be written, $y' = a + bx$, wherein y' and x are co-ordinates of any point on the line. The symbol a represents the y'-intercept or the point on the y'-axis where the (extended) line cuts through it, and b is the slope of the line, or the amount of vertical rise (or fall) in the line per unit change in horizontal distance. The following diagram (Fig. 12–2) gives the geometrical interpretation of a and b.

On this diagram we have shown 0 on both axes and extended the line until it cuts through the y' axis. We see that for any x value

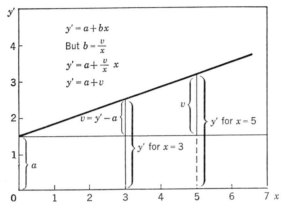

FIGURE 12–2.   Geometric Interpretation of a and b in $y' = a + bx$

y' must be equal to $a + v$. The diagram also shows that the slope of the line is given by v/x. But we have said that b is the slope of the line. Substituting v/x, then, for b in $y' = a + bx$, we have $y' = a + v$. We can, of course, find the values of a and b approximately by reading the appropriate values from the graph. We see directly that $a \doteq 1.5$ and that $b = \dfrac{v}{x} \doteq \dfrac{2.5 - 1.5}{3} = .33$, choosing $x = 3$ for the latter computation. The equation for this particular line, then, is approximately $y' = 1.5 + .33x$. We can check our figures by substituting an arbitrary value of x in the equation, computing y', and then seeing if we read the same value of y' from the graph directly above the chosen value of x.

THE LEAST SQUARES CRITERION

The basic problem in fitting any straight line, of course, is to evaluate a and b in terms of the observations. We should have a reasonable basis for determining what these values shall be. In fitting the line shown in Figure 12–1, we have used the criterion of *least squares*. Figure 12–3 will aid us in understanding this criterion. The first plotted point on the graph has been selected for purposes of illustration, but the notations relating to it apply to every other plotted point. Directly above (or below) each plotted point there is a point on the regression line. The ordinate of the plotted point is denoted by y_i and the ordinate of the regression line is denoted by y'.

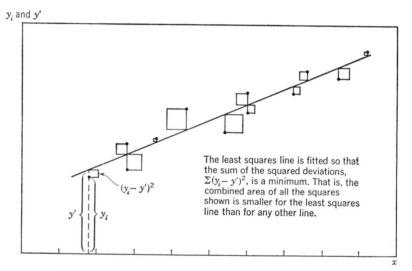

FIGURE 12–3.   Geometric Interpretation of the Least Squares Criterion

The deviation of a plotted point from the line (or the vertical distance by which it falls off the line) is given by $(y_i - y')$. In Figure 12–3, the squares of these deviations are indicated by square areas along the line. Now the criterion for fitting the least squares line is simply this: The line should be fitted in such a manner that the *sum* of the squared deviations, $\Sigma(y_i - y')^2$, is a minimum. This means that from the indefinitely large number of straight lines that could conceivably be fitted to the data, we must select that one for which the sum of the squared deviations is smallest. To do this we must construct appropriate expressions involving the observed values of x_i and y_i so that we can solve for a and b. Since $y' = a + bx$, we substitute $a + bx$ for y' in $\Sigma(y_i - y')^2$ giving $\Sigma(y_i - a - bx_i)^2$. Then by a mathematical process (which we do not cover in elementary books) we minimize this sum to yield two equations in a and b. These are called the *normal equations* for fitting a line of least squares, and we solve them simultaneously to find values of a and b. They are as follows:

$$\Sigma y_i = na + b\Sigma x_i \qquad \text{(Eq. 12–1)}$$

$$\Sigma x_i y_i = a\Sigma x_i + b\Sigma x_i^2 \qquad \text{(Eq. 12–2)}$$

By multiplying Equation 12–1 by Σx_i^2 and Equation 12–2 by Σx_i, we could form two new equations and subtract one from the other so as to eliminate the terms in b. Similarly, we could multiply Equation 12–1 by Σx_i and Equation 12–2 by n and add the resulting new equations so as to eliminate the terms in a. The process is much simpler, however, if we put it in terms of determinants and utilize Cramer's rule. This rule tells us that a and b may be found by computing the ratios of determinants.

These ratios are as follows:

$$a = \frac{\begin{vmatrix} \Sigma y_i & \Sigma x_i \\ \Sigma x_i y_i & \Sigma x_i^2 \end{vmatrix}}{\begin{vmatrix} n & \Sigma x_i \\ \Sigma x_i & \Sigma x_i^2 \end{vmatrix}}, \qquad b = \frac{\begin{vmatrix} n & \Sigma y_i \\ \Sigma x_i & \Sigma x_i y_i \end{vmatrix}}{\begin{vmatrix} n & \Sigma x_i \\ \Sigma x_i & \Sigma x_i^2 \end{vmatrix}}$$

The determinant which forms the denominator in both ratios is made up of the coefficients of a and b in the normal equations. In the ratio for determining a, the numerator would be the same as the denominator, except that the coefficients of a have been replaced by the "constant terms" in the normal equations, that is, those terms to the left of the equality signs. In the numerator of the b ratio, we find that the coefficients of b have been replaced by the constant terms. Cramer's rule merely summarizes the steps necessary in constructing the ratio of determinants to solve for any unknown: *The value of an unknown is given by the ratio of two determinants, the denominator being formed from the coefficients of the unknown terms and the numerator being similarly formed except that the coefficients of the unknown being solved for are replaced by the constant terms in the equations.*

Determinants of the type we have here are evaluated by a simple process of cross multiplication. In each determinant, we start with the term in the upper left-hand corner and multiply it by the term in the lower right corner (see Table 12–2). From this product we subtract the other cross product in the determinant. Thus we see that:

$$a = \frac{\Sigma y_i \Sigma x_i^2 - \Sigma x_i y_i \Sigma x_i}{n \Sigma x_i^2 - \Sigma x_i \Sigma x_i}$$

The student may wish to verify the fact that this result is exactly what he would get if he multiplied each normal equation by an appropriate term so as to form new equations that could be added algebraically to eliminate the terms in b.

Evaluating the determinants in the ratio for b gives us:

$$b = \frac{n \Sigma x_i y_i - \Sigma x_i \Sigma y_i}{n \Sigma x_i^2 - \Sigma x_i \Sigma x_i}$$

Incidentally, the student wishing to go on to advanced work in statistics, econometrics, or management science would do well to arrange his program so as to include the study of determinants and matrices.

Let us now show how we fit the line of least squares to the sample of modern novels as shown in Figure 12–1. The appropriate work sheet is set forth in Table 12–2.

The values of n, Σx_i, and Σy_i are readily determined from the original observations. The only other summations we need in order to fill out the normal equations are $\Sigma x_i y_i$ and Σx_i^2. We have set up columns (3) and (4) in our worksheet to get the latter summations. In Table 12–2, $\Sigma x_i y_i$ is the figure shown at the bottom of column (3) and Σx_i^2 is the figure shown at the bottom of column (4). Using determinants, we find that $a = .6262$ and that $b = .008158$. Thus by substituting these values in $y' = a + bx$ we may write the equation for our least squares line as $y' = .6262 + .008158x_i$.

To draw the line on the graph, we need only choose two arbitrary values of x_i and substitute them, in turn, in the equation of the line. Two values of y' result. Plotting these values of y' opposite their corresponding x_i values, we have two points which determine the line.

By substituting the remaining values of x_i in the regression equation one by one, we can find a y' value for every pair of observations (x_i, y_i) in the sample.

CHARACTERISTICS OF THE LEAST SQUARES LINE

In addition to satisfying the basic criterion, the least squares line possesses other characteristics which are similar to those of the arithmetic mean. First, the algebraic sum of the deviations from

TABLE 12–2

Regression Line Fitted by Least Squares
(Sample of Twelve Modern Novels)

x_i (no. of pages)	y_i (retail price)	$x_i y_i$	x_i^2
(1)	(2)	(3)	(4)
190	2.00	380	36,100
240	2.90	696	57,600
240	2.20	528	57,600
280	3.00	840	78,400
320	3.80	1216	102,400
370	3.20	1184	136,900
400	4.20	1680	160,000
400	3.70	1480	160,000
460	4.20	1932	211,600
480	4.80	2304	230,400
520	4.60	2392	270,400
560	5.30	2968	313,600
4460	43.90	17,600	1,815,000

$$a = \frac{\begin{vmatrix} \Sigma y_i & \Sigma x_i \\ \Sigma x_i y_i & \Sigma x_i^2 \end{vmatrix}}{\begin{vmatrix} n & \Sigma x_i \\ \Sigma x_i & \Sigma x_i^2 \end{vmatrix}} = \frac{\begin{matrix} 43.90 \diagdown \nearrow 4460 \\ 17,600 \diagup \searrow 1,815,000 \end{matrix}}{\begin{matrix} 12 \diagdown \nearrow 4460 \\ 4460 \diagup \searrow 1,815,000 \end{matrix}} = \frac{79,678,500 - 78,496,000}{21,780,000 - 19,891,600}$$

$$= \frac{1,182,500}{1,888,400} = .6262$$

$$b = \frac{\begin{vmatrix} n & \Sigma y_i \\ \Sigma x_i & \Sigma x_i y_i \end{vmatrix}}{\begin{vmatrix} n & \Sigma x_i \\ \Sigma x_i & \Sigma x_i^2 \end{vmatrix}} = \frac{\begin{matrix} 12 \diagdown \nearrow 43.90 \\ 4460 \diagup \searrow 17,600 \end{matrix}}{\begin{matrix} 12 \diagdown \nearrow 4460 \\ 4460 \diagup \searrow 1,815,000 \end{matrix}} = \frac{211,200 - 195,794}{21,780,000 - 19,891,600}$$

$$= \frac{15,406}{1,888,400} = .008158$$

the line is equal to zero. That is, $\Sigma(y_i - y') = 0$. Thus the sum of deviations above the line is equal to the sum of deviations below the line. This is similar to the center of gravity characteristic of the arithmetic mean. Second, the line passes through the mean of the system. That is, the line always passes through the point designated by $\bar{x}$, $\bar{y}$. For the data of Table 12–2, $\bar{x} = 371.7$ and $\bar{y} =$

3.658. Substitution of 371.7 for x_i in the equation, $y' = .6262 + .008158x_i$, will give $y' = \bar{y} \doteq 3.658$. By referring to Figure 12–1, the student should verify the fact that the line passes through the point designated by the two mean values.

It is important to remember that the line fitted to the observed data is an estimate of the true regression line, which we represent by the symbols $Y = \alpha + \beta X$.

ASSUMPTIONS OF REGRESSION ANALYSIS

Before making use of the regression line to compute an estimate, we should familiarize ourselves with the assumptions of linear regression analysis. The first of these assumptions is that the x_i values have been measured without error, that is, they are taken as parameters. To use the sample of novels again, the values of x_i were selected in advance and then from the group of books having a given x_i value, one or more were selected at random. In Table 12–2, we see that from the books that were 240 pages long, two have been selected at random, these having prices of $2.90 and $2.20. From the books that were 370 pages long, one was selected, the price being $3.20.

The second assumption is that for each of the x_i values, the population of y values is assumed to be normally distributed with the mean located on the true regression line.

In the third place, all of these normal distributions of y values are assumed to have equal variances.

If our observations conform to these assumptions, we may estimate the mean value of y for a given value of x_i and construct confidence limits for the estimate.

To show how the estimate and confidence limits are constructed, let us return to the example of the modern novels. Suppose that the publisher is about to put on the market a new novel that will be 350 pages in length. To estimate the price that should be charged for the book, we substitute 350 for x_i in the estimated regression equation and solve for y'. We have $y' = .6262 + .008158(350)$ or $y' = .6262 + 2.8553 = 3.4815$. Our estimate of the price is, then, $3.48. This, as stated earlier, is an estimate of the mean price of books having 350 pages.

We may compute confidence limits for this estimate from the following formula:

$$y' \pm \text{“}t\text{”} \cdot s_E \sqrt{\frac{1}{n} + \frac{(x_c - \bar{x})^2}{\Sigma(x_i - \bar{x})^2}} \qquad \text{(Eq. 12–3)}$$

where "t" is an appropriate value selected from the table of Student's "t" distribution with df $= (n - 2)$, s_E is the *standard error of estimate*,

given by $s_E = \sqrt{\dfrac{\Sigma(y_i - y')^2}{n - 2}}$, n is the number of pairs of observa-

tions, and x_c is the value of x_i for which we are estimating y'.

The standard error of estimate is similar to the standard deviation except that in the former case we take deviations from y', the ordinates of the regression line, and we divide the sum of the squared deviations by $n - 2$ instead of $n - 1$.

A 95% confidence interval for the estimate of the average price of a novel 350 pages in length is

$$3.48 \pm 2.228 \times .33386 \times .29396 \text{ or}$$

$$3.48 \pm .22, \text{ giving confidence limits of}$$

$$3.26\text{--}3.70$$

A worksheet showing detailed steps in the computation is given in Table 12–3. In the computations, we have rounded the value of $\bar{x}$ so that it appears as 372 rather than 371.7.

Confidence intervals of this type, though centered on the estimated regression line, become gradually wider as x_c values differ more widely from $\bar{x}$. Thus at a given probability level, smaller confidence intervals will result if the x_c values are near the middle of the x_i range. Values of x_c should not be selected beyond the range of the sample data unless one has good reason to believe that the linear relationship extends into such a region. In any case, we must remember that estimates of the mean y for a given x value always require that the relationship between x and y hold through time. For many types of experimental data, this requirement is automatically fulfilled, but for survey data, such as we deal with in business and economics, it often is not.

TEST OF A HYPOTHESIS CONCERNING β

Of the many tests that can be carried out in linear regression, one of the most common is the test of the hypothesis that β, the slope of the true regression line, is 0. In other words, this is a test of the hypothesis that the true regression line is horizontal. If this hypothesis is true, then the probability that random samples of y values (for each x value) would give a large absolute value of b is slight. We choose a level of significance and divide the region of rejection equally

TABLE 12–3

Construction of a 95% Confidence Interval for Estimating the Mean y for a Given x_i
(Estimate of Mean Price of Novel Having 350 Pages)

x_i	bx_i	$y' =$ $a + bx_i$	y_i	$y_i - y'$	$(y_i - y')^2$	$x_i - \bar{x}$	$(x_i - \bar{x})^2$
190	1.550	2.176	2.00	−.176	.030976	−182	33,124
240	1.958	2.584	2.90	.316	.099856	−132	17,424
240	1.958	2.584	2.20	−.384	.147456	−132	17,424
280	2.284	2.910	3.00	.090	.008100	−92	8464
320	2.611	3.237	3.80	.563	.316969	−52	2704
370	3.018	3.644	3.20	−.444	.197136	−2	4
400	3.263	3.889	4.20	.311	.096721	28	784
400	3.263	3.889	3.70	−.189	.035721	28	784
460	3.753	4.379	4.20	−.179	.032041	88	7744
480	3.916	4.542	4.80	.258	.066564	108	11,664
520	4.242	4.868	4.60	−.268	.071824	148	21,904
560	4.568	5.194	5.30	.106	.011236	188	35,344
4460					1.114600		157,368

$$s_E^2 = \frac{\Sigma(y_i - y')^2}{n - 2} = \frac{1.114600}{12 - 2} = .11146$$

$$s_E = \sqrt{.11146} \doteq .33386$$

$$\sqrt{\frac{1}{n} + \frac{(x_c - \bar{x})^2}{\Sigma(x_i - \bar{x})^2}} = \sqrt{\frac{1}{12} + \frac{(350 - 372)^2}{157,368}}$$

$$= \sqrt{\frac{1}{12} + \frac{484}{157,368}} = \sqrt{.083333 + .00307559}$$

$$= \sqrt{.08641} \doteq .29396$$

$$y' \pm \text{``}t\text{''} \cdot s_E \sqrt{\frac{1}{n} + \frac{(x_c - \bar{x})^2}{\Sigma(x_i - \bar{x})^2}} \doteq 3.48 \pm 2.228(.33386)(.29396)$$

$$\doteq 3.48 \pm .22$$

$$\boxed{3.26\text{--}3.70}$$

between both tails of the "t" distribution. We compute a value of "t" from the formula, "t" $= \dfrac{b - 0}{s_b}$, where s_b is the standard error of b. The ratio, $\dfrac{b - 0}{s_b}$, is distributed as "t" with $n - 2$ degrees of freedom. We define s_b according to the following formula:

$$s_b = \sqrt{\frac{s_E{}^2}{\Sigma(x_i - \bar{x})^2}} \qquad \text{(Eq. 12–4)}$$

We compare the computed value of "t" with the appropriate tabular value to determine whether or not to reject the hypothesis.

Let us make this test for the modern novels at the 5% level of significance. From our estimation problem, we know that the critical value of "t" is ± 2.228. To get the computed value, we substitute as follows:

$$\text{"}t\text{"} = \frac{b - 0}{s_b} = \frac{.008158 - 0}{\sqrt{\dfrac{.11146}{157{,}368}}} = \frac{.008158}{\sqrt{.0000007082761}}$$

$$= \frac{.008158}{.0008415914} \doteq 9.693$$

Since 9.693 is greater in absolute value than 2.28, we reject the null hypothesis that $\beta = 0$ and conclude that β must be significantly different from 0, a linear relationship being indicated with the line probably sloping upward from left to right.

Similar procedures may be used to test the hypothesis that $\beta = 1$, that is, that the true regression line forms an angle of 45° with the horizontal axis. Tests may also be carried out with regard to α, one of the common ones being the test of the hypothesis that α equals zero, the regression line, under such circumstances, going through the origin.

LINEAR CORRELATION

We have seen that linear regression is concerned with the fitting of a line to a set of observations and the making of estimates and tests when certain basic assumptions are satisfied. Linear correlation, however, is concerned with measuring the goodness of fit of the regression line or the "closeness" of association between the two variables.

A statistic appropriate to this type of measurement is the Pearsonian *coefficient of correlation*, which is denoted by r. If there is no relationship between the two variables, x and y, with the points on the scatter diagram being contained in an area roughly like a circle or with all of the points along a perfectly horizontal line, the value of r is 0. If the relationship is perfect, all points lying on a least squares line that is upward sloping to the right, r equals 1. If the relationship is perfect, but with all points on a least squares line downward sloping to the right, r equals -1.

The statistic r is similar to the coefficient of variation discussed in Chapter 6 in that it is an abstract number not tied to any specific unit of measurement. The coefficient of variation is also a simple proportion, and it so happens that the *square* of the correlation coefficient may be interpreted as a ratio or proportion. That is, r^2 may be looked upon as the proportion of total "squared error" that is accounted for or that is "due to" the linear relationship.

Understanding of this interpretation is facilitated by the scatter diagram of Figure 12–4. Here we see three types of deviation in the y variable, namely, "data to mean" $(y_i - \bar{y})$; "line to mean" $(y' - \bar{y})$; and "data to line" $(y_i - y')$. Now total squared error is defined as $\Sigma(y_i - \bar{y})^2$, which is equal to $\Sigma(y' - \bar{y})^2 + \Sigma(y_i - y')^2$. Thus $\dfrac{\Sigma(y' - \bar{y})^2}{\Sigma(y_i - \bar{y})^2} = r^2$, the proportion of total squared error which is associated with the regression line. The numerator of the r^2 formula is the summation of the squared deviations designated as "line

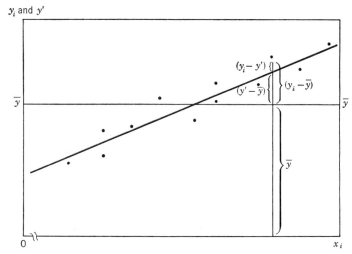

FIGURE 12–4. Deviations Relating to the Interpretation of r^2

to mean." This summation is, then, the amount of squared error that is "accounted for" by the linear relationship of x to y, that is, the amount that is "explained" by fitting the line. The expression for r^2 is simply this amount of squared error expressed as a proportion of total squared error.

Now we do not use the above formula for computing r^2 or r. A rather simple formula for r that may be transformed into convenient forms for computing is $r = \dfrac{s_{xy}}{s_x s_y}$. The numerator of this formula is called the sample *covariance* of x and y and is defined as follows:

$$s_{xy} = \frac{\Sigma(x_i - \bar{x})(y_i - \bar{y})}{n - 1}$$

We see from this formula that if $(x_i - \bar{x})$ were substituted for $(y_i - \bar{y})$, we would have s^2 or s_x^2, the sample variance from Chapter 6. The variance, then, is just a special case of the covariance. The symbol, s_x, of course, represents the standard deviation of the x_i observations, and s_y represents the standard deviation of the y_i observations.

If we were to substitute the standard formulas for s_{xy}, s_x, and s_y in the formula for r and make a simple cancellation, we would have:

$$r = \frac{\Sigma(x_i - \bar{x})(y_i - \bar{y})}{\sqrt{\Sigma(x_i - \bar{x})^2}\sqrt{\Sigma(y_i - \bar{y})^2}}$$

Squaring both sides gives:

$$r^2 = \frac{[\Sigma(x_i - \bar{x})(y_i - \bar{y})]^2}{\Sigma(x_i - \bar{x})^2 \Sigma(y_i - \bar{y})^2}$$

A useful exercise is to utilize our knowledge of the regression line to show that the two formulas for r^2 are equivalent, that is,

$$r^2 = \frac{\Sigma(y' - \bar{y})^2}{\Sigma(y_i - \bar{y})^2} = \frac{[\Sigma(x_i - \bar{x})\Sigma(y_i - \bar{y})]^2}{\Sigma(x_i - \bar{x})^2 \Sigma(y_i - \bar{y})^2}$$

Now, since the regression line passes through the point $(\bar{x}, \bar{y})$, we see that $y' = \bar{y} + b(x - \bar{x})$. In turn, $y' - \bar{y} = b(x_i - \bar{x})$. Further, $(y' - \bar{y})^2 = b^2(x_i - \bar{x})^2$ and $\Sigma(y' - \bar{y})^2 = b^2\Sigma(x_i - \bar{x})^2$. Thus:

$$r^2 = \frac{\Sigma(y' - \bar{y})^2}{\Sigma(y_i - \bar{y})^2} = \frac{b^2\Sigma(x_i - \bar{x})^2}{\Sigma(y_i - \bar{y})^2}$$

Now from the determinant on page 235, we see that $b = \dfrac{n\Sigma x_i y_i - \Sigma x_i \Sigma y_i}{n\Sigma x_i^2 - (\Sigma x_i)^2}$.

Remembering our short-method formulas for computing the variance, we may rewrite this formula for b as $b = \dfrac{\Sigma(x_i - \bar{x})(y_i - \bar{y})}{\Sigma(x_i - \bar{x})^2}$.

Squaring this and substituting it for b^2 in the last expression for r^2 above, we have:

$$r^2 = \frac{[\Sigma(x_i - \bar{x})(y_i - \bar{y})]^2}{\Sigma(x_i - \bar{x})^2 \Sigma(x_i - \bar{x})^2} \frac{\Sigma(x_i - \bar{x})^2}{\Sigma(y_i - \bar{y})^2}$$

which yields, after canceling,

$$r^2 = \frac{[\Sigma(x_i - \bar{x})(y_i - \bar{y})]^2}{\Sigma(x_i - \bar{x})^2 \Sigma(y_i - \bar{y})^2}$$

this being the required result.

For purposes of computation, we may wish to write this formula in the following form:

$$r^2 = \frac{(n\Sigma x_i y_i - \Sigma x_i \Sigma y_i)^2}{[n\Sigma x_i^2 - (\Sigma x_i)^2][n\Sigma y_i^2 - (\Sigma y_i)^2]} \qquad \text{(Eq. 12-5)}$$

Use of this formula does *not* require the computation of $\bar{x}$, $\bar{y}$, and the deviations, $(x_i - \bar{x})$ and $(y_i - \bar{y})$.

COMPUTATION OF r^2

We may now return to the data on the sample of modern novels and compute r^2. All of the necessary figures for the substitution in Equation 12-5 are given in Table 12-2, except for Σy_i^2, which, it turns out, is equal to 172.19. Substituting in the formula for r^2, we have:

$$r^2 = \frac{[12(17,600) - 4460(43.90)]^2}{[12(1,815,000) - (4460)^2][12(172.19) - (43.90)^2]}$$

$$= \frac{(211,200 - 195,794)^2}{(21,780,000 - 19,891,600)(2066.28 - 1927.21)}$$

$$= \frac{(15,406)^2}{1,888,400(139.07)} = \frac{237,344,836}{262,619,788}$$

$$\doteq .9038$$

In this particular case, then, about 90% of the total squared error in y is accounted for by the estimated linear relationship.

This computation can be simplified considerably if we first code the data. We may add a constant to each x_i observation and then multiply the sum by another constant. We may do the same on the y_i observations. The constants need not be the same and the coding operations do not alter the value of r^2.

Let us code the x_i observations by adding -400 to each of them and then multiplying the difference by $\frac{1}{10}$. Then let us code the y_i observations by adding -4.20 to each of them and multiplying the difference by $\frac{1}{10}$. The results of these coding operations and the substitutions in the required formulas are shown in Table 12–4.

The interpretation of r^2 as the proportion of the total squared error that is due to regression follows from the least squares method of fitting the line. However, this interpretation does not seem to lead to any specific inferences that reach very far beyond the particular observations that have been used in the computations. It seems we can infer only this much: If the relationship $y' = a + bx$ is a close estimate of $Y = \alpha + \beta X$, then the stated interpretation of r^2 will be a fairly precise one regardless of the population distributions of the x variable and the y variable. However, if we wish to take r as an estimator of a corresponding parameter, $\rho = \dfrac{S_{xy}}{S_x S_y}$, or test hypotheses concerning ρ, we find it necessary to place rather far-reaching restrictions on the population distribution of the x and y variables. (ρ is the Greek letter "rho.")

The restrictions consist of the assumption that the x and y variables form a bivariate normal population. ρ is a parameter of such a population distribution. The value of ρ is 0 when x and y are statistically independent. Statistical independence means that the relative frequency (or probability) of x values in a given range is the same regardless of the relative frequencies of the associated values of y.

The bivariate normal distribution may be graphed in three-dimensional space with the x- and y-axes at right angles to each other in the horizontal plane and frequencies measured by volumes of vertical columns standing over the related pairs of values on the x, y plane. If $\bar{x}$ and $\bar{y}$ are positive, then the bivariate normal frequency distribution will resemble a sombrero sitting on the floor in the corner of a room, the edges of the floor representing the x- and y-axes in the positive quadrant.

TABLE 12–4

Coded Computation of r^2
(Price and Size of Twelve Modern Novels)

x_i	y_i	$v_i = \dfrac{x_i - 400}{10}$	$w_i = \dfrac{y_i - 4.20}{10}$	v_iw_i	v_i^2	w_i^2
190	2.00	-21	$-.22$	4.62	441	.0484
240	2.90	-16	$-.13$	2.08	256	.0169
240	2.20	-16	$-.20$	3.20	256	.0400
280	3.00	-12	$-.12$	1.44	144	.0144
320	3.80	-8	$-.04$	.32	64	.0016
370	3.20	-3	$-.10$	.30	9	.0100
400	4.20	0	.00	.00	0	.0000
400	3.70	0	$-.05$	.00	0	.0025
460	4.20	6	.00	.00	36	.0000
480	4.80	8	.06	.48	64	.0036
520	4.60	12	.04	.48	144	.0016
560	5.30	16	.11	1.76	256	.0121
4460	43.90	-34	$-.65$	14.68	1670	.1511

$$r^2 = \frac{[n\Sigma v_iw_i - \Sigma v_i\Sigma w_i]^2}{[n\Sigma v_i^2 - (\Sigma v_i)^2][n\Sigma w_i^2 - (\Sigma w_i)^2]}$$

$$= \frac{[12(14.68) - (-34)(-.65)]^2}{[12(1670) - (-34)^2][12(.1511) - (-.65)^2]}$$

$$= \frac{(176.16 - 22.10)^2}{(20,040 - 1156)(1.8132 - .4225)}$$

$$= \frac{(154.06)^2}{18,884 \times 1.3907} = \frac{23,734.48}{26,261.98}$$

$$\doteq .9038$$

If ρ equals 0, the sombrero will be perfectly round in horizontal cross section, but as ρ approaches 1, this cross section will become more and more elongated, as though the sombrero were being fitted to successively more narrow-skulled eggheads, with, however, the edges tapering off as do the tails of the normal curve. Figure 12–5 represents a bivariate normal distribution having $\rho = 0$.

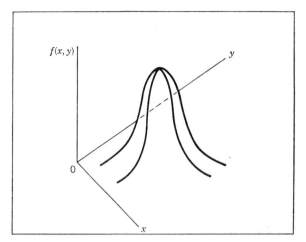

FIGURE 12–5.   Bivariate Normal Distribution, $\rho = 0$

ESTIMATION AND TESTS CONCERNING ρ

Now if we have drawn a random sample of elements from a bivariate normal population, without, of course, choosing the x values in advance, as in the case of linear regression, then both x and y are random variables, and we may take r as an estimator of ρ. It should be remembered that r is a biased estimator. That is, the mean of the r values over all possible samples of a given size will not equal ρ.

We may also test hypotheses concerning ρ, one of the most common being that $\rho = 0$, that is, the hypothesis that in the population there is no correlation between x and y. To make the test, we select a random sample, tabulate the x and y measurements and then compute a value of "t" as follows:

$$\text{``}t\text{''} = \frac{r - 0}{s_r} = \frac{r}{\sqrt{1 - r^2}/\sqrt{n - 2}}$$

which is distributed as Student's "t" distribution with $n - 2$ degrees of freedom. Of course,

$$s_r = \frac{\sqrt{1 - r^2}}{\sqrt{n - 2}}$$

Next we compare the computed value of "t" with the appropriate tabular value of "t" to indicate whether or not the hypothesis should be rejected.

We shall not give an example of this type of computation, for the assumption of a bivariate normal population is rarely satisfied in business and economic data.

CORRELATION IS NOT CAUSE

Now it is possible for us to find a very large value (nearly 1 or -1) for r and to reject the hypothesis that $\rho = 0$ at a significance level of perhaps .02 or less, even when the x and y variables have very little actual connection with each other. This fact serves to emphasize that r is a measure of *linear association* and not necessarily an indicator of anything else.

Although an absolute value of r close to 1 indicates that two variables are quite closely associated in a linear relationship, such a value is not sufficient to demonstrate a relationship of causality. Furthermore, even if there is a causal relationship, the value of r does not indicate the direction of causality, that is, x to y or y to x. We cannot say, for example, that higher prices of novels are caused by greater numbers of pages or vice versa, just because these two variables give rise to a correlation coefficient of, say, .90 or more. There *may* be a thread of causality in this particular case, for, all other factors remaining constant, a large book should cost more to produce than a small one, and cost is one of the important elements considered in setting the price. However, it is not uncommon for very close relationships to exist between two variables which actually have very little influence upon each other. Someone noticed in the years 1951, 1952, and 1953, for example, that when a certain New York baseball team was winning most of its games the stock market was high, but when the team hit a losing streak, the market went down. We would hardly expect a causal relationship here, unless, perhaps, betting losses were so severe among the team's fans that resulting forced sales of their securities caused the market to drop!

There is also reported to be a close direct relationship between frequency of laughter and social status. The more you laugh, the higher you are on the social scale (however this may be calibrated). Do people laugh their way up the social ladder, we might ask, or does an increasingly successful climb cause them to laugh more often at the less fortunate individuals struggling down below on the lower rungs?

Bankers have noticed that practically all embezzlements are carried out by employees who drink or gamble. It is tempting to jump to the conclusion that gambling and drinking cause embezzling, but it could possibly be the other way around, and, of course, embezzling, drinking, and gambling could, all three, be effects of some unknown common cause.

RANK CORRELATION

In economics and business we sometimes hear statements to the effect that "you get only what you pay for" or "the higher the price, the better the goods." Such statements imply that quality is directly proportional to price. We should like to be able to test such a hypothesis, but it is extremely difficult to measure this thing called "quality." However, it is possible to *rank* a sample of items according to judgments of quality and according to price and then compute a measure of association between the ranks. The highest-priced item will have a price rank of 1, the next highest priced a rank of 2, and so on.

It is possible to compute a coefficient of rank correlation by falling back upon the formula for r^2, with which we are already familiar.

To show how the computations are carried out, let us consider the following data, which represent price ranks and quality ranks as found on seventeen tank-type vacuum cleaners by a consumer testing bureau.

Cleaner	x_i (Quality rank)	y_i (Price rank)
A	1	8
B	2	2
C	3	11
D	4	12
E	5	4
F	6	3
G	7	16
H	8	5
I	9	7
J	10	10
K	11	13
L	12	9
M	13	1
N	14	14
O	15	15
P	16	6
Q	17	17

We see that the highest-priced cleaner ranked thirteenth in quality.

Table 12–5 shows the worksheet for getting the values to substitute in Equation 12–5 so as to find the coefficient of rank correlation. Let us denote this statistic by r_r.

TABLE 12–5

Computation of r_r

(Quality Ranks (x_i) and Price Ranks (y_i) of Seventeen Vacuum Cleaners)

x_i	y_i	$x_i y_i$	x_i^2	y_i^2
1	8	8	1	64
2	2	4	4	4
3	11	33	9	121
4	12	48	16	144
5	4	20	25	16
6	3	18	36	9
7	16	112	49	256
8	5	40	64	25
9	7	63	81	49
10	10	100	100	100
11	13	143	121	169
12	9	108	144	81
13	1	13	169	1
14	14	196	196	196
15	15	225	225	225
16	6	96	256	36
17	17	289	289	289
153	153	1516	1785	1785

$$r_r{}^2 = \frac{(n\Sigma x_i y_i - \Sigma x_i \Sigma y_i)^2}{[n\Sigma x_i^2 - (\Sigma x_i)^2][n\Sigma y_i^2 - (\Sigma y_i)^2]}$$

$$= \frac{[17(1516) - 153(153)]^2}{[17(1785) - 153^2]^2}$$

$$= \frac{(2363)^2}{(6936)^2} = \frac{5,583,769}{48,108,096}$$

$$= .116067$$

$$r_r = \sqrt{.116067} \doteq .34069$$

Although the vacuum cleaner data are hypothetical, they are quite similar to data which have, in the past, been found to exist in the case of many electrical appliances. Results shown in connection with Table 12–5 indicate that there is hardly anything in the way of a linear relationship between the price ranks and quality ranks. On the basis of such evidence, it would seem quite unwise to make any grandiose generalizations to the effect that quality is always directly related to price. Implicit in all of this, of course, is confidence in the findings of the consumer testing bureau.

We see from the data of Table 12–5 that $\Sigma x_i = \Sigma y_i$ and $\Sigma x_i^2 = \Sigma y_i^2$. These relationships suggest that a simplified formula for computing the coefficient of rank correlation could be developed. A bit of mathematics enables us to develop such a formula from the formula for r. The result is:

$$r_r = 1 - \frac{6\Sigma d_i^2}{n^3 - n} \qquad \text{(Eq. 12–6)}$$

where d_i represents the differences between the paired ranks, that is, $d_1 = (x_1 - y_1)$, $d_2 = (x_2 - y_2)$, and so on. This statistic is known as Spearman's coefficient of rank correlation. In Table 12–6 we have computed r_r by this simplified formula to verify the fact that it gives the same result as would have been found from the standard formula for r.

If the sample is large, then under the hypothesis that the rank correlation is 0 the sampling distribution of r_r will be nearly normal in form with mean 0 and standard error $1/\sqrt{n-1}$. Computed values of Z will thus be compared with critical values of ± 1.65 in testing hypotheses at the 10% level of significance. We need not assume in such cases that the x_i and y_i were drawn from a bivariate normal population or any other specific population distribution.

The simplified formula and the regular r formula will always yield identical results unless there are ties in ranks. But the discrepancy is slight if there are not too many ties. We handle ties by assigning each tied item a rank equal to the mean of the tied ranks. Suppose, for example, that in the case of the vacuum cleaners, two cleaners were tied for second place in quality. In the absence of the tie, they would have had ranks 2 and 3. Thus we assign each of them a rank of 2.5, that is, $\dfrac{2+3}{2}$. If three cleaners had been tied for second place, we would have assigned each of them the value 3, which is the mean of 2, 3, and 4. Handling ties in this fashion assures us that Σx_i will equal Σy_i, but does not assure us that Σy_i^2 will equal Σx_i^2.

Let us take one more example of the use of rank correlation. In seeking to show that there is little direct relationship between two

TABLE 12–6

**Use of Simplified Formula to
Compute r_r
(Quality Ranks (x_i) and Price
Ranks (y_i) of Seventeen
Vacuum Cleaners**

x_i	y_i	d_i	d_i^2
1	8	−7	49
2	2	0	0
3	11	−8	64
4	12	−8	64
5	4	1	1
6	3	3	9
7	16	−9	81
8	5	3	9
9	7	2	4
10	10	0	0
11	13	−2	4
12	9	3	9
13	1	12	144
14	14	0	0
15	15	0	0
16	6	10	100
17	17	0	0
153	153		538

$$r_r = 1 - \frac{6\Sigma d_i^2}{n^3 - n} = 1 - \frac{6(538)}{4913 - 17}$$

$$= 1 - \frac{3228}{4896} = 1 - .65931$$

$$= .34069$$

particular variables, Professor Sumner Slichter computed the co-efficient of rank correlation for a group of fifteen countries, the variables being per cent increase in consumer price index from 1948 to 1957 and per cent increase in real product per capita over the same period. The value of r_r turned out to be slightly more than 0.5 in this case.[1]

---

[1] U.S. Congress, Joint Economic Committee, *Employment, Growth, and Price Stability,* Hearings Pursuant to Sec. 5(a) of Public Law 304 (79th Congress), 86th Congress, 1st Session, Part 1, March 20, 23, 24, 25, 1959, p. 11.

NONLINEAR RELATIONSHIPS

Confining ourselves to the consideration of two variables, we may extend regression analysis to cover cases of nonlinear relationships, that is, situations where some sort of curve rather than a straight line indicates how x is associated with y. Such a curve may be parabolic, and in such circumstances, a least squares fit is fairly easily accomplished. But the fitting of the parabola and other, more difficult, types of curves is customarily reserved for more advanced courses. Measures of association analogous to the correlation coefficient may, of course, be computed, estimates constructed, and tests of hypotheses made.

MULTIPLE REGRESSION AND CORRELATION

Regardless of whether the relationship is linear or not, it is possible to extend regression analysis to cover cases where more than two variables are involved. Instead of looking upon values of y as being determined by values of x, we may think of y as depending upon two or more other variables. Going beyond three variables, we cannot give the usual spatial representation to the regression relationship. Thus we navigate in n-dimensional space by analogy to the two-dimensional and three-dimensional cases. Here again the techniques include the fitting of the regression equation and the computation of measures of association, together with the making of estimates and tests of hypotheses. Relationships between sets of more than two variables are most readily analyzed (as far as the labor of computation is concerned) if they are linear in form, the regression equation representing a plane in three-dimensional space and a hyperplane in n-dimensional space.

SUMMARY

We can sometimes acquire important information about populations by making observations on two characteristics of each selected element. If a relationship between the variables is discernible, a regression equation representing it may be fitted to the observations. Plotting the data on a scatter diagram aids us in determining the type of relationship. We have considered here only the case of linear relationships between two variables. Further, we have fitted the straight line by the method of least squares, which means we have selected that line for which the sum of squared deviations, $\Sigma(y_i - y')^2$, is a minimum.

The standard equation for a straight line may be written $y' = a + bx$, where a is the y' intercept and b is the slope of the line. The fitting process is accomplished by finding values of a and b that minimize the sum of the squared deviations. Two normal equations must be solved simultaneously in evaluating a and b. This procedure is facilitated if we make use of Cramer's rule, which gives directions for solving simultaneous linear equations by constructing ratios of determinants.

The least squares line has certain characteristics which are similar to those of the arithmetic mean. The sum of the deviations from the line, $\Sigma(y_i - y')$, equals zero. As we know, the sum of the *squared* deviations is a minimum. Finally, the line passes through $\bar{x}$, $\bar{y}$, the mean of the system.

The fitted line is an estimate of the true regression line, $Y = \alpha + \beta X$.

In linear regression analysis, it is very important to be aware of the basic assumptions involved: (1) the x_i values are chosen in advance, that is, they are treated as parameters; (2) for each selected x_i value, one or more y_i values are taken at random; (3) the populations of y_i values associated with each of the x_i values are assumed to be normally distributed with equal variances.

The mean y_i value for a given x_i value may be estimated and a confidence interval constructed according to the following formula:

$$y' \pm \text{``}t\text{''} \cdot s_E \sqrt{\frac{1}{n} + \frac{(x_c - \bar{x})^2}{\Sigma(x_i - \bar{x})^2}} \qquad \text{(Eq. 12–3)}$$

Hypotheses concerning α and β may be tested, one of the most common ones being the hypothesis that β is equal to zero. In making this test we utilize the fact that $\dfrac{b - 0}{s_b}$ is distributed as Student's "t" distribution with $n - 2$ degrees of freedom.

In order to measure the "strength" of the linear relationship, or the degree of association between the two variables, we compute r or r^2, the former being known as the Pearsonian coefficient of correlation. Perhaps r^2 is the more useful from the standpoint of interpretation, for it may be looked upon as the proportion of total squared error that is accounted for by the linear relationship or that is "due to" regression.

$$r^2 = \frac{\Sigma(y' - \bar{y})^2}{\Sigma(y_i - \bar{y})^2}$$

For purposes of computation, we find it convenient to use the following formula:

$$r^2 = \frac{(n\Sigma x_i y_i - \Sigma x_i \Sigma y_i)^2}{[n\Sigma x_i^2 - (\Sigma x_i)^2][n\Sigma y_i^2 - (\Sigma y_i)^2]} \qquad \text{(Eq. 12–5)}$$

The two formulas for r^2 may be shown, by algebra, to be equivalent.

We may code the data prior to computing r, to reduce the labor involved. Adding a constant to each observation, dividing by a constant, or a combination of these operations has no effect upon the value of r^2. The constants need not have the same value for both variables.

In taking r as an estimator of the parameter ρ, we must assume that our observations are made on a sample selected from a bivariate normal population, an assumption that is not often satisfied in the case of business or economic data.

It is possible to find close linear relationships between pairs of observations which have no connection with each other except that they happen to coincide in time or space. The value of r in such cases may be nearly 1 or -1. This situation serves to point up the important fact that r (and r^2) are measures of association only and do not necessarily indicate a relationship of causality.

In cases where variables are difficult to measure but can be ranked, we may, in the case of two variables, find an indication of the degree of linear association between the ranks by computing r_r, which is known as Spearman's coefficient of rank correlation and which may be readily computed from the following formula:

$$r_r = 1 - \frac{6\Sigma d_i^2}{n^3 - n} \qquad \text{(Eq. 12–6)}$$

Regardless of the population distributions of x_i and y_i, if the samples are large, then under the hypothesis that its true value is 0, r_r will be approximately normally distributed with mean 0 and standard error $1/\sqrt{n - 1}$.

Going beyond the one-semester course in elementary statistics, we may expect to find techniques for analyzing nonlinear relationships and relationships (linear and nonlinear) involving more than two variables. The latter are often given the designation *multiple regression and correlation*.

TERMS TO PONDER

1. Linear Relationship
2. Scatter Diagram
3. Least Squares Criterion
4. Normal Equations
5. Cramer's Rule
6. Standard Error of Estimate
7. Coefficient of Correlation
8. Covariance
9. Bivariate Normal Population
10. Rank Correlation

EXERCISES

1. Data on national income and personal consumption expenditures for the United States are given below:

Year	National income (billions of dollars)	Consumption expenditures (billions of dollars)
1949	218	181
1950	242	195
1951	279	210
1952	292	220
1953	306	233
1954	302	238
1955	330	257
1956	349	269
1957	364	284
1958	361	291

Source: U.S. Congress, Joint Committee on the Economic Report, *Economic Indicators* (Washington, D.C., U.S. Government Printing Office, June, 1959), pp. 2, 3. Figures rounded.

a. Plot these data on a scatter diagram with national income measured on the horizontal axis and consumption expenditures along the vertical axis.

b. Fit a straight line to the data by the method of least squares.

c. Do you think that these data satisfy the assumptions of linear regression analysis? Why or why not?

2. Twenty-four employees of the Random Corporation are ranked according to salary and intelligence (IQ score) as shown below:

Employee	Salary rank	Intelligence rank	Employee	Salary rank	Intelligence rank
A	1	8	M	13	16
B	2	21	N	14	5
C	3	6	O	15	9
D	4	17	P	16	7
E	5	15	Q	17	13
F	6	2	R	18	22
G	7	24	S	19	20
H	8	18	T	20	11
I	9	12	U	21	19
J	10	3	V	22	14
K	11	4	W	23	1
L	12	10	X	24	23

a. Compute the coefficient of rank correlation (r_r) for the given data.

b. Assuming that n is large enough for r_r to be normally distributed, test the hypothesis that the true value of r_r is zero. Use a 10% level of significance.

3. The following data were collected by an imaginary spark plug manufacturing company for the purpose of constructing a break-even chart on an average cost basis:

x_i (production of spark plugs: thousands per month)	y_i (mean cost of production: cents)
26.0	2.4
25.1	6.3
20.0	9.8
21.2	16.0
26.0	19.0
16.3	22.0
17.0	28.0
9.8	34.1
11.2	33.0
10.0	44.2
6.5	47.0
5.0	50.0

a. Plot these data on a scatter diagram.

b. Fit a straight line of least squares to the observations.

c. Compute a point estimate of the mean cost of producing 30,000 spark plugs per month. Estimate the total cost of producing the 30,000 spark plugs.

d. If average gross *revenue* is 32 cents per plug at an output of 30,000 plugs, use your estimate in c to estimate net profit at this level of output.

e. Do you think that these data conform to the assumptions of linear regression analysis? Why or why not?

4. It is said that there is a positive correlation between intelligence and susceptibility to arthritis. In other words, the higher the IQ, the greater the chance of developing arthritis. Suppose that you are able to quantify both variables and demonstrate that there is a close linear relationship between them. Would you say that there was a causal relationship here? If not, how would you explain the relationship?

5. The following observations refer to a sample of motor trucks. The x_i values are miles traveled and the y_i values are maintenance expenditures. For each of the selected x_i values, a y_i value was chosen at random.

x_i (thousands of miles)	y_i (hundreds of dollars)
5	1.0
10	1.5
12	2.0
22	3.2
35	8.4
40	7.5
50	8.0
58	13.0
60	14.5
64	12.2

a. Plot the data on a scatter diagram.

b. Fit a straight line of least squares to the observations.

c. Draw the fitted line on the scatter diagram.

d. Using the regression equation found in b, estimate mean maintenance expenditures for trucks that have traveled 50,000 miles.

e. Find 95% confidence limits for the estimate found in d.

f. Compute r, the Pearsonian coefficient of correlation, for the data given.

g. Compute r^2 and give a meaningful interpretation of this statistic in terms of the least squares regression line.

SELECTED REFERENCES

EZEKIEL, Mordecai, and FOX, Karl, *Methods of Correlation and Regression Analysis,* 3d ed. (New York, John Wiley and Sons, Inc., 1959), Ch. V.

MCCARTHY, Philip J., *Introduction to Statistical Reasoning* (New York, McGraw-Hill Book Co., Inc., 1957), Ch. XII.

SPROWLS, R. Clay, *Elementary Statistics* (New York, McGraw-Hill Book Co., Inc., 1955), Ch. X.

13

INDEX NUMBERS

===

IN BUSINESS AND ECONOMICS, an index number is usually nothing more than a ratio or an average of several ratios; it is used to show a comparison over time. Essentially, two time periods are involved; one of these is called the base period and the other is called the given period. A number referring to the base period serves as the basis of comparison and appears in the denominator of the ratio(s), while a number referring to the given period appears in the numerator of the ratio(s). It is important to remember that index numbers are statistical estimates constructed from data, which, more often than not, constitute judgment samples.

EXAMPLE OF AN ELEMENTARY INDEX NUMBER

Business expenditures for new plant and equipment during each of several years are given below: [1]

Year	Expenditures (billions of dollars)
1953	28.3
1954	26.8
1955	28.7
1956	34.9

Now suppose we wish to convert each of these figures to an index with 1954 serving as the base year. We merely divide each

---

[1] U.S. Bureau of the Census, *Statistical Abstract of the United States, 1956* (Washington, D.C., U.S. Government Printing Office, 1956), Table No. 596, p. 498. Figures rounded.

of the figures by the 1954 figure and express the result as a percentage. It is a fundamental convention that all index numbers be expressed as percentages, although the per cent sign does not appear. We indicate that the 1954 figure is serving as the basis of comparison in each index by writing the notation (1954 = 100). The indexes of new plant and equipment expenditure appear as follows:

Expenditures for New Plant and Equipment

Year	*Index* *(1954 = 100)*
1953	106
1954	100
1955	107
1956	130

This particular index is merely a form of simple ratio, such as we studied in Chapter 2. It is also, as we shall see later, a form of *value* index. Again, the index for each year shows a comparison involving two time periods, the given year and 1954, the base year.

Fundamental to the study of index numbers are *price* indexes, which, in general, show how given period prices of certain goods compare with base period prices of these same items. After learning the basic forms of price indexes, we can easily make transitions to other important types of indexes, namely, quantity indexes and value indexes.

PRICE INDEXES

There are five basic types of price indexes. They divide into two classes, simple indexes and weighted indexes. The simple indexes are important as an aid in explaining the idea of a price index and introducing the symbols used in the formulas, but beyond these textbook uses, they have no important applications. The five types of price indexes may be listed as follows:

1. Simple aggregative index ⎫
2. Simple mean of price relatives ⎬ Simple indexes
3. Weighted aggregative indexes ⎫
   a. Laspeyres
   b. Paasche ⎬ Weighted indexes
4. Fisher's ideal index
5. Weighted mean of price relatives ⎭

From the standpoint of practical applications, the weighted indexes are of most importance. A form of Fisher's ideal index (number 4 in the list) is used in the field of international trade, but other than that it is not widely used, largely because some of the necessary data cannot readily be acquired in each given period.

COMPUTATION OF THE VARIOUS PRICE INDEXES

Let us imagine a sample of food items for which we have found prices and quantities in two years, 1956 and 1947. We shall use these data to construct price indexes of the various types we have designated. The given year will be 1956 and the base year 1947. Let the data be as follows:

TABLE 13–1

Data for Computing Price Indexes

Item	p_n (average price, 1956)	p_o (average price, 1947)	q_n (quantity, 1956)	q_o (quantity, 1947)	Price relatives (p_n/p_o)
Bread, lb.	.16	.12	15	10	1.33
Meat, lb.	.60	.80	8	20	.75
Cheese, lb.	.50	.30	2	3	1.67
	1.26	1.22			3.75

In constructing price indexes, the U.S. Bureau of Labor Statistics usually uses hundreds of items. We will use this very small sample so that the student can readily follow the computations.

The prices are given in dollars per unit. For each item in the example, the unit is one pound. Quantities are given in billions of units sold during the specified periods. Quantities do not enter into the computation of the simple indexes, but they become important in the case of the weighted indexes.

For purposes of writing index number formulas, we use the symbol p to represent a price and the symbol q to represent a quantity. Subscripts tell us the period (base or given) to which the prices and quantities refer, the subscript o denoting the base period, and the subscript n denoting the given period. Thus p_o is the price in the base period of an item and q_n is the quantity of some item in the given period.

SIMPLE AGGREGATIVE PRICE INDEX

To compute a simple aggregative price index, we merely divide the sum of given year prices by the sum of base year prices. The quotient is, of course, expressed as a percentage. Using the symbol I_p to indicate a price index, the appropriate formula and the substitution are as follows:

$$I_p = \frac{\Sigma p_n}{\Sigma p_o} \times 100 = \frac{1.26}{1.22} \times 100 = 103$$

In this formula, the subscripts n and o are not, of course, a part of the summation notation. They are fixed subscripts which do not take on varying numerical values. The subscript i is omitted in index number summations to keep the notation from becoming unduly cumbersome.

SIMPLE MEAN OF PRICE RELATIVES

In order to compute the simple mean of price relatives, we must first find the price relative of each item in the list. The price relative of an item is the ratio of its given year price to its base year price. In symbols, the price relative is given by p_n/p_o. Taking the mean of such ratios, we have the second of the simple price indexes:

$$I_p = \frac{\Sigma \dfrac{p_n}{p_o}}{k} \times 100 \text{ (where } k \text{ is the number of items)}$$

$$= \frac{3.75}{3} \times 100 = 125$$

The two indexes we have just computed have one important characteristic in common: they both give equal weight to each price (or price relative) entering into the computation. As a matter of experience, we know that all prices are *not* of the same importance to the purchaser. The weighted index numbers seek to give expression to these varying degrees of importance so as to reflect more accurately the real life situation. In the case of food, the prices of bread, milk, meat, and potatoes are, we would guess, more important for most buyers than the prices of other food items.

In order to compute the weighted aggregative indexes, we must add several columns to our table of data. These columns are as follows:

Item	$p_n q_o$	$p_o q_o$	$p_n q_n$	$p_o q_n$
Bread	1.60	1.20	2.40	1.80
Meat	12.00	16.00	4.80	6.40
Cheese	1.50	.90	1.00	.60
	15.10	18.10	8.20	8.80

WEIGHTED AGGREGATIVE PRICE INDEX (LASPEYRES FORM)

For purposes of discussing the two types of weighted aggregative index, let us call the list of items stated in base period quantities the "base list"; similarly, let us call the list of items stated in given period quantities the "given list." Now to compute the Laspeyres (or base-weighted) aggregative index, we first compute two summations, (1) the base list priced at given year prices ($\Sigma p_n q_o$), and (2) the base list priced at base period prices ($\Sigma p_o q_o$). We divide (1) by (2) and express the result as a percentage to get the index. For the data we are using, we have:

$$I_p = \frac{\Sigma p_n q_o}{\Sigma p_o q_o} \times 100 = \frac{15.10}{18.10} \times 100 = 83.4$$

Although the simple indexes showed price increases, this index (being less than 1) shows a price decrease. This Laspeyres index tells us that on the average the base list would cost, in 1956, 83.4% as much as it would in 1947.

The Laspeyres form of the weighted aggregative index is the basic theoretical model for several price indexes published by the U.S. Department of Labor, although equivalent weighted means of price relatives are usually used for purposes of actual computation.

WEIGHTED AGGREGATIVE PRICE INDEX (PAASCHE FORM)

To get the Paasche form of the weighted aggregative index, we again compute two summations: (1) the given period list priced at given period prices ($\Sigma p_n q_n$), and (2) the given period list priced at base period prices ($\Sigma p_o q_n$). For the illustrative data, we have:

$$I_p = \frac{\Sigma p_n q_n}{\Sigma p_o q_n} \times 100 = \frac{8.20}{8.80} \times 100 = 93.2$$

This result tells us that on the average the *given period list* would cost 93.2% as much in the given period as it would in the base period.

FISHER'S IDEAL INDEX

Although the formula for Fisher's ideal index sometimes appears to be quite frightening to the beginning student, it is rather simple and easy to remember if one has mastered the weighted aggregative indexes. (At this point, we may forget the formulas for the simple indexes without suffering any great loss.) Fisher's index is simply the geometric mean of the two weighted aggregative indexes. To get it, then, we multiply the Laspeyres form by the Paasche form and take the square root of this product. Briefly, we have:

$$\text{Fisher's index} = \sqrt{\text{Laspeyres} \times \text{Paasche}} \times 100$$

Taking the trouble to write out the formula in terms of p's and q's, we have:

$$\text{Fisher's index} = \sqrt{\frac{\Sigma p_n q_o}{\Sigma p_o q_o} \times \frac{\Sigma p_n q_n}{\Sigma p_o q_n}} \times 100$$

This index is named for the late Dr. Irving Fisher, who was a professor of economics at Yale University some years ago. He is not to be confused with Sir Ronald A. Fisher of Cambridge University, England, who is the most noted statistician in the world today.

For the illustrative data we have been using, Fisher's index is easily computed by taking $\sqrt{.834 \times .932} \times 100 \doteq 88.2$. We shall see later that Fisher's index is "ideal" in the sense that it satisfies certain logical criteria of a good index number. No other index will satisfy all of these criteria. However, Fisher's index is almost always difficult to apply because of practical considerations.

WEIGHTED MEAN OF PRICE RELATIVES

Before we can compute the weighted mean of price relatives, we must have a set of weights, one weight for each item in the list. In constructing an index of food prices, we might interview a sample of housewives and ask them to assign point values from 1 to 10 to each item in the index number list, the most important items receiving the highest scores and the least important the lowest scores. From a tabulation of the results, we could draw up a set of weights, perhaps using the median point score for each item as its weight. In our illustrative data, suppose we apply an arbitrary weight of 8 to bread, 7 to meat, and 5 to cheese. Each of the price relatives must be multiplied by its appropriate weight as shown in the following columns:

Item	Price relative $\dfrac{p_n}{p_o}$	Weight (w)	Weighted relative $\dfrac{p_n}{p_o} w$
Bread	1.33	8	10.64
Meat	.75	7	5.25
Cheese	1.67	5	8.35
		20	24.24

We may write the formula and show the computation of the index as follows:

$$I_p = \frac{\Sigma \left(\dfrac{p_n}{p_o} w \right)}{\Sigma w} \times 100 = \frac{24.24}{20} \times 100 = 121.2$$

Weights are usually formulated in a manner different from that described. For example, if we decide that the appropriate weight to apply to each item is the dollar volume spent on that item in the base period, we have $w = p_o q_o$. Now, when—and only when—we define w in this fashion, the weighted mean of price relatives is exactly equal to the Laspeyres index. All we need do is substitute $p_o q_o$ for w in the formula of the former index to show that the equivalence holds.

We begin with:

$$I_p = \frac{\Sigma \left(\dfrac{p_n}{p_o} w \right)}{\Sigma w} \times 100 \qquad (1)$$

If $w = p_o q_o$, we have:

$$I_p = \frac{\Sigma \left(\frac{p_n}{p_o} p_o q_o \right)}{\Sigma p_o q_o} \times 100 \tag{2}$$

$$= \frac{\Sigma p_n q_o}{\Sigma p_o q_o} \times 100 \tag{3}$$

In the summation that forms the numerator of (2), each and every term contains two p_o values that cancel each other. Thus the numerator becomes $\Sigma p_n q_o$.

Note that formula (2) is equal to $\Sigma \left(\frac{p_n}{p_o} \cdot \frac{p_o q_o}{\Sigma p_o q_o} \right) \times 100$. This formula clearly shows that we can compute price relatives and their *proportionate* weights separately. This is the procedure actually followed in the construction of the Consumer Price Index.

When the weights w are set equal to $p_o q_o$, they are called *value weights* of the base period.

QUANTITY INDEXES

For each and every type of price index there is a corresponding quantity index. The weighted price indexes we have computed (with the exception of Fisher's index) show the relative change in prices under the assumption that the quantities of items (or weights) remain the same. The corresponding quantity indexes show relative changes in quantities under the assumption that prices remain the same. A simple rule tells how to get from a given price index to the corresponding quantity index: *In the price index formula, change the p's to q's and the q's to p's but do not alter the n's and o's.*

Taking the Laspeyres index as an example, we begin with $I_p = \frac{\Sigma p_n q_o}{\Sigma p_o q_o} \times 100$. Making the changes specified in the rule, we arrive at $I_q = \frac{\Sigma q_n p_o}{\Sigma q_o p_o} \times 100$. Of course, $q_o p_o$ is equal to $p_o q_o$, so the denominator is the same for both the Laspeyres price index and its quantity index. We shall use I_q as a general symbol for a quantity index.

Perhaps the most widely known quantity index is the Federal Reserve Board Index of Industrial Production. This index shows changes in the physical quantities of output of mining, manufacturing, and utility industries. This index is computed separately on two bases: 1947–49 and 1957.

THE VALUE INDEX

We shall define the value index I_v as the ratio of two sums: (1) the given period list priced in the given period, and (2) the base period list priced in the base period. The second sum is the denominator of the ratio. The formula is $I_v = \frac{\Sigma p_n q_n}{\Sigma p_o q_o} \times 100$. The name of the index obviously comes from the fact that price times quantity equals value. It is the basic model for the indexes of department store sales computed for each Federal Reserve district by the Board of Governors of the Federal Reserve System. The base period for these indexes is 1947–49.

LOGICAL CRITERIA OF A GOOD INDEX NUMBER

Having discussed quantity indexes and the value index, we are in a position to understand certain logical criteria which have been devised for deciding which index is the "ideal" index. We shall discuss only two of these criteria. The first is called the *factor reversal test*: The product of a price index and its corresponding quantity index should be equal to the value index. Fisher's index will pass this test. None of the other indexes we have discussed will do so. By writing the formulas for the Laspeyres index and its quantity index, the reader can readily show that the product of the two does *not* equal the value index.

The second criterion is the *time reversal test*: An interchange of the base period and the given period should yield the reciprocal of the index. Starting with the formula for a price index, we interchange the two periods by changing n's to o's and o's to n's. Again taking the Laspeyres index, $\frac{\Sigma p_n q_o}{\Sigma p_o q_o} \times 100$, we interchange the two time periods to get $\frac{\Sigma p_o q_n}{\Sigma p_n q_n} \times 100$. This result is *not* equal to the Laspeyres index turned upside down, that is, $\frac{\Sigma p_o q_o}{\Sigma p_n q_0} \times 100$. Thus, the Laspeyres index does not pass this test. Fisher's ideal index will, however.

Although Fisher's ideal index would, in view of these logical criteria, appear to be the best index of all, it is not widely used in practice. One of the reasons for this we have mentioned already: the index requires a new list of given period quantities each time it is computed. In addition, the ideal index may not give the type of comparison that we wish to show. The Laspeyres price index isolates the price change completely because the quantities are held constant. Fisher's index does not do this because two sets of quantities are involved in its computation and given period quantities change for each new computation of the index. We would find that most of the important price and quantity indexes computed today are variations of the Laspeyres index or the weighted mean of price relatives.

THE REPRESENTATIVE PERIOD

So far in discussing index numbers, we have considered only two time periods, the base period and the given period, for these are the only ones provided for in the basic index number models. However, in practice, we often find it desirable to introduce a third time period, which we shall call the "representative period." This period is usually one in which data on weights or quantities of items are collected. Suppose, for example, that we are computing a weighted aggregative price index of the Laspeyres form for consumer goods. Suppose further that the given period is 1956 and the base period is 1947. The basic model formula for the index is $I_p = \dfrac{\Sigma p_n q_o}{\Sigma p_o q_o} \times 100$.

Now, q_o represents the quantity of an item purchased in the base period, 1947. If, however, quantities of items purchased in the base period were widely different from more recent quantities, particularly those of the given period, then our index number would not give an accurate reflection of price changes for the current pattern of consumer purchases. If automatic washing machines, television sets, and hi-fi record players were purchased only in small quantities, during 1947 but in very large quantities during 1956, for example then it would be advisable to choose a representative period in which quantities of these items were more nearly like the 1956 quantities. Let us choose 1952 as our representative period. Then in computing our index, we would utilize quantities of items sold in 1952 and find the average prices of these items in the base period (1947) as well as in 1956. The formula for the index number would then be altered to appear as:

$$I_p = \frac{\Sigma p_n q_r}{\Sigma p_o q_r} \times 100$$

where r indicates the representative period. Thus this index compares the *representative list* at given period prices with the representative list at base period prices.

In constructing a particular index number, figures indicating a specific period are sometimes used as subscripts in the formula. For the example under discussion, we may write:

$$I_p = \frac{\Sigma p_{56} q_{52}}{\Sigma p_{47} q_{52}} \times 100$$

CHAIN INDEXES

To introduce the idea of a chain index, suppose we utilize the modified Laspeyres price index formula letting 1947 be the base period and 1952 the representative period. If we begin with the index for 1948 on base 1947, multiply it by the index for 1949 on base 1948 and then multiply that product by the index for 1950 on base 1949, we end up with the index for 1950 on the 1947 base. In this sequence, the given period of any index becomes the base period for the succeeding index. We may show in symbols how the successive indexes were linked together:

$$\frac{\Sigma p_{48} q_{52}}{\Sigma p_{47} q_{52}} \times \frac{\Sigma p_{49} q_{52}}{\Sigma p_{48} q_{52}} \times \frac{\Sigma p_{50} q_{52}}{\Sigma p_{49} q_{52}}$$

The reader will notice that, as we have said, the numerator of each index cancels with the denominator of the succeeding index, the final result being $\dfrac{\Sigma p_{50} q_{52}}{\Sigma p_{47} q_{52}}$, the index for 1950 on base 1952.

The chain may, of course, have any number of links. By using the device, we may compute a current index by linking it to the index of the period immediately preceding. Successive computations of the Consumer Price Index are combined in this fashion, the formula being:

$$I = I_{n-1} \times \Sigma \left(\frac{p_n}{p_{n-1}} \cdot \frac{p_{n-1} q_{52}}{\Sigma p_{n-1} q_{52}} \right) \times 100 = \frac{\Sigma p_n q_{52}}{\Sigma p_{47-49} q_{52}} \times 100$$

where the subscript $(n - 1)$ denotes the period immediately prior to the given period.

PURCHASING POWER OF THE DOLLAR

As prices go up, the purchasing power of the dollar goes down. In recent times, the reader may have heard such statements as "The dollar nowadays is worth only 80 cents." The statement is incomplete. What it means is that a dollar (spent on certain goods) nowadays will buy only 80% as much as it would in some base period. Taking the base period dollar as 100 cents, then, the current dollar is worth only 80 cents.

Since a price index represents the level of prices, a reciprocal relationship exists between the price index and the purchasing power of the dollar. To get the purchasing power of the dollar corresponding to a given price index, then, we first change the index to ordinary decimal form and then take its reciprocal. The result is in terms of dollars. For example, the Consumer Price Index (1947–49 = 100) in April, 1960, was 126.2. Changing this to a decimal and taking its reciprocal, we have $1/1.262 = \$.792$ or 79.2 cents. Thus the consumers' dollar in April, 1960, was worth 79.2 cents and would, on the average, buy 79.2% as much as it would in the base period (1947–49).

In the above example, we were talking about the *consumers' dollar,* that is, the purchasing power figure applied to dollars spent on consumers' goods. If we used the wholesale price index to compute the purchasing power of the dollar, our result would be in terms of the *wholesale commodities dollar.* That is, the purchasing power figure would apply to dollars spent on commodities in primary markets.

In addition to the comprehensive Consumer Price Index, separate indexes are computed (by the Bureau of Labor Statistics) for various classes of items entering into the construction of this index. There is an index of food prices, an index of apparel prices, an index of transportation prices, and so on. Thus we can compute the purchasing power of the consumers' food dollar, his apparel or clothing dollar, and so on.

Items entering into the construction of the Wholesale Price Index are also divided into classes, with separate indexes being computed for each class. To list just a few of the categories, we have farm products, processed foods, textile products and apparel, lumber and wood products, and metals and metal products.

ADJUSTMENT OF CURRENT DOLLAR DATA FOR PRICE CHANGES

Money measurements expressed in terms of the price level obtaining at the time of measurement are called "current dollar data." Often such measurements form a time series, such as the Disposable Income figures shown below: [2]

Year	Disposable Income (billions of dollars)
1952	237.4
1953	250.2
1954	254.5
1955	270.2
1956	287.2

Now these figures are increasing over time, but we know that not all of the increase from year to year necessarily represents increased buying power; part or all of the increase may be due to price rises. In order to compare these different income figures in terms of the goods and services each would buy, we must express them in "constant dollars."

Since disposable income is either spent on consumer goods or saved, the purchasing power of the consumers' dollar would be the appropriate statistic to use in adjusting our data. We will need a purchasing power figure for each of the years in the time series. The purchasing power of the consumers' dollar in 1952 (1947–49 = 100) was $.881 or 88.1 cents. Each 1952 dollar will only buy 88.1% as much as a base period dollar. Thus to express the 1952 disposable income figure in terms of what it would buy in the base period, we must multiply it by .881. Similarly, the 1953 income figure (250.2) must be multiplied by .874 to put it in terms of base period dollars. Carrying out like operations on the remaining disposable income figures, we have Table 13–2, the adjusted figures appearing in column (4).

The adjusted income figures are said to be in "real" terms, in terms of constant dollars, or in terms of constant prices.

Since the purchasing power figures (column (3)) are reciprocals of price indexes, we may adjust the data directly by dividing each income figure by the appropriate index number. The index

[2] *Federal Reserve Bulletin* (Washington, D.C., Board of Governors of the FRS, August, 1957), p. 972.

TABLE 13-2

Adjusting Disposable Income Figures for Price Changes

Year	Disposable Income (billions of dollars)	Purchasing power of consumers' dollar (1947–49 = 100)	Adjusted Disposable Income
(1)	(2)	(3)	(4)
1952	237.4	.8811	209.2
1953	250.2	.8741	218.7
1954	254.5	.8711	221.7
1955	270.2	.8734	236.0
1956	287.2	.8606	247.3

number must be changed to decimal form before dividing. For 1952, we have 237.4/1.135 = 209.2 or 209. This procedure eliminates the intermediate step of computing the purchasing power figure.

Due, perhaps, to the fact that most prices have been steadily rising since World War II, the process of adjustment for price changes is nowadays often called "deflating." The Department of Commerce computes a standard "deflator" for adjusting the Gross National Product, this statistic being a special type of price index.

SHIFTING THE BASE OF AN INDEX NUMBER

The Consumer Price Indexes used to compute the purchasing power figures appearing in column (3) of Table 13–2 are as follows:

Year	Consumer Price Index [3] (1947–49 = 100)
1952	113.5
1953	114.4
1954	114.8
1955	114.5
1956	116.2

Each of these indexes is, of course, on the 1947–49 base. Now suppose we wished to convert all of them to the base year 1954. The hard way of accomplishing the task would be to recompute the indexes from the original data with 1954 as the base year. The

[3] *Ibid.*, p. 970.

easy way would be to divide each of the indexes by the 1954 index and express the results as percentages. In a similar manner, any other year in the list could be made to serve as a new base. The original indexes with the base shifted to 1954 and to 1956 are shown in Table 13–3.

TABLE 13–3

Shifting the Base of an Index Number

Year	Consumer Price Index (1947–49 = 100)	Base shifted to 1954	Base shifted to 1956
(1)	(2)	(3)	(4)
1952	113.5	98.9	97.7
1953	114.4	99.7	98.5
1954	114.8	100.0	98.8
1955	114.5	99.7	98.5
1956	116.2	101.2	100.0

In the case of the Consumer Price Index formula, which embodies a representative period, the values of the index on the new bases would be equivalent to the values that would result if the index were completely reconstructed on the new bases. For example in shifting the base of the 1953 index to 1954, we divide by inverting the 1954 index and multiplying the 1953 index by it:

$$\frac{\Sigma p_{53}q_{52}}{\Sigma p_{47-49}q_{52}} \times \frac{\Sigma p_{47-49}q_{52}}{\Sigma p_{54}q_{52}} = \frac{\Sigma p_{53}q_{52}}{\Sigma p_{54}q_{52}}$$

Other index number formulas may not behave in this fashion when the base period is shifted. By shifting the base of the Consumer Price Index, we could express the disposable income figures of Table 13–2 in 1952 dollars, 1953 dollars, and so on, up to 1956 dollars.

PRICE INDEXES: GENERAL PROBLEMS OF CONSTRUCTION

A fundamental problem in the construction of any index number is the specification or definition of important terms and concepts. The sector of the economy covered by the index must be clearly delineated. The Consumer Price Index covers only prices of goods bought by families of city wage earners and clerical workers; other indexes may cover only wholesale prices or prices of stocks traded on the New York Stock Exchange. The type of outlet (chain, mail-order house, and so on) at which prices are collected must be clearly set forth. The goods and services that are to be priced must be specified precisely (as to grade, quality, and quantity) so that price changes from one given period to another will be reflected accurately.

Problems of definition merge with problems of sampling. We must decide whether to use probability samples or judgment samples. The design (including size) of the sample must be determined. Not only must we determine the places in which data are to be collected; we must also decide on the number of prices to be taken for each item, and the times (for example, days of the week) at which the prices are to be collected. The manner of collecting information (whether by direct interview or by mail) is another problem of sampling.

We may, of course, choose to let the representative period be identical with the base period. But in most cases we will want to select a separate representative period for determining the quantities purchased or weights for the index. This period must not be too remote from the given period, for it should reflect current patterns of purchases as to types and qualities of goods. For example, 1935 would not be an acceptable representative period for the current Consumer Price Index, for television sets and frozen foods would not be important consumer items in that year. Representative periods must be changed from time to time so as to reflect changes in buying patterns arising out of product and service innovation and altered consumer tastes.

Finally, the base period must be selected with care. This period should be one in which prices are neither extremely high nor extremely low relative to the levels of the given period. Obviously, prices at a peak or a trough of the business cycle should be avoided. An average of prices over several years is often thought to give a satisfactory base. We have already seen that the 3-year period, 1947–49, serves as the base of several important indexes. The base period must not be too remote from the representative period, for the representative list must, of course, be priced at base period prices.

PRICE INDEXES: PROBLEMS OF USE AND INTERPRETATION

In interpreting price index numbers, the most important single fact to bear in mind is that the index is an *estimate* of the *general level* of a *certain class* of prices. Between two successive given periods, some individual prices within the class may rise, while others may decline. Taking weights into account, if the total decline is more than enough to offset the influence of the rise, the index will decrease. If the two influences are equal, the index will not change. If price declines are not sufficient to offset price rises, the index will increase. If the index stands at 115.0, it means that prices in the given period are, on the average, 15% above base period prices. Or, since our money units are on the metric system, we may say that it now (in the given period) takes $1.15 to buy the same things that could have been bought for $1.00 in the base period.

We should not assume that there is a necessary connection between the class of prices covered by an index and the prices outside that class. The Consumer Price Index, which reflects price changes in the items bought by city wage-earner and clerical-worker families, may not be strictly applicable to prices of items bought by farmers, doctors, dentists, movie stars, or bank presidents.

It is very important to remember that whenever we state the value of an index number or the purchasing power of the dollar we should, in addition to mentioning the class of prices referred to, mention the relevant base period. A recent publication of an economic interest group contained the statement that the dollar currently is worth only about 50 cents. This statement, as it stands, is meaningless, for there is no mention of the types of goods the dollar is to be spent on and the relevant base period is not stated. Propagandists can minimize a price rise or sometimes even change a rise to a decline by an unannounced shift of the base period. By the same device, a moderate rise may be converted to a precipitous one.

Although we try to specify as closely as possible the quality and quantity of items that are to be priced in constructing an index, implicit price changes do occur. These changes are not measured by the index. If a seller maintains his price but deteriorates product quality or gives short measure, an implicit price rise occurs. If a packer of frozen foods, for example, puts 12 ounces of peas in a 35-cent package labeled "14 ounces," a price rise has occurred. Also, in periods of national emergency when prices are controlled, implicit price rises often take place. On the other hand, if product quality is improved while the price remains constant, there is an implicit price decline. Implicit price declines may occur in markets characterized by vigorous nonprice competition.

SOME SPECIFIC INDEXES IMPORTANT IN BUSINESS AND ECONOMICS

1. The Consumer Price Index. This index, as we already know, covers prices of goods and services purchased by families of urban wage earners and clerical workers. In constructing the index, the Bureau of Labor Statistics prices about 300 items in 46 different cities throughout the country. From the population of all urban places having 2500 or more inhabitants in 1950, a probability sample of 97 cities was selected for purposes of ascertaining quantities and qualities of goods and services bought. Then a probability sub-sample of 46 cities was selected from the 97 cities for purposes of pricing the goods and services in the index number list. Probability sampling methods were also used to select the places in each of the 46 cities at which food prices and the places at which rents are collected. Other prices are collected on the basis of judgment samples. The index is computed and published monthly. The base period is 1947–49 and the representative period is the year ending June 30, 1952. The basic formula for computation is the weighted mean of price relatives with value weights.

We noted previously (p. 270) that separate indexes are computed for the various classes of goods and services covered by the Consumer Price Index. In addition, separate indexes of all items are computed and published for 20 cities. These indexes, it should be noted, do not show comparative price levels from city to city. They merely show the extent that prices have risen in each city since the base period. That is, if the index for Detroit is 113 and that for Cincinnati is 116, we cannot say that consumer prices in Cincinnati are higher than they are in Detroit. Such a statement could be made only if prices had been the same in both cities during the base period.

The national or all-city CPI is formed by averaging indexes of all 46 cities, each city index bearing a weight proportional to the number of wage-earner and clerical-worker families it represents.

At present, over a million workers are covered by labor-management contracts containing price-wage escalator clauses. Wage rates of these workers are tied to the Consumer Price Index. If the index increases by, say, 1 percentage point, then the workers receive an automatic wage increase of 1 cent per hour. Decreases in the index, similarly, lead to decreases in wages. Cost of living bonuses for workers not covered by escalator clauses are sometimes based on changes in the CPI.

The CPI together with other data is used to construct other indexes such as the Retail Price Index and the deflator for Gross National Product.

2. The Wholesale Price Index. The name of this index is somewhat misleading, for the prices covered are those at which producers sell in the primary markets, not the prices at which wholesalers sell. All kinds of commodities, from raw materials to fabricated products, are priced in constructing the index. Altogether, about 2000 items are covered. Price data on agricultural commodities are furnished by the organized exchanges or by government agencies, while other data are taken from trade publications or furnished directly by producers. Most of the price data on fabricated products come directly from the producers. Probability sampling methods are not used.

The basic formula for calculation of the index is a modified weighted mean of price relatives, with value weights being used. The base period is 1947–49 and the representative period consists of the two years 1952–53, weights being the average value of shipments for this period. The index is computed and issued monthly by the U.S. Bureau of Labor Statistics.

An important use of the Wholesale Price Index involves the adjustment of money sums for price changes in long-term contracts of various types. If a businessman enters into a long-term purchase contract, leasing arrangement or patent licensing agreement, he often would like to have the contract drawn so as to specify, as nearly as possible, payments in "constant dollars." In such arrangements, therefore, a base price is established and provision is made for periodic adjustment of the contract payments in accordance with movements in the Wholesale Price Index. Defense contracts ordinarily carry a clause providing for adjustment of the contract price in accordance with changes in the Wholesale Price Index.

In addition to the monthly Wholesale Price Index, a weekly and a daily index are issued by the Bureau of Labor Statistics. The former statistic represents an attempt to estimate short-term changes in the monthly index. It is based on a small sample of less than 200 items. The latter index is a simple geometric mean of 22 price relatives. The 22 items covered by the index are raw or semifinished materials traded in spot markets or on the organized exchanges. Products near or at the final stages of production are not included. The base period of the index is 1947–49.

Use of the geometric mean in averaging the price relatives gives rise to an interesting and desirable characteristic in the index. If, in passing from one period to the next, each of a certain number of prices is multiplied by a and if at the same time each of an equal number of prices is multiplied by $1/a$, then the index will not change in value. For example, if three prices doubled and three others were cut in half, the index would not change.

3. The Federal Reserve Board Index of Industrial Production. This highly publicized business indicator is a quantity index showing relative changes in physical outputs. It is of basic importance, for the industries covered by it—mining, manufacturing, and electric and gas utilities—account for more than a third of the national income.

Probability sampling techniques are not used. The index is constructed from data compiled originally for other purposes, these data being supplied by private business sources as well as government agencies.

The 1959 revisions of the index provide for two different base periods, 1947–49, which was the old base period, and 1957. The new representative period is 1957, which has been carried back in the revised values of the index to January, 1953. For values of the index covering the time span from January, 1947 to December, 1952, the representative period is 1947.

The formula used for computing the index is a weighted mean of quantity relatives. Value weights rather than prices are used in the computation, but they are in terms of value added rather than gross value. Value added is the difference between the value of the final product and the cost of materials and supplies used in its production. The value added figures are, of course, relevant to the representative period.

The various series of data from which the quantity relatives are computed are divided into industry groups according to the 1957 version of the Standard Industrial Classification Manual issued by the U.S. Bureau of the Budget. The major industry groupings are Durable Manufactures, Nondurable Manufactures, Mining, and Utilities. In addition to the industry classes, market categories are used for grouping the series, the major ones here being Consumer Goods, Equipment, and Materials. Separate indexes have been computed for each of the major categories. There is, for example, a Durable Manufactures index and a Consumer Goods index. As in the case of the total index, each major group index is computed on both the 1947–49 base and the 1957 base.

Together with other indicators, the Index of Industrial Production is used to ascertain the state of the aggregate economy. An analysis of individual industry production indexes indicates those sectors which are the most important contributors to a general upturn or downturn, as the case may be. Also, an individual business may measure its own production performance in comparison with that of its particular industry group by examining the relevant production index figures.

SUMMARY

Fundamentally, an index number is a ratio or average of several ratios showing a comparison of prices, quantities, or values over time. In this comparison, two time periods are involved, a base period and a given period. Sometimes weighting factors are relevant to still another period, which we have called the representative period. An index number is an estimate computed from a sample.

Of basic importance in the study of all types of indexes are price indexes. We may list five basic price indexes and group them into two categories, simple indexes and weighted indexes. In the former category, we have the simple aggregative index and the simple mean of price relatives. In the latter category, we have the weighted aggregative index of the Laspeyres form and that of the Paasche form, Fisher's ideal index, and the weighted mean of price relatives. Fisher's ideal index is the geometric mean of the Laspeyres and Paasche indexes. If value weights are used in computing the weighted mean of price relatives, it becomes identical with the Laspeyres index.

A price index may be changed to its corresponding quantity index by changing the p's to q's and the q's to p's in the price index formula.

We defined the value index as total value of the sample items in the given period divided by their total value in the base period.

Two important logical criteria of a good index number are (1) the factor reversal test and (2) the time reversal test. Of the index numbers given in the chapter, only Fisher's ideal index will pass both these tests.

A price index number represents relative changes in the general price level of a certain class of items. The purchasing power of a dollar spent on some class of items is given by the reciprocal of the index number for that class. The purchasing power is, we must note, relative to the base period of the index number.

Price indexes may be used to adjust current dollar data for price changes, such data being converted to constant dollars or real terms.

If we have the values of a price index number for several given periods, we may shift the base of the index to any one of these periods by selecting the one we desire to be the base and dividing all values of the index by the value having the selected given period.

In the construction of index numbers, very difficult problems of definition, specification, and sampling often arise. All of these problems call for the exercise of informed judgment. Frequently, probability sampling techniques are difficult to utilize in the construction of index numbers. Thus measures of precision do not usually accompany the stated values of the indexes.

Examples of important price indexes are the Consumer Price Index and the Wholesale Price Index, which are both issued by the U.S. Bureau of Labor Statistics. An example of an important quantity index is the Index of Industrial Production issued by the Federal Reserve System.

TERMS TO PONDER

1. Simple Index
2. Weighted Index
3. Laspeyres
4. Paasche
5. Fisher's Ideal Index
6. Weighted Mean of Price Relatives
7. Quantity Index
8. Value Index
9. Factor Reversal Test
10. Time Reversal Test
11. Representative Period
12. Purchasing Power
13. Constant Dollars

EXERCISES

1. Hypothetical data on certain prices and quantities of cost of living items are given at the top of page 281. (Prices are given in cents per unit.) Using the data, construct the following cost of living price indexes with 1956 as the given year and 1949 as the base year:

   a. A simple average of price relatives.

   b. A weighted average of price relatives. (Use arbitrary weights given in the last column.)

   c. A weighted aggregative index of the Laspeyres form.

2. Using the data of Exercise 1 and retaining 1949 as the base year, construct the following indexes:

Item	Unit	Av. price 1949	Av. price 1956	Quantity 1949	Quantity 1956	Arbitrary weight
Bread	1 lb.	14.0	20.0	8.0	10.0	10
Beef	1 lb.	55.6	48.2	1.4	1.8	6
Pork	1 lb.	73.6	69.4	3.5	2.5	25
Butter	1 lb.	72.3	82.4	5.0	5.2	40
Eggs	1 doz.	76.9	80.2	4.5	6.0	40
Milk	1 qt.	20.8	24.0	9.0	12.0	18
Apples	1 lb.	10.1	14.1	2.0	1.5	2
Beans	1 lb.	16.8	15.2	1.5	2.0	3
Potatoes	15 lb.	80.1	76.2	4.3	7.2	32
Coffee	1 lb.	52.4	94.4	3.0	2.0	15
Shirts	ea.	355.0	325.0	1.0	1.5	36
Shoes	pr.	1000.0	1200.0	2.0	1.5	50
Suits	ea.	3850.0	4200.0	1.0	1.0.	60
Dresses	ea.	1250.0	1500.0	1.0	1.0	50

    a. A quantity index of the Laspeyres form.

    b. A value index.

3. State the time reversal test and by use of its formula show that Fisher's ideal index passes this test.

4. Using the price index computed in Exercise 1*c*, find the purchasing power of the cost of living dollar in 1956 relative to 1949.

5. Following are given the figures for personal income in the United States for selected years. The Consumer Price Index (1947–49 = 100) for each of the selected years is given also. Express each of the personal income figures in real terms, that is, in 1947–49 dollars.

Year	Personal income (billions of dollars)	Consumer Price Index (1947–49 = 100)
1929	85.8	73.3
1933	47.2	55.3
1941	96.3	62.9
1950	227.0	102.8
1951	255.3	111.0
1952	271.8	113.5
1953	286.0	114.4
1954	287.3	114.8
1955	305.9	114.5
1956	326.9	116.2

Source: *Economic Report of the President* (Washington, D.C., U.S. Government Printing Office, 1958), pp. 128, 160.

6. Shift the base of the indexes given in Exercise 5 to the year 1952.
7. The federal government enters into a contract for the production of $56,358 worth of electronic devices in 1956 when the Wholesale Price Index is 114.3 (1947–49 = 100). An escalator clause in the purchase contract states that payment shall be made upon delivery and that the contract price shall be adjusted in accordance with the change in the Wholesale Price Index. If the order is delivered in December, 1957, when the Wholesale Price Index stands at 118.5, how much will the government have to pay for the order?

SELECTED REFERENCES

CROXTON, Frederick E., and COWDEN, Dudley J., *Applied General Statistics*, 2d ed. (Englewood Cliffs, N.J., Prentice-Hall, Inc., 1955), Chs. XVII, XVIII.

MILLS, Frederick C., *Introduction to Statistics* (New York, Holt, Rinehart and Winston, Inc., 1956), Chs. XIII, XIV.

NETER, John, and WASSERMAN, William, *Fundamental Statistics for Business and Economics* (New York, Allyn and Bacon, Inc., 1956), Ch. XII.

14

TIME SERIES

IN ECONOMICS AND BUSINESS, most populations change as time passes. In designating a population, therefore, we usually state the relevant date or other short period of time at which observations are made. If instead of confining our study to one point in time, however, we make observations on the population at several points in time, the observations or estimates resulting therefrom make up a *time series*. We shall consider only the common case where the time intervals between successive observations may be assumed equal. Familiar examples of time series are monthly estimates of department store sales, daily averages of stock prices, quarterly estimates of Gross National Product, and the number of freight-car loadings each month.

For a given time series, the specification of the population (except for time) and the characteristics observed, as well as the basic method of estimating, should remain the same. Otherwise, the statistics will not be comparable from one time interval to another. As an example, let us take the monthly estimates of the number of unemployed persons in the United States. These estimates are made as a part of the Current Population Survey by the U.S. Bureau of the Census. Prior to January, 1957, a person was classified as employed if he was laid off with definite instructions to return to his job within 30 days. But beginning in January, 1957, such a person was considered unemployed. Thus the monthly estimates prior to January, 1957, formed one time series, and the estimates beginning with January, 1957, formed another. Recently, all estimates were adjusted so as to conform to the 1957 definitions.

REPRESENTATIONS OF TIME SERIES

We often represent a time series by listing the time designations and setting the corresponding observations opposite them. More frequently, perhaps, we draw a line graph of the series, with the time intervals laid off along the horizontal scale and the observations or estimates parallel to the vertical scale. A time series represented in the former manner is shown in Table 14–1 and in the latter by Figure 14–1.

TABLE 14–1

Stocks Owned by U.S. Life Insurance Companies (Millions of Dollars)

Year	Amount	Year	Amount
1946	1249	1951	2221
1947	1390	1952	2446
1948	1428	1953	2573
1949	1718	1954	3268
1950	2103		

Source: *Life Insurance Fact Book* (New York, Institute of Life Insurance, 1958), p. 79.

The illustrative time series presented in this chapter will really be small pieces of time series. Usually a very large number of observations is desirable. We wish here, however, to guard against

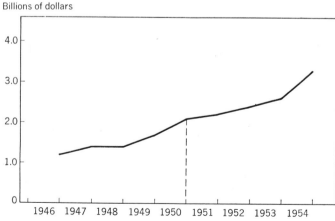

FIGURE 14–1.   Line Graph.   Stocks Owned by U.S. Life Insurance Companies

having the point of the exposition blunted by the impact of great masses of numbers.

On the line graph the data in the series are, of course, represented by lengths of vertical lines, such as the dashed line drawn at 1950 in Figure 14–1. Only the top points of these vertical lines are plotted. Successive plotted points are joined by solid lines so as to emphasize the changes in the data over time.

The positioning of the plotted points in relation to the intervals of the horizontal scale is usually governed by the nature of the data. Certain data are called *cumulative*, that is, they can be added over successive time intervals to give a meaningful result. Take, for example, department store sales. The monthly sales figures for January, February, and March can be added to get a meaningful sales figure for the first quarter of the year. Cumulative data are usually plotted opposite the middle of the time interval to which they refer.

Noncumulative data cannot be added over successive intervals so as to give a meaningful result. The figures on amounts of stocks owned by life insurance companies (Table 14–1) are of this type. Each figure relates to a particular instant (December 31 in this particular case) in its time interval. Noncumulative data are usually plotted opposite the point in each interval to which they refer.

Observing noncumulative quantities is, then, the taking of snapshots in accordance with the analogy used to describe balance sheet accounts. Observing cumulative quantities involves the moving-picture idea of the operating statement accounts. Cumulative data are analogous to flows, while noncumulative data are analogous to stocks.

Averages of either noncumulative or cumulative data may appear in a time series. Such an average should always be plotted at the middle of the time interval over which it is computed. Average weekly earnings in retail trade serve as an example. (See Fig. 14–2.) Here weekly figures have been averaged over a year.

Once the data are plotted, the time intervals may be numbered off according to an arbitrary scale. We will find it convenient in certain computations to locate 0 at the middle of the time scale.

THE USES OF TIME SERIES

Having learned something about the representation of time series, we naturally inquire about their more important purposes

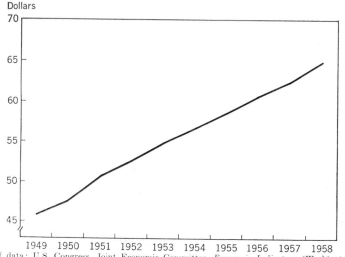

Dollars

Source of data: U.S. Congress, Joint Economic Committee, *Economic Indicators* (Washington, D.C., U.S. Government Printing Office, May, 1959), p. 15.

FIGURE 14–2.   Average Weekly Earnings in Retail Trade (Current Prices)

and uses. First, and quite obviously, arranging data in the form of a time series *facilitates comparisons* between data occurring at different points in time. Such comparisons give meaning to observations that otherwise would signify virtually nothing. When we say that prices are high, for example, we are implicitly comparing the current price level with that of some past period or periods. Second, time series may serve as valuable *historical records*. They exhibit patterns of historical growth and change. Analysis of these patterns may lead to a better understanding of important economic events of the past. A study of the interrelationships implied by coincident troughs in several well-known "business cycles," for example, may lead to a better understanding of the causes of the depression of the 1930's. Third, time series may aid us in *making forecasts*. Since, in the strict sense, we know nothing of the future and only a part of the past, estimates and predictions as to the future must be made on the basis of observed patterns and tendencies of the past. We may sometimes infer that known tendencies of the immediate past will continue for a limited period into the future and thus forecast successfully for relatively short terms. Long-term forecasts are, however, fraught with many hazards unless the predicted quantities are very largely determined by what has already happened. For example, persons who will be in the labor force 10 years hence are already born. These persons may be assumed to be subject to the disability, death, and labor-force participation rates of the immediate past. Thus the size of the labor force 10 years hence can be estimated with fair accuracy.

THE CLASSICAL TIME SERIES MODEL

Time series analysis arises out of the need for an answer to the question, "How did the series get in the shape it is in?" There are, of course, innumerable approaches that could be taken in attempting to answer this question, but the appropriate one for the beginner is the study of the classical time series model. This model is not a good representation for *all* time series, but even if the complete model is inappropriate, parts of it may often be utilized in making important adjustments, such as adjustments for seasonal variation.

In the complete model, each observation or estimate in the series is assumed to consist of four components, trend, seasonal, cyclical, and irregular.

The trend is the general long-term movement of the series. The life insurance stock data of Figure 14–1, for example, exhibit a long-term upward movement, that could, it seems, be approximated by an upward sloping straight line. The data on agricultural employment (Fig. 14–3), on the other hand, show a generally downward, though very gradual, trend.

Strictly speaking, a seasonal variation is a periodic pattern taking place over an entire year. The monthly estimates of agricul-

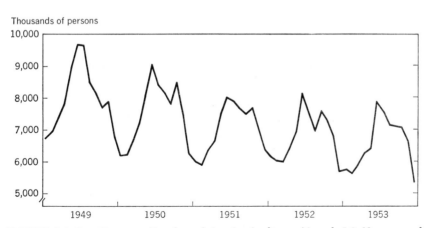

FIGURE 14–3. Persons Employed in Agriculture (Aged 14 Years and Over)

tural employment exhibit quite regular ups and downs due to the varying labor requirements of the planting and harvesting seasons (Fig. 14–3). Data on sales of department stores would, of course, show high levels at Christmas time and Easter time year after year. The term *seasonal* is sometimes used loosely to mean any relatively regular periodic fluctuation, whether it runs its course in a year or some shorter period.

The cyclical component gets its name from the type of fluctuation that has been called the "business cycle," and which represents the familiar alternating periods of expansion and contraction in general business activity. The expansion phase is associated with "good" business conditions: high levels of employment, production and sales; "firm" or rising prices; increasing optimism and willingness to take risks. On the other hand, the contraction phase is a period of worsening business conditions: declining levels of employment, production, and sales; a tendency for prices to "weaken" or decline; increasing pessimism, less willingness to take risks, and increasing clamor for governmental action directed toward improving business conditions.

In the past, several different types of business fluctuation have been identified. These different "cycles" vary in average length, the Kitchin cycles being very short and Kondratieff's "long waves" having an average length of perhaps 45 years. The study of the nature, causes, and cure of the business "cycle" is a subject in and of itself, the study of the classical time series model being only one of the important preliminary requirements. "Cycles" are exhibited by the graph of the Index of Industrial Production in Figure 14–4. This series has been adjusted for seasonal variation, that is, the seasonal component has been "taken out" of each of the original data, but the cyclical component is very much in evidence, with the recessions of 1953–54 and 1957–58 being quite readily identifiable.

The last of the components is the irregular, which in classical analysis is combined with the cyclical component in the form of a residual.

We symbolize the trend component by T, the seasonal by S, the cyclical by C, and the irregular by I. If the model is an appropriate one for a given series, then each of the model data will be represented by Y, Y being made up of a combination of T, S, C, and I. The question of how the components should be combined could conceivably be answered in a great many different ways, but the

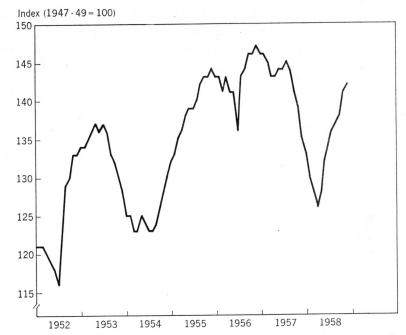

Index (1947·49 = 100)

FIGURE 14–4. Industrial Production (FRB, Seasonally Adjusted)

classical model specifies that the components be combined by multi-plication, that is, $Y = T \times S \times C \times I$. Each of the data in the series, then, is assumed to be made up of the *product* of four values, the first representing the influence of the trend, the second the sea-sonal, the third the cycle, and the fourth the irregular. The trend component is in the same units as the original series data, but the seasonal is in the form of an index, that is, a ratio or proportion. The C and I components are combined, their product being ex-pressed as a ratio.

Annual data (one observation per year) will, of course, show no seasonal pattern and may be represented by the model, $Y = T \times C \times I$.

THE PROCESS OF ANALYSIS

The first step in classical time series analysis is to evaluate each of the components of the model. This is done by taking the given time series observations as values of Y. Then values of T are found by fitting a trend equation to the Y values, this trend equa-tion showing up as a line representing the general sweep or movement of the plotted points on the line graph. Next, values of a seasonal index, S, are computed. Finally, the CI components are found in combined form as residuals by a process of adjustment whereby the trend and seasonal components are eliminated from the original series.

In this process of adjustment, we start with the equation for our model: $Y = T \times S \times C \times I$.

Having found a T value and an S value for each Y value, we divide each Y by its corresponding T and S:

$$\frac{Y}{T \times S} = \frac{T \times S \times C \times I}{T \times S}$$

or

$$\frac{Y}{T \times S} = C \times I$$

If we merely wish to adjust for trend, we divide both sides of the model equation by T only, and if we wish to adjust only for seasonal variation, we divide by S only. In making an adjustment for trend only, we get an abstract number, a ratio or proportion that is not expressed in units of the data. On the other hand, adjustment only for seasonal variation gives us a number that is expressed in units of the data.

THE FORECAST

If we were to use the classical model as the basis of a forecast, we would, of course, have to estimate for a given future date, values of each component, T, S, and $C \times I$. Then we could multiply these values in accordance with the model so as to get an estimated future value of Y. As we have implied before, forecasting in this fashion, especially for long periods ahead, can be extremely hazardous. We may do quite well, however, for short-term forecasts, within one phase of the cycle, where the trend is consistent, the seasonal fairly regular and the $C \times I$ components small or slowly changing. But we know that in many series the C and I components can be very large and quite erratic. Thus simple forecasts of this type can seldom foretell the turning points in the cycle, and it is almost necessary to combine time series analysis with several other techniques and add a measure of sound judgment, some common sense, a little hope, and a lot of plain luck in order to make a successful forecast.

EVALUATING *T* FOR ANNUAL DATA

In fitting a trend line, so as to find values of T, let us first take the very simple case of *annual* data. Here, as previously noted, the data will show no seasonal variation, the model being $Y = T \times C \times I$. To illustrate the computations, let us take the series of Table 14–1, Stocks Owned by U.S. Life Insurance Companies. Each of the observations will be rounded to the nearest tenth of a billion so that we will be working with simple two-digit numbers. The time scale or x_i scale is rewritten with 0 placed at the middle year, 1950, as shown in column 2 of Table 14–2 (p. 292), the observations being shown in the y_i column. Remember that y_i represents the actual observed values, which are only approximations to the "ideal" Y values of the model.

As in the case of linear regression (see pp. 231–232), we must decide upon (1) the type of trend line that is appropriate for our data, and (2) the method of fitting the line. For the series at hand, an examination of the line graph indicates that a straight line appears to be a fairly good representation of trend, and we shall fit such a line by the method of least squares.

The standard form equation of the straight line is $y = a + bx$, and the problem in fitting the line is, of course, to find appropriate values of a and b to substitute in the equation. For purposes of time series analysis, let us rewrite the equation as $T = a + bx$, for we wish to use it to estimate values of T, the trend ordinates in our classical time series model.[1] In the equation, a represents the trend ordinate at the point where $x = 0$ and b represents the slope of the line.

Because we have transformed our time scale, we will not have to rely upon Cramer's rule for a solution of the normal equations, as we did in Chapter 12. A much simpler solution is possible, for on our transformed x_i scale $\Sigma x_i = 0$. Thus any term containing Σx_i in the normal equations will become 0. The normal equations are:

$$\Sigma y_i = na + \boxed{b\Sigma x_i} \qquad (1)$$

$$\Sigma x_i y_i = \boxed{a\Sigma x_i} + b\Sigma x_i^2 \qquad (2)$$

The circled terms are the ones that become 0. We see immediately that a is found by dividing both sides of the first equation by

---

[1] Note that we are using T to indicate a theoretical component as well as the estimates of that component.

n, that is, $a = \dfrac{\Sigma y_i}{n}$, and that the second equation is solved for b as follows, $b = \dfrac{\Sigma x_i y_i}{\Sigma x_i{}^2}$.

Table 14–2 shows the computations necessary for evaluating a and b for the series on stocks of life insurance companies. The trend equation turns out to be $T = 2.033 + .242x$ (origin December 31, 1950).

Now to find the value of T, the trend ordinate, for any year, we find the x_i value for that year and substitute it for x in the trend equation. For the year 1946, the value of x_i is -4. Thus for 1946, $T = 2.033 + .242\,(-4) = 2.033 - .968 = 1.065$. The T values for the entire series are shown in column (6) of Table 14–2.

To draw the trend line on the graph, we need only select two T values, plot them opposite the appropriate points on the time

TABLE 14–2

Fitting Linear Trend by the Method of Least Squares
(Stocks of U.S. Life Insurance Companies)

Year	x_i	y_i	$x_i y_i$	$x_i{}^2$	T	$\dfrac{y_i}{T}$
(1)	(2)	(3)	(4)	(5)	(6)	(7)
1946	-4	1.2	-4.8	16	1.065	1.13
1947	-3	1.4	-4.2	9	1.307	1.07
1948	-2	1.4	-2.8	4	1.549	.90
1949	-1	1.7	-1.7	1	1.791	.95
1950	0	2.1	0.0	0	2.033	1.03
1951	1	2.2	2.2	1	2.275	.97
1952	2	2.4	4.8	4	2.517	.95
1953	3	2.6	7.8	9	2.759	.94
1954	4	3.3	13.2	16	3.001	1.10
		18.3	14.5	60		

$$T = a + bx$$

$$a = \frac{\Sigma y_i}{n} = \frac{18.3}{9} = 2.033$$

$$b = \frac{\Sigma x_i y_i}{\Sigma x_i{}^2} = \frac{14.5}{60} = .242$$

$$T = 2.033 + .242x \text{ (origin December 31, 1950)}$$

scale, and then draw a straight line through them. Using the T
values for 1947 and 1952, we have drawn the trend line in Figure
14–5. In making *adjustments* for trend, of course, we will need *all*
of the T values, not just two.

Suppose that in early 1955 we wished to make a simple forecast
of the trend value for 1956 by projecting our least squares line. On
our time scale we find that the x_i value for 1956 is 6. Substituting
this value in our trend equation, we have $T = 2.033 + .242(6) = $

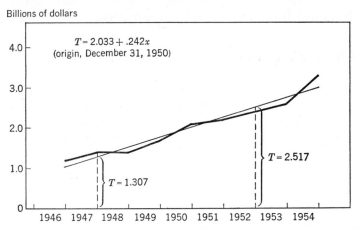

**FIGURE 14–5. Stocks Owned by U.S. Life Insurance Companies (Linear
Trend Fitted by the Method of Least Squares)**

$2.033 + 1.452 = 3.485$. The actual value of stocks owned by U.S.
life insurance companies in 1956 was 3.503 billion dollars. Our forecast has turned out quite well only because the trend line fits the
series quite closely, the $C \times I$ component is small, and we have forecast for only a short period beyond the last time period in the series.

Of course, we have here "forecast" with benefit of hindsight
(which is the only completely foolproof method existing). But, had
we refused the benefits of hindsight and tried to forecast the trend
value for 1957, our result would have been considerably in error.
Our trend equation gives 3.727 billion dollars for 1957, but the actual
value of stocks owned by U.S. life insurance companies in that year
was $3.391 billion.

ADJUSTMENT OF THE DATA FOR TREND

We are taking as our model for the life insurance stock data,
$Y = T \times C \times I$, the seasonal component being omitted. In the

model, we see that the trend is eliminated if we divide both sides of the equation by T. the result, of course, is $Y/T = C \times I$. Since we, of course, do not know the theoretical values of Y, we substitute values of y_i for Y and carry out the adjustment by computing so-called ratio-to-trend values, y_i/T. These values are shown in column (7) of Table 14–2. They are abstract numbers and if plotted on a line graph would show up as points fluctuating about a horizontal line drawn at a distance of "1" above the horizontal axis. This type of graph is exactly what we would expect for a series from which the trend had been extracted.

CENTERING ZERO IN AN EVEN NUMBER OF TIME PERIODS

The data on stocks owned by U.S. life insurance companies consisted of observations made at 9 successive time intervals. The number 9 being odd, it was very easy to set 0 opposite the middle time point. If, however, the series involved an *even* number of periods, we would have to make a slight adjustment. We would locate 0 halfway between the middle two points in time, the first observations on each side of the 0 point being located at ½ a time period from 0. A series on average hourly earnings in building construction which involves an even number of time periods is given in Table 14–3, with the transformed time scale in column (2).

These earnings data are centered at the middle (July 1) of the years. Thus 0 on the x_i scale is at January 1, 1955. We have fitted a trend line by the method of least squares as in the case of the series on stocks of life insurance companies. The only added inconvenience arising from the even number of time periods is that there are now more two-digit numbers in the x_i column. The trend equation is $T = 2.8025 + .0981x$, the value of b indicating a rise of about 10 cents per hour per year in real earnings. The series is graphed in Figure 14–6.

EVALUATING *T* FOR QUARTERLY DATA

Let us now fit a linear trend to a series of quarterly data which show a downward rather than an upward trend and which exhibit a very definite and quite regular pattern of seasonal variation. Such a series is the one shown in Table 14–4. It consists of quarterly estimates of the number of persons aged 14 years and over who are employed in agriculture. These data are of the noncumulative type.

TABLE 14–3

Average Hourly Earnings, Building Construction (1958 Prices)

Year	x_i	y_i (earnings)	x_iy_i	x_i^2	T
(1)	(2)	(3)	(4)	(5)	(6)
1951	-3.5	\$ 2.44	-8.540	12.25	2.459
1952	-2.5	2.51	-6.275	6.25	2.557
1953	-1.5	2.68	-4.020	2.25	2.655
1954	$-.5$	2.80	-1.400	.25	2.753
	0.0				
1955	.5	2.87	1.435	.25	2.852
1956	1.5	2.98	4.470	2.25	2.950
1957	2.5	3.04	7.600	6.25	3.048
1958	3.5	3.10	10.850	12.25	3.146
		22.42	4.120	42.00	

Source: U.S. Congress, Joint Economic Committee, *Economic Indicators* (Washington, D.C., U.S. Government Printing Office, March, 1959), p. 14.

$$T = a + bx$$

$$a = \frac{\Sigma y_i}{n} = \frac{22.42}{8} \doteq 2.8025$$

$$b = \frac{\Sigma x_iy_i}{\Sigma x_i^2} = \frac{4.120}{42.00} = .0981$$

$$T = 2.8025 + .0981x \quad \text{(origin January 1, 1955)}$$

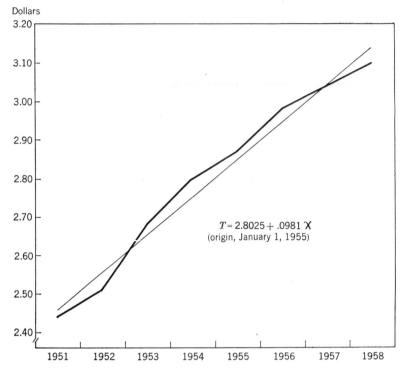

FIGURE 14–6. **Average Hourly Earnings in Building Construction (1958 Prices)**

Thus we have tabulated estimates which were made at the middle or nearly at the middle of each quarter.

A line graph of the series appears in Figure 14–7. The seasonal pattern is immediately evident as well as the gradually downward sloping trend. This type of slope is called negative and will be indicated in the trend equation by a negative value of b.

The first step in fitting a linear trend by least squares is, again, to transform the time scale. There are an even number of quarters in the series, so we shall locate 0 between the middle two quarters, this point being at July 1, 1951. Denoting the estimates in the series by y_i and the time scale values by x_i, we proceed to compute Σy_i, $\Sigma x_i y_i$, and Σx_i^2. These computations are shown in Table 14–5. The trend equation is then $T = 7.1425 - .0872x$ (origin July 1, 1951). The line is fitted to the graph in Figure 14–7 by evaluating T for the x_i values, -8.5 and $+8.5$. All 20 values of T, computed from the trend equation, are shown in column (7) of Table 14–5. We shall return to this series somewhat later, in our discussion of

TABLE 14–4

**Persons Employed in Agriculture
(Aged 14 Years or Over)**

Year	Quarter	Millions
	1	6.99
1949	2	8.97
	3	8.51
	4	7.88
	–	——
	1	6.22
1950	2	8.06
	3	8.16
	4	7.55
	–	——
	1	5.93
1951	2	7.44
	3	7.69
	4	7.02
	–	——
	1	6.06
1952	2	6.96
	3	6.96
	4	6.77
	–	——
	1	5.37
1953	2	6.39
	3	7.27
	4	6.65

Source: U.S. Bureau of the Census, *Current Population Survey, Annual Report on the Labor Force* (Washington, D.C., U.S. Government Printing Office, 1950, 1951, 1952, 1953, 1955).

Millions of persons

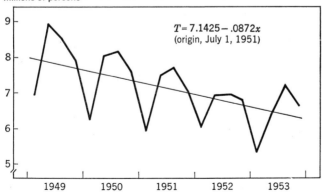

FIGURE 14–7.   Persons Employed in Agriculture (Aged 14 Years or Over)

TABLE 14–5

Fitting a Linear Trend by Least Squares to Quarterly Data
(Persons Employed in Agriculture)

Year	Quarter	x_i	y_i	x_iy_i	x_i^2	T
(1)	(2)	(3)	(4)	(5)	(6)	(7)
	1	−9.5	6.99	−66.405	90.25	7.971
1949	2	−8.5	8.97	−76.245	72.25	7.884
	3	−7.5	8.51	−63.825	56.25	7.796
	4	−6.5	7.88	−51.220	42.25	7.709
	1	−5.5	6.22	−34.210	30.25	7.622
1950	2	−4.5	8.06	−36.270	20.25	7.535
	3	−3.5	8.16	−28.560	12.25	7.448
	4	−2.5	7.55	−18.875	6.25	7.360
	1	−1.5	5.93	−8.895	2.25	7.273
1951	2	−.5	7.44	−3.720	.25	7.186
	3	.5	7.69	3.845	.25	7.099
	4	1.5	7.02	10.530	2.25	7.012
	1	2.5	6.06	15.150	6.25	6.924
1952	2	3.5	6.96	24.360	12.25	6.837
	3	4.5	6.96	31.320	20.25	6.750
	4	5.5	6.77	37.235	30.25	6.663
	1	6.5	5.37	34.905	42.25	6.576
1953	2	7.5	6.39	47.925	56.25	6.488
	3	8.5	7.27	61.795	72.25	6.401
	4	9.5	6.65	63.175	90.25	6.314
			142.85	−57.985	665.00	

$$a = \frac{\Sigma y_i}{n} = \frac{142.85}{20} = 7.1425 \qquad b = \frac{\Sigma x_iy_i}{\Sigma x_i^2} = \frac{-57.985}{665.00} = -.0872$$

$$T = 7.1425 - .0872x \text{ (origin July 1, 1951)}$$

seasonal indexes, but let us digress for the moment to discuss linear trends on the ratio scale.

LINEAR TRENDS ON THE RATIO SCALE

The time series that we have dealt with so far have all exhibited straight line trends when plotted upon arithmetic scales. In such cases, constant differences in successively plotted values of T are represented on the vertical scale by constant distances. But let us

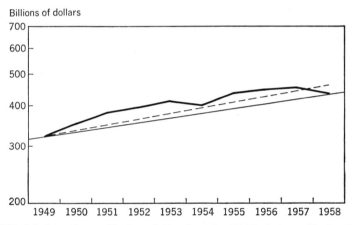

FIGURE 14–8.   Gross National Product in 1958 Prices (Ratio Scale)

now examine a straight line drawn on graph paper having a ratio (or semilogarithmic) scale. Such a line appears on the graph of Gross National Product figures in Figure 14–8. The ratio scale is on the vertical dimension and is laid off in distances which are proportional to the logarithms of the numbers appearing beside the scale. (The horizontal scale is the same as for ordinary graph paper.)

In order to gain a clear understanding of the ratio scale, let us review some aspects of common logarithms. We know that log $10 = 1$, log $100 = 2$, log $1000 = 3$, and so on. Taken in the order of size, these *logarithms* are separated by a constant *difference* of 1, but the corresponding numbers (10, 100, 1000) are separated by a constant *multiplier* of 10. That is, the logarithms form an arithmetic sequence, but the corresponding numbers (antilogs) form a geometric sequence. On the ratio scale, the distance between 10 and 100 would be the same as the distance between 100 and 1000 or the same as that between 1000 and 10,000, and so on.

Let us select another set of numbers which form a geometric sequence: 200, 300, and 450. These numbers are separated by the constant multiplier 1.5. By laying a ruler alongside the vertical scale of Figure 14–8, the student can verify the fact that on a ratio scale the distance between 200 and 300 is the same as the distance between 300 and 450. Also, the distance between 300 and 600 is the same as the distance between 350 and 700, the constant multiplier being 2 in this case. In general, the distance between any number and k times that number is a constant distance on the ratio scale, this distance representing the multiplier, k.

Now a point moving along a straight line, of course, rises (or falls) a constant vertical distance for each unit of horizontal travel. Thus if the ordinates of a straight line are spaced out equally along the horizontal axis, successive ordinates will differ in height by a constant amount. So again, on ordinary graph paper, these equal successive amounts represent equal successive differences, but on ratio paper they represent equal successive multipliers. Therefore, if a time series graphs as a straight line on ratio paper, the relative rate of change is constant, that is, each observation is a constant multiple or proportion of the one immediately preceding. It is rarely the case that all the observations in a time series will fall exactly on a straight line, but the constant relative rate holds approximately if the straight line is a good fit. In general, we should remember that for a line graph on a ratio scale, a constant slope represents a constant relative rate of change. When the slope changes, the rate changes.

If a straight line appears to represent well the trend of a series plotted on semilog paper, we may fit a straight line of least squares to the logarithms of the observations. However, it is sometimes the case that we wish only to draw a straight line representing the *average growth rate* in the series. This task is accomplished easily, after the data are plotted on a ratio scale, by drawing a straight line between the first point and the last. The validity of this method is apparent at once if we review our discussion in Chapter 5 of the geometric mean, wherein we learned that the average growth rate depended only upon the first and last observations and the number of periods separating them. Such a line is the solid line drawn in Figure 14–8, indicating the average growth rate in 10 GNP figures.

Suppose now that we wished to compare the series of 10 GNP figures with a trend line representing some hypothetical growth

rate, such as 4% per year.   (See the dashed line of Fig. 14–8.)
After plotting the observations on ratio paper, we would join the
first plotted point with another point lying on the 4% growth line
at an arbitrary number of time intervals from the first.   It is easier
to draw the line if the second plotted point is a considerable distance
horizontally from the first, so let us plot the second point at the
last time period, which will be the tenth in this case.   The appropriate value to plot is the first GNP figure multiplied by $(1.04)^{10-1}$,
where .04 is the hypothetical growth rate and the exponent $(10 - 1)$
is one less than the number of periods in the series.   (There is one
observation per period.)   We now merely join the two points with
a straight line.   In Figure 14–8 the first GNP figure is 324.0.   We
see that $(1.04)^9 \times 324.0$ gives 461.2 as the 1958 value on the 4%
growth line.

A general formula for finding this second point would be $Y_n = y_1(1 + \bar{r})^{n-1}$, where Y_n is the ordinate of the second point, y_1 is the
first observation in the series, $\bar{r}$ is the hypothetical growth rate, and
n is the number of the time periods in the series.   Notice that the
formula is just a variation of the old compound interest formula from
the mathematics of finance.

We have used a capital Y in Y_n because it represents a hypothetical or theoretical value.   If the actual average rate of growth
were equal to the hypothetical, then y_n (the last observation in the
series) would equal Y_n.   Suppose that this is the case.   Then we may
substitute y_n in the formula we have developed and solve for $(1 + \bar{r})$,
which we know from Chapter 5 to be the geometric mean of the relative rates formed from the observations in the series.   We find that

$$(1 + \bar{r}) = \sqrt[n-1]{\frac{y_n}{y_1}}$$

just as we did in our discussion of the geometric mean, again reveal-
ing the fact that the average growth rate depends only upon the first
and last observations and the number of time periods separating
them.

To refresh our memories, let us work through a simple problem
involving the use of this formula.   Our objective is to find $\bar{r}$, the
average growth rate of the observations in a time series.   The Gross
National Product of the United States was 441.7 billion dollars in
1958 (1958 prices) and 402.1 billion dollars in 1954 (1958 prices).

Let us find the average growth rate in the GNP for the five years, 1954 to 1958 inclusive. Substituting in the formula, we have

$$(1 + \bar{r}) = \sqrt[5-1]{\frac{441.7}{402.1}} = \sqrt[4]{1.0984830} \doteq 1.02376 \doteq 1.0238$$

$\bar{r} \doteq 1.0238 - 1 = .0238$, or 2.38% per year.

When an economist states, as is frequently the case nowadays, that a certain average growth rate in real GNP is necessary for the economy to fully employ its resources, and if he is measuring average growth rate by the method we have shown, he should specify the level of GNP at which he wishes the given rate to begin. A given average growth rate of, say, 4% per year can be represented on a ratio scale by an infinite number of parallel straight lines (upward sloping to the right). A 4% growth rate beginning with the GNP of 1932 will give vastly different levels of GNP for subsequent years than will a 4% rate beginning with 1929. Taking real GNP figures in terms of 1958 prices, for example, we find that a 4% growth rate from the year 1929 would give us an expected real GNP of 626.8 billion dollars for 1958. However, a 4% growth rate from the year 1932 would yield an expected real GNP of 396.7 billion dollars in 1958. The actual value of the 1958 GNP (at 1958 prices) was 437.7 billion dollars. A *three* per cent rate of growth measured from 1949 would give an expected GNP of 422.7 billion dollars for 1958 (1958 prices).

The dashed line in Figure 14–8, as we have said, represents a growth rate of 4% per year, beginning of course with 1949.

NONLINEAR TRENDS

The student should not get the idea that no other trends exist except straight lines. Many trend *curves* are treated in more advanced courses, among them the various growth curves. The equations of most growth curves fall into a category known as transcendental functions, and it is often difficult, if not impossible, to find directly the normal equations necessary for a least squares fit. However, special methods of fitting such curves have been devised.[2]

---

[2] For a discussion of these methods, see F. E. Croxton and D. J. Cowden, *Applied General Statistics*, 2d ed. (Englewood Cliffs, N.J., Prentice-Hall, Inc., 1955), Ch. 13.

EVALUATION OF S, THE SEASONAL COMPONENT

Returning now to the classical time series model, we wish to learn how to evaluate S, the seasonal component. This task is accomplished by constructing a set of seasonal indexes. For purposes of illustration, we shall use the data on persons employed in agriculture, wherein each seasonal pattern is represented by four observations, because the computations are simpler for quarterly data than for monthly data. (See Table 14–4 and Fig. 14–7.) Our final results will be in the form of four seasonal indexes, one for each quarter of the year.

The procedure we shall follow is called the ratio-to-moving-average method. A necessary preliminary is the examination of the concept of a moving average.

THE MOVING AVERAGE

A moving average (mean) is a device for smoothing out the fluctuations in a time series. A perfectly regular periodic pattern can, in fact, be eliminated entirely from the series by the use of an appropriate moving average. To illustrate, let us take the following hypothetical series, which exhibits a perfectly regular seasonal pattern and a perfectly regular linear trend, each seasonal pattern being represented by a set of three observations. (See Table 14–6.)

The first step in getting the moving average is to compute a moving total. Since there are three observations in each seasonal pattern, we compute a three-term moving total. We add the first three observations (5, 9, 3), then, sliding through the series one period at a time, we add successive sets of three observations each. That is, after adding $5 + 9 + 3$, we add $9 + 3 + 7$, then $3 + 7 + 11$, and so on. At each shift of the moving total, one observation is subtracted from it and another is added to it. These two values will always be in corresponding positions in the seasonal pattern if the pattern is regular and if the moving total contains as many observations as there are in one seasonal pattern. In Table 14–6, we see that in moving from $(5 + 9 + 3)$ to $(9 + 3 + 7)$ the total has lost 5 but gained 7. Both 5 and 7 are first-period values. If the seasonal remained perfectly regular and there were no trend or other components present, all first-period values would be equal, all second-period values would be equal, and all thirds would be

TABLE 14–6

Computation of Hypothetical Moving Average

Year	Period	Observation	Three-term moving total	Three-term moving average
	1	5		
1	2	9	17	5.67
	3	3	19	6.33
	4	7	21	7.00
2	5	11	23	7.67
	6	5	25	8.33
	7	9	27	9.00
3	8	13	29	9.67
	9	7	31	10.33
	10	11	33	11.00
4	11	15	35	11.67
	12	9		

equal. In such circumstances, the moving total would, of course, be constant throughout the series, as would the moving average. Had there been no trend in the observations of Table 14–6, they would have appeared as repeated patterns of 5, 9, 3, throughout, giving a constant moving total of 17 and a constant moving average of 5.67.

Each total in Table 14–6 is centered opposite the middle observation included in the total. Values of the moving average are, of course, found by dividing each total by 3. They exhibit a perfectly regular upward linear trend, the seasonal having been eliminated entirely.

Now actual time series observations do not exhibit perfectly regular seasonals or perfectly regular trends. In application, the moving average will not smooth out *all* fluctuations around the trend.

CONSTRUCTION OF THE SEASONAL INDEXES

Let us now compute the appropriate moving average for the series on agricultural employment. Four-term moving totals are shown in column (4) of Table 14–7. Since there are an even number (four) of observations in each seasonal pattern, values of the

TABLE 14–7

Construction of Seasonal Indexes
Ratio-to-Moving-Average Method
(Persons Employed in Agriculture)

Year	Quar-ter	y_i	Four-term moving total	Over-lapped total	Centered moving average (ma)	Seasonal relatives (y_i/ma)	Seasonal adjustment y_i / S	Trend and seasonal adjustments y_i / $S \times T$
(1)	(2)	(3)	(4)	(5)	(6)	(7)	(8)	(9)
	1	6.99					8.36	1.049
1949	2	8.97	32.35				8.54	1.083
	3	8.51	31.58	63.93	7.991	1.065	7.83	1.004
	4	7.88	30.67	62.25	7.781	1.013	7.67	.995
	1	6.22	30.32	60.99	7.624	.816	7.44	.976
1950	2	8.06	29.99	60.31	7.539	1.069	7.68	1.019
	3	8.16	29.70	59.69	7.461	1.094	7.51	1.008
	4	7.55	29.08	58.78	7.347	1.028	7.35	.999
	1	5.93	28.61	57.69	7.211	.822	7.09	.975
1951	2	7.44	28.08	56.69	7.086	1.050	7.09	.987
	3	7.69	28.21	56.29	7.036	1.093	7.07	.996
	4	7.02	27.73	55.94	6.992	1.004	6.84	.975
	1	6.06	27.00	54.73	6.841	.886	7.25	1.047
1952	2	6.96	26.75	53.75	6.719	1.036	6.63	.970
	3	6.96	26.06	52.81	6.601	1.054	6.40	.948
	4	6.77	25.49	51.55	6.444	1.051	6.59	.989
	1	5.37	25.80	51.29	6.411	.838	6.42	.976
1953	2	6.39	25.68	51.48	6.435	.993	6.09	.939
	3	7.27					6.69	1.045
	4	6.65					6.48	1.026

Arrays of Seasonal Relatives

Quarter

1	2	3	4
.816	.993	1.054	1.004
.822	1.036	1.065	1.013
.838	1.050	1.093	1.028
.886	1.069	1.094	1.051

Medians

.830	1.043	1.079	1.020

Mean of the median relatives = .9930.
Each median relative is divided by .9930
to get the seasonal indexes.

Quarter	*Seasonal indexes* (S)
1	.836
2	1.050
3	1.087
4	1.027

moving total and moving average should logically be centered between the middle two observations in each total. But we prefer to have a moving average that can logically be placed directly opposite each of our original observations. The desired centering results if we "overlap" the four-term totals. In Table 14–7, we add the first total value to the second, and the following result is achieved in terms of the individual observations:

Quarter	First four-term moving total	Second four-term moving total	
1	6.99		
2	8.97	8.97	Sum equals
3	8.51	8.51	32.35 + 31.58
4	7.88	7.88	or
		6.22	63.93

The sum of these eight values gives us a total that can be centered on the third quarter observation, for the weighting is symmetrical about this point. Succeeding overlapped totals will be centered directly opposite the original observations in the series. The process of computing the overlapped totals, of course, amounts to taking a two-term moving total of the four-term totals.

Each of the overlapped totals is divided by 8 to get values of the moving average, shown in column (6) of Table 14–7.

Next, *seasonal relatives* are found by computing the ratio of each observation to the corresponding value of the moving average. These ratios are shown in column (7) of Table 14–7. Then we sort out the seasonal relatives by quarters, there being four relatives for each in this example. Seasonal relatives are arrayed by quarters at the bottom of Table 14–7. We can now select the median seasonal relative for each quarter, .830, 1.043, 1.079, and 1.020. If these median relatives have an average (mean) value of 1.00, as they should if the seasonal pattern is regular, we take them as our seasonal indexes. If, however, they do not, we adjust them and then take the adjusted values as our indexes.

For our example, we must adjust the median relatives, for their mean is .9930. Dividing each of them by this amount gives us our indexes:

Quarter	Seasonal index
1	.836
2	1.050
3	1.087
4	1.027
	4.000

At this point let us summarize the steps followed in constructing the seasonal indexes for quarterly data.

1. Compute a four-term moving total, the first value being centered between the second and third quarters of the first year.
2. "Overlap" values of the four-term total by forming a two-term moving total from them. The first value of the overlapped total is centered directly opposite the third-quarter observation of the first year.
3. Divide each of the overlapped total values by 8 to get values of the moving average.
4. Divide each of the observations (except the first two and the last two) by the corresponding moving average value. The results are called seasonal relatives.
5. Sort out the seasonal relatives by quarters. Find the median relative for each quarter.
6. If the median seasonal relatives have a mean of 1.00, take them as the seasonal indexes. If not, make an adjustment by dividing

each median relative by the mean of all four relatives. These adjusted median relatives are the seasonal indexes.

For monthly data, we would compute a twelve-term moving total. The values of this total would be overlapped by pairs and the first value of the overlapped total would be centered opposite the seventh month in the first year. There would be twelve seasonal indexes, of course, instead of four. In various studies of the business cycle, the basic data are monthly series which have been adjusted for seasonal variation.

Instead of taking the median seasonal relative for each quarter or month, we sometimes take a *positional mean*. That is, we take the mean of several relatives in the middle of each array. The number of middle items taken should be the same, of course, for each array.

ADJUSTMENT OF OBSERVATIONS FOR SEASONAL VARIATION

We may now carry out the process of seasonal adjustment by dividing each of the original observations by the appropriate seasonal index, all first-quarter figures being divided by the first-quarter index, all second-quarter figures by the second-quarter index, and so on. (This process is similar to adjusting current dollar data for price changes, a process explained in our discussion of price indexes, p. 271.) The results of these adjustments for the agricultural employment data are shown in column (8) of Table 14–7. The adjusted data are shown in graphical form in Figure 14–9. Those

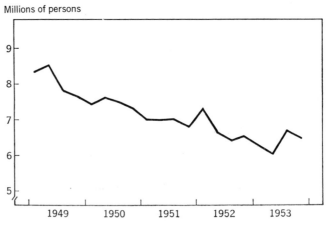

FIGURE 14–9.   Persons Employed in Agriculture Aged 14 Years and Over (Adjusted for Seasonal Variation)

components that have not been adjusted for are very much in evidence, that is, the downward sloping trend and the cyclical-irregulars.

Since the trend ordinates have already been evaluated for the agricultural employment data (see column (7) of Table 14–5), we need only divide each y_i/S by the appropriate value of T to complete the adjustment process. For the first quarter of 1949, we have

$$\frac{y_i}{S \times T} = \frac{6.99}{.836 \times 7.971} = 1.049.$$

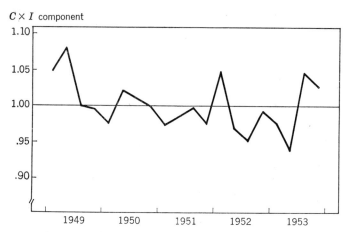

FIGURE 14–10. **Persons Employed in Agriculture Aged 14 Years and Over (Adjusted for Trend and Seasonal Variation)**

Data adjusted for both seasonal variation and trend are shown in column (9) of Table 14–7 and are graphed in Figure 14–10, where we see the characteristic fluctuation of the CI components about a horizontal line drawn at a level of one.

PROJECTION OF $S \times T$

Let us now see if we can project the model beyond 1953 and estimate the seasonal and trend components of agricultural employment in the fourth quarter of 1954. On the time scale, the appropriate value of x_i would be 13.5. Substituting in our trend equation, we find $T = 7.1425 - .0872(13.5) = 7.1425 - 1.1772 \doteq 5.965$. Multiplying this result by our fourth-quarter seasonal index (1.027) we have $S \times T = 1.027 (5.965) = 6.126$ million persons. The actual value of agricultural employment in the fourth quarter of 1954 was 6.154 million persons, indicating a discrepancy of 28,000, which we may ascribe to the cyclical and irregular components, if we have faith in the classical model. If we wish to adjust the $S \times T$ value for cyclical and irregular components, we might try a trick that sometimes works fairly well in forecasting weather, that is, the technique of assuming that the weather tomorrow will be the same as it is today. In the case of the agricultural employment data, we notice that CI is above 1 (greater than trend) in the fourth quarter of 1953, so we assume it will remain at about the same level in the fourth quarter of 1954. Taking the CI component (1.026) for the fourth quarter of 1953, then, we compute $T \times S \times CI = 1.027$ (5.965) (1.026) = 6.285 million persons. But this value is off by 131 thousand, a result which seems to indicate there is something wrong with this particular technique, and indeed there is. Our model postulates that the CI components are irregular, so it is not a consistent application of the model if we decide that CI will remain constant over two successive fourth quarters of the year.

In simple forecasts of this type it is best to make a projection of $S \times T$ only. And this should be done only for short time intervals beyond the last time point in the series. In addition, the trend line should be a good fit, there should be some reasonable ground for believing that it will continue to be a good fit, the seasonal should be quite regular, and the cyclicals and irregulars should be very small. In order to see the dangers of projecting a trend (extrapolating) too far into the future, the reader should extend the linear trend of the agricultural employment series 30 years beyond 1953 and then try to give a meaningful interpretation of the result.

Although it should not be used to forecast CI components, the weather trick has been used in forecasting the trend of semiannual and annual data. Department stores (and presumably many other businesses) have forecast sales volume up to a year in advance by assuming that next year will be like this year—plus or minus a few percentage points. Such forecasts have been found accurate enough for purposes of inventory control.

SOME SIMPLE TECHNIQUES OF FORECASTING

Usually forecasting involves much more than a simple extrapolation of a time series. A good forecaster must have a thorough knowledge of the type of business involved, the interrelationships of the firms in the particular industry, and their relationship to

the economy as a whole. It will often be the case that the exercise
of informed judgment is of much more importance than the mechanics involved in the forecast. To illustrate the way in which
human judgment enters into the forecast, let us take an example
involving the use of survey data to forecast sales for a mythical
motorcar company.

It is March, 1959. The company is Behemoth Motors, Inc.
Sales have been comparatively slow during the winter months and
plans have been made to introduce a smaller car (to be called the
Moth) in the summer if sales do not take a turn for the better during
the remainder of the year. The task of the forecaster (H. J. Squint)
is to determine whether sales will be sufficiently good that the introduction of the new smaller car can be postponed until 1960. It is
decided that if sales of about 2.0 billion dollars can be made in the
remainder of 1959 on the conventional style car, the new Moth need
not be introduced in 1959.

In order to get some idea of the demand for new cars, the forecaster looks up a currently available government survey on intended consumer spending in the remainder of 1959. He finds that
an estimated 7.5% of the households in the country plan to buy
new cars in 1959 and that they plan to spend, on the average, $3100
for each car, this average being a mean.

Now, since it is known that there are about 50 million households in the country (data furnished by another government bureau), we see that about 3.75 million households (.075 × 50) intend
to buy new cars in the remainder of 1959. Apparently, the thing
to do next is to multiply the mean expenditure ($3100) by the
number of families expecting to buy new cars (3.75 million) to get
an estimate of total sales for the industry. However, Squint knows
that several adjustments must be made before attempting any
such estimate.

First, he has to deal with the FA factor. This stands for frus-
trated anticipations and refers to the proportion of households who
are unable to carry out their plans to purchase new cars. Of course,
there may be households that did not intend to buy new cars at
the time of the government survey but that decide later to do so.
The result of this situation is the RI (reversed intentions) factor.
The net effect of these two factors, Squint judges, on the basis of
past experience, will be to reduce the number of purchasing households to 3.5 million, but to have no effect on the mean expenditure.

Now our forecaster multiplies 3.5 million by $3100 to get

$10.85 billion, a first approximation to expected total sales for the industry. However, he realizes that he must reduce this figure in order to take into account the FC (foreign car) factor and the FP (false prestige) factor.

Some of these 10.85 billion dollars are going to go into the foreign car market. Squint estimates on the basis of past years' experience that the amount will be about 10%, so that leaves him with about 9.76 billion dollars.

The FP factor is a tricky thing to deal with. Lately, it seems to Squint to have diminished somewhat, but he feels that it will never get down to the abominably low level where it languished in the dark days when the automobile was intended to perform the function of transportation. In the present, when the auto is designed primarily to sit in front of the house (on a very wide street) to amaze the neighbors and arouse their envy, persons are bound to overstate the amount that they say they intend to spend on a new car. The FP factor, Squint judges, is down to about 5%. So he reduces the $9.76 billion by 5% to get $9.27 billion. Now our forecaster applies Behemoth Motors' traditional share of the market (25%) to the 9.27 billion dollars and arrives at his forecast of 2.3 billion. This value is more than the target sales value of $2.0 billion, so the production of the smaller car is postponed until 1960.

The forecaster's troubles are not over, however. Some of the households who intend to buy cars may have made up their minds to buy only if the rumored new Moth is introduced early in the season. Behemoth's decision not to introduce the small car, if publicized, may cause these households to refrain from buying or to purchase foreign cars. This situation illustrates the general principle that an announced business forecast affects the data on which the forecast was based.

BUSINESS FORECASTING BY TRADITIONAL INDUSTRY SHARE, AND SO ON

We saw that the forecaster in the Behemoth Motors case applied his firm's traditional share of the industry's market in arriving at his final estimate. This technique is fairly common. Frequently a government forecast of the physical output of an industry can be found. A business may then apply a ratio representing its traditional share of such output to the forecast for its own planning purposes. Such a ratio may be adjusted from past levels, depending upon the judgment of the decision makers in the firm.

For almost any business, the level of demand will be related to the level of some income or expenditures aggregate. If the relationship is stable, good short-term forecasts are possible. The amount of money annually spent in the U.S. on clothing and shoes has been a slowly declining proportion of total personal consumption expenditures, except for the World War II period, the proportion being .119 in 1929 and .082 in 1955.[3] An accurate independent forecast of personal consumption expenditures and a knowledge of the relationship will enable one to forecast the amount of expenditure on clothing and shoes fairly accurately.

Forecasting future sales is, of course, the basic type of forecast for a business firm, for practically all other business planning depends upon it. Often forecasts are made by noting the trends or tendencies in some one variable or several variables that have a common-sense correlation with sales of a given firm, industry, or line of business. Real-estate agents, builders, and land speculators are interested in such quantities as rates of family formation, age at marriage, in-migration and out-migration at metropolitan areas, and geographical income distributions. Textbook publishers are deeply interested in estimates of the numbers of persons who will be attending elementary school, high school, and college at various future dates.

At times a mathematical equation is used to indicate the hypothesized relationship between the variables. The equation may involve one dependent variable and one independent variable (as in simple linear regression) or one dependent variable and several independent variables (as in multiple regression).

In all these cases the quantity to be forecast is, of course, assumed to depend upon some other quantity or quantities. This relationship of dependence is an association noted in the past and *assumed to hold in the future*. But one cannot be sure that the assumption will be borne out by future events. This fact makes life interesting (and sometimes painful) for the forecaster. It is much easier to trip and fall when walking into the future backward—and no forecaster yet has discovered the secret of how to turn around.

[3] Thomas Jeff Davis, *Cycles and Trends in Textiles*, U.S. Department of Commerce (Washington, D.C., U.S. Government Printing Office, 1958), p. 46.

Not too many years ago a well-known executive of a retail merchandising concern received considerable notice in the press because of his persistent prediction of a rather severe business contraction following World War II. His forecast was based on the method of "superimposed cycles" of commodity prices. He noted that in every United States war since 1812, wholesale commodity prices had gone up during the war, then reached a peak and declined rather sharply after the war. Superimposing these cycles graphically, he came to the conclusion that a rather severe decline in wholesale prices (and business in general) would occur shortly after World War II, for this had always happened after previous wars. This conclusion led to a policy of contraction by the firm, closing down stores, reducing inventories, and maintaining a highly liquid financial condition. Meanwhile, the leading competitor of the firm (which had not used this one-cylinder method of forecasting) followed a policy of expansion and was able to increase its share of the market considerably.

Differences in methods and judgment invariably lead to diverse forecasts. In the foretelling of any important economic event, some one forecaster is very probably going to be correct simply because there are so many forecasts taking so many different directions at so many different rates.

QUALITATIVE CONSIDERATIONS

We must not overlook the fact that qualitative considerations may be of great importance in determining the outlook of a firm or industry. Governmental policy is particularly important nowadays. This factor may be crucial in such industries as ocean shipping, air transportation, railroads, motor carriers, power, banking, housing, and agriculture, all of these industries being subject to a good deal of governmental aid or regulation or both. In the case of an electric power company—to take just one example—future changes in revenues may depend primarily upon how judges are going to react when the company appeals a regulatory commission's rate order. Even in the case of nonregulated industries, such as manufacturers of electronic equipment, the major portion of annual revenues may come from sales on defense contracts to the federal government. Thus governmental policy on defense and weapons development is a prime consideration for such firms.

SCIENCE, TIME, AND ECONOMICS

The study of time series brings to the surface important and somewhat unique difficulties that we frequently encounter in applying statistical methods to business and economic data. Time series analysis is one of the most important areas of statistics from the standpoint of economic and business applications, yet a study of these techniques leaves one with feelings of dissatisfaction and doubt. We are dissatisfied because we should like to have methods which were firmly grounded in the theory of probability, but to date the theory of probability has not helped to yield very useful results as far as *economic* time series are concerned.

This situation is not due so much to the techniques involved as to the nature of the populations concerned. As we have said, most populations in business and economics change over time, and they often change suddenly, drastically, and with little or no warning. As a result, economics cannot very often provide laws or principles that are consistently useful for prediction or policy formation. Such predictions as are made are tentative, approximate.

To get a better focus on the problem of time in economics, we must understand a few elementary considerations relating to the nature of science. Science may be defined in at least two different ways. First, and we think most importantly, science is a method, the essence being the statistical method: observation of the phenomena of experience, framing hypotheses regarding relationships between these phenomena, testing the hypotheses, and with the accumulation of substantiating evidence, giving the hypothesized relationships the status of scientific laws.

Second, science can be regarded as the body of laws or principles that has been discovered as a result of applying the scientific method. These laws are generalizations concerning populations. Now if the relevant populations are stable over time or periodic, as in the physical sciences, the laws are operational, that is, useful for the purpose of making predictions and hence a dependable basis for human action. The astronomer can predict an eclipse of the sun many years in advance, for the solar system is a population of bodies that move with reference to each other in precise periodic patterns. The chemist assumes that Boyle's law will always work when applied to certain populations of confined gases and his assumption is borne out. Now if the solar system were jarred by an erratic cosmic fist every so often, so that the old laws of motion no longer applied, or if gases underwent unpredictable changes that made Boyle's law inapplicable, the situation would be similar to that in economics.

Important economic principles or "laws" have usually arisen out of attempts to solve difficult problems, often of vital human concern. We have the problem of what constitutes value, the problem of unemployment, the problem of inflation, the problem of distribution, to name only a few. Laws resulting from an attack on these problems at one time and place may be irrelevant at another time and place, the time specification on the economic population being critical.

This situation has led certain economists to seek elements of constancy, slow change, or periodicity in economic populations. Legal and sociological institutions may be studied by some, business "cycles" by others. But the objective, whether explicit or not, is the same: a type of population that will make economics more like the physical sciences, that will take its laws and principles out of the spirit world and make them operational, dependable, and (in more than a rough sort of way) useful for policy formation. As yet these objectives have not been fully realized.

Perhaps economic phenomena are of an evolutionary character, but hardly evolving in accordance with any predictable pattern. If this is so, then what is the lot of the statistician attempting to apply his methods to the slippery world of economic change? It seems to be the case that he must be as much an economist as a statistician, if not more so. And, we hasten to add, this does not imply that he will not be much of a statistician. But it does imply that he will often have to rely on judgment, the wisdom gained from past experience, rather than "standard objective methods." Each new problem will be different to a rather large degree from those that have gone before and his success will, perhaps, depend more than anything else upon his willingness to throw overboard old principles that are no longer relevant and to seek others which are, for the time being, operational and therefore useful.

For purposes of forecasting, the use of alternative techniques may be found helpful. In some cases the extrapolation of time series may give satisfactory results, in others regression analysis may work out quite well, and in still others, the use of surveys to ascertain what certain persons intend to do in the future will work better than other methods. The survey method has been used with some degree of success in estimating intended consumer expenditures and intended investment expenditures of various types.

The techniques of statistical estimation have done a great deal in helping to ascertain the state of the economy as of a given time in the recent past, but much remains to be done as far as developing consistently reliable techniques of forecasting is concerned.

SUMMARY

A time series consists of a set of observations or estimates made on a population at different points in time. We have considered the common case where equal time intervals separate the successive observations. Time series are frequently represented by line graphs, wherein the time intervals are laid off along the horizontal scale and the ordinates of the time series data parallel to the vertical scale. Time series data may be either of the *cumulative* type, that is, analogous to a flow, or of the *noncumulative* type, that is, analogous to a stock.

Time series facilitate comparisons between observations occurring at different points in time, serve as historical records, and aid one in making forecasts.

A proper introduction to the study of time series consists of a consideration of the classical time series model. In this model, each of the data is assumed to consist of four components: the trend, the seasonal, the cyclical, and the irregular. Letting Y stand for a model datum, T for trend, S for seasonal, C for cyclical, and I for irregular, we combine the components by multiplication, $Y = T \times S \times C \times I$.

Annual data, which contain no seasonal, may be represented by the model, $Y = T \times C \times I$.

The first step in classical time series analysis is to evaluate each of the components. Values of T are found by fitting a trend equation to the series. Here we have confined our discussion to the fitting of linear trends. Seasonal indexes may be evaluated by the ratio-to-moving-average method. After we adjust the data for trend and for seasonal variation, we find that the product of the C and I components remains as a residual. In symbols, the adjustment process is as follows:

$$\frac{Y}{T \times S} = \frac{T \times S \times C \times I}{T \times S} = C \times I$$

Since we do not know the model values of Y, we substitute y_i values —the actual observations in the series—for Y in the adjustment process.

Having fitted a trend line and evaluated our seasonal indexes, we may estimate the trend value for some future date by substituting the appropriate x value in the trend equation. The resulting T value may be multiplied by the appropriate seasonal index to form a forecast of the $S \times T$ components. This forecast may be quite accurate for short terms if the trend line is a good fit, if there are reasonable grounds for assuming it will continue to be so, if the seasonal is quite regular, and if the C and I components are small. Adjusting the forecast of $T \times S$ for C and I is a hazardous process, for these components, by nature, are highly unstable.

Straight-line trends on a ratio scale represent constant relative rates of change. For an ordinary line graph on a ratio scale, the relative rate of change is constant as long as the slope of the line is constant.

The projection of a time series may play only a minor part in the making of a business or economic forecast. Computations may involve nothing more than simple ratios. Skill in the exercise of judgment is important in any forecast, for all predictions must be based upon patterns and tendencies observed in the past.

The formulation of "timeless laws" which are useful for purposes of planning and prediction is hardly possible in economics, for such generalizations must either be nonoperational or be applied in a rough sort of way to highly unstable, nonperiodic populations. Much progress has been made in ascertaining the state of the economy as of a given time in the recent past, but much remains to be done as far as developing consistently reliable techniques of forecasting is concerned.

TERMS TO PONDER

1. Cumulative Data
2. Noncumulative Data
3. Trend
4. Seasonal
5. Cyclical
6. Irregular
7. Trend Equation
8. Adjustment for Trend
9. Ratio Scale
10. Average Growth Rate
11. Moving Total
12. Moving Average
13. Seasonal Relative
14. Seasonal Index
15. Seasonal Adjustment
16. Extrapolation

EXERCISES

1. The following data represent private nonfarm housing starts in the United States. Observations are in terms of thousands of units per quarter.

Year	Quarter	y_i
	1	227
1952	2	295
	3	298
	4	249
	1	237
1953	2	315
	3	281
	4	234
	1	232
1954	2	326
	3	339
	4	304
	1	288
1955	2	397
	3	358
	4	267

Source: *Economic Report of the President* (Washington, D.C., U.S. Government Printing Office, 1954, 1956, 1957, 1958), and U.S. Congress, Joint Economic Committee, *Economic Indicators* (Washington, D.C., U.S. Government Printing Office, September, 1954), p. 18.

Plot the series on a line graph.

a. Assuming that the classical model is appropriate for this series, evaluate T by fitting a line of least squares.

b. Construct the appropriate seasonal indexes by the ratio-to-moving-average method.

c. Adjust the observations for trend and seasonal fluctuations.

2. Consider the data at top of page 320 on commercial and industrial sales of publicly owned electric utilities in the Tennessee Valley area.

a. Fit a straight line of least squares to these data.

b. By projecting the trend line to 1959, estimate average sales per customer for that year.

3. If the Gross National Product was 438 billion dollars in 1958 (at 1958 prices), what average growth rate would be necessary to achieve a 500-billion-dollar Gross National Product (1958 prices) in 1963?

4. Classify each of the following examples of time series data as either cumulative or noncumulative:

a. Monthly estimates of the size of the labor force.

b. Annual figures on net worth of General Motors.

c. Quarterly figures on total operating expenses of the Westinghouse Electric Company.

Year	Average sales per customer (thousands of kilowatt-hours)
1946	32.2
1947	35.0
1948	37.5
1949	38.2
1950	39.3
1951	45.2
1952	48.2
1953	51.9
1954	55.0
1955	59.7
1956	64.2
1957	67.3

Source: U.S. Federal Power Commission, *Statistics of Electric Utilities in the United States, 1957, Publicly Owned* (Washington, D.C., U.S. Government Printing Office, n.d.), p. XII.

 d. Weekly figures on the total national debt in the United States.
 e. Daily values of the Temperature-Humidity Index taken at 2 o'clock in the afternoon, Washington, D.C.
5. Suppose you are contemplating the construction of an apartment house in suburban Washington, D.C. What specific types of statistical data would be of value in helping you to decide whether or not to go ahead with the project? Would time series data be of any value to you?

SELECTED REFERENCES

Lewis, Edward E., *Methods of Statistical Analysis in Economics and Business* (Boston, Houghton Mifflin Company, 1953), Chs. X, XI.

Paden, Donald W., and Lindquist, E. F., *Statistics for Economics and Business*, 2d ed. (New York, McGraw-Hill Book Co., Inc., 1956), Chs. XII, XIII, XIV.

Steiner, Peter O., *An Introduction to the Analysis of Time Series*, preliminary ed. (New York, Holt, Rinehart and Winston, Inc., 1957).

15

PRESENTING THE

FINAL RESULTS

Upon completing a statistical study, we must find ways to convey the results clearly and concisely. Often this involves writing a report. The dictum "Keep it brief and simple" almost always presents a real challenge to the writer. If the methods or subject matter are highly technical, the report may become excessively detailed as a result of an attempt to achieve clarity. On the other hand, too much brevity may result only in vagueness.

In general, a statistical report will contain the following major sections: (1) a statement of the circumstances giving rise to the study and the purposes it seeks to achieve, (2) a brief description of the methods and procedures, (3) a statement of the findings of the study, and (4) the conclusions and recommendations.

If appropriate, section (1) may include a brief review of previous work that has been done on the subject of the report. Fundamentally, this section ties in with the basic objectives of one applying the statistical method. Thus we need a clear statement therein as to the new knowledge sought, the problems to be solved, or the decisions to be made. If the methods and procedures are highly technical, a detailed discussion of these matters may be placed in an appendix. However, an attempt should be made to give a brief, clear statement on these matters in section (2) of the report.

Section (3), in presenting the findings, should refer back to section (1) so as to maintain a sense of direction and continuity. In some reports, the findings may comprise several chapters.

Section (4) is sometimes divided, for often a condensed statement of the main conclusions and recommendations is given at the beginning of the report. Such a statement is not infrequently demanded by the busy executive who cannot take the time to read the entire report.

Some reports, which are basically for the purpose of conveying factual information, will not include a set of recommendations. Such is the case with the *Monthly Report on the Labor Force* issued by the U.S. Bureau of the Census. Also in this report, since the circumstances giving rise to it and its purposes are generally well known, the findings occupy the prominent place. The major findings are summarized in tabular form on the first page of the report.

The *Economic Report of the President,* on the other hand, will contain policy recommendations on such things as monetary and fiscal matters, antitrust legislation, the tariff, and agricultural aid programs, to name only a few.

Two extremely important aids to good statistical presentation are tables and graphical devices. We are familiar with these devices to a degree, for they have been employed throughout this book. But the use of tables and graphs in the exposition of statistical methods is a bit different from their use in statistical reports. Let us begin with tables.

STATISTICAL TABLES

Basically, a statistical table is simply an arrangement of data in rows and columns. The table may be of an informal sort, employed much like a parenthetical phrase in an ordinary sentence. In this case no title is given, the table is not numbered or ruled, and the number of data is small. Such tables are sometimes called "leader work." [1] For example, national income for the United States from 1954 to 1958 (billions of current dollars) ran as follows: [2]

1954	301.8
1955	330.2
1956	349.4
1957	364.0
1958	360.8

---

[1] Bruce L. Jenkinson, *Manual of Tabular Presentation,* U.S. Bureau of the Census (Washington, D.C., U.S. Government Printing Office, 1950), p. 1.

[2] U.S. Congress, Joint Economic Committee, *Economic Indicators, June 1959* (Washington, D.C., U.S. Government Printing Office, 1959), p. 3.

This is, of course, simply a listing of data according to time designations. Other types of data may be listed by qualitative categories, such as the types of tobacco which go into most American cigarette blends: [3]

Flue-cured	50%
Turkish	5
Maryland	2 to 3
Burley	remainder

If the information is of a more complicated sort, with data classified according to two or more categories, a formal table is preferable. Let us take as an example a table summarizing some of the findings of the *Monthly Report on the Labor Force* for May, 1959 (p. 13). The various parts of this table are identified in Table 15–1.

The *heading* includes the number and title of the table plus the *headnote,* if necessary. The title should contain a statement of the nature of the data and the time and place to which they refer. The headnote amplifies the title by adding more detail.

The *stub* is the column on the extreme left of the table. It lists, by means of *line captions,* the types of data that are distributed through the other columns.

To the right of the stub at the top of the table we have the *box head,* which contains the *spanners* and *column heads.* A spanner indicates a category that includes the classifications of two or more columns.

Below the box head we find the *field* of the table, which contains the *cells* of the various columns.

Footnotes may be included below the table. They may be of a general nature, applying to the whole table, as in the case of the illustration in Table 15–1, or they may refer to specific column heads. A *source note* should be included if data have been taken from other statistical work.

In general, the categories of major emphasis are listed in the stub. The title will indicate just where this emphasis lies. In the example of Table 15–1, the reasons for not working received major emphasis. Numbers of workers in each of these categories appear

---

[3] Bureau of Business and Economic Research, University of Maryland, "Southern Maryland, A Tobacco Economy," *Studies in Business and Economics* (Vol. 7, No. 4), March, 1954, p. 24.

TABLE 15–1

The Main Parts of a Formal Table

Heading { "Table 8. Employed Persons with a Job but Not at Work, by Reason for Not Working and Pay Status, for the United States: Week of May 10–16, 1959"

Headnote { (Thousands of persons 14 years of age and over)

Reason for not working	Total	Nonagricultural industries		
		Total	Wage and salary workers	
			No.	% paid
Total with a job but not at work............	2,007	1,891	1,681	50.3
Bad weather............	31	16	11	.....
Industrial dispute............	66	66	66	.....
Vacation............	661	654	605	85.6
Illness............	918	845	725	34.1
All other............	331	309	211	22.3

Footnote {

NOTE.—Persons on temporary (less than 30-day) layoff and persons scheduled to start new wage and salary jobs within 30 days no longer included in the category "With a job but not at work." These groups numbered 104,000 and 198,000, respectively in May.

324

in columns, figures in the same column being more easily compared than those in the same row.

The "all other" category is important. Its omission can lead to confusion, particularly when percentage figures are given which will not add to 100 without it.

Data in the same column of a table should be rounded to the same degree of accuracy, the least accurate figure serving as the guide. Failure to round properly, in the manner indicated, occurs fairly often in cases where data from diverse sources are brought together in one column of a table.

We shall conclude our brief discussion of statistical tables at this point. For a more detailed treatment of the subject, the student should consult the reference given in footnote 1.

GRAPHICAL DEVICES

In Chapter 4 the student was exposed to some graphical devices which are used in connection with frequency distributions: the histogram, frequency polygon, and ogive. If such devices are used in a statistical report, they should be titled properly, so that the nature of the data and the time and place to which they refer will be apparent. Also, the axes must be labeled clearly with the unit designations included. Source notes should be given at the bottom of the graphs where appropriate. The same requirements hold for line graphs, which were treated in connection with the discussion of time series in Chapter 14.

In addition to the graphs relating to frequency distributions and time series, statistical reports may include such devices as column charts, bar charts, pie charts, picture diagrams, and statistical maps for purposes of giving a visual effect to certain comparisons.

A column chart is illustrated in Figure 15–1. Such charts often serve a function similar to that of a line graph, for time is commonly measured along the horizontal axis. In this particular example, the columns show the number of life insurance policyholders in the United States. A line graph showing the amount of life insurance in force is superimposed on the column chart.

A bar chart is shown in Figure 15–2. Here a comparison between two points in time is shown for amounts of life insurance purchased in nine different geographical regions. The time comparison requires the drawing of two bars for each region. On

Life Insurance Ownership in the United States

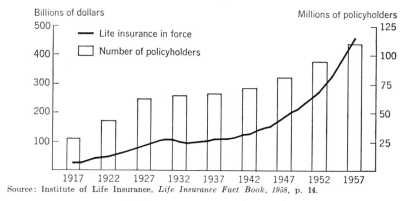

Source: Institute of Life Insurance, *Life Insurance Fact Book, 1958*, p. 14.

FIGURE 15–1.   A Column Chart

simpler bar charts, the time comparison may be omitted.   In other cases, time only may be shown on the vertical axis.

In both bar and column charts, the widths of the bars should be uniform, for we are, in such cases, making linear comparisons. Also, 0 should always be shown on the linear scale and the scale should be broken only in exceptional cases, for if these requirements are not met, distorted comparisons between lengths of bars or columns may very well result.

Pie charts are often used in showing how the consumer's dollar flows into various types of expenditures, how the tax dollar divides into various types of governmental expenditures categories, and

Ordinary Life Insurance Purchases in the United States

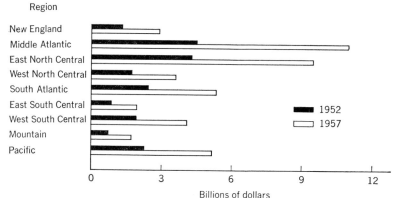

Source: Institute of Life Insurance, *Life Insurance Fact Book, 1958*, p. 21.

FIGURE 15–2.   A Bar Chart

Distribution of Gross National Product, 1957
Total $440 Billion

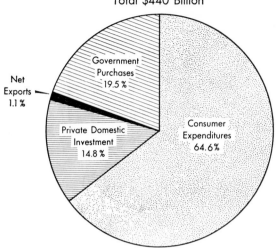

Source: U.S. Department of Commerce, *U.S. Income and Output* (Washington, D.C., U.S. Government Printing Office, 1958), p. 81.

FIGURE 15–3. Pie Chart

so on. The diagram is a circle with each subdivision (or pie slice) proportional in area to the quantity of money or other variable it represents. A pie chart which divides the Gross National Product into its major components is shown in Figure 15–3.

A picture diagram is often similar to a bar chart, except that a row of picture symbols instead of a bar is used to indicate the number of objects or size of the characteristic under consideration. In using picture diagrams, one must be very cautious that distortions do not occur which would give rise to misinterpretations. If the sizes of several figures are to be compared, the attribute of comparison should be indicated, whether it be length, area, or volume. Comparison based on length may lead to ludicrous-appearing figures in the cases where the symbols represent persons.

The picture diagram device is best used in popular presentations where each symbol or picture represents a count of objects. One picture of a tractor may represent 1000 tractors, one cornstalk may represent 1000 bushels of corn, and so on. A picture diagram is shown in Figure 15–4. A report containing a great many picture diagrams is the condensed popular treatment of *America's Needs and Resources* called *U.S.A. in New Dimensions*, both works produced by the Twentieth Century Fund, the latter being published by the Macmillan Company.

HOW BIG IS A TON OF INGOT STEEL?

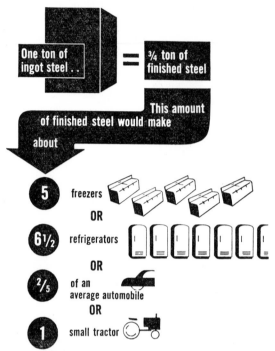

Source: American Iron and Steel Institute, *Charting Steel's Progress* (New York, 1959), p. 17.

FIGURE 15–4. A Picture Diagram

Students have been exposed to statistical maps ever since elementary-school geography courses. These sometimes take the form of dot maps, where each dot represents 1000 sheep, 10,000 bushels of wheat, or some other quantity. Also, a variety of shadings, crosshatchings, and colors may be employed to put various quantities in their appropriate geographical environments. Rather frequent use of statistical maps is made in the publication, *The European Common Market and Its Meaning to the United States* (New York, Committee for Economic Development, 1959).

Regardless of the particular type of graphical device contemplated, these general considerations should be borne in mind:

1. Make sure that the title indicates clearly the nature of the data, the time and the relevant place.
2. Choose a scale that will utilize most of the available space without giving rise to misleading impressions, and label scales so as to designate the quantitative unit clearly.

3. Use source notes unless the data arose from your own firsthand research. Use footnotes where necessary to clarify and amplify important points.

4. Do not use a graph for its own sake. If it does not add to the clarity of the presentation or provide appropriate added emphasis, leave it out.

SOURCES OF READY-MADE STATISTICS

In seeking to acquire new knowledge, solve problems, or make decisions, one saves a great deal of time and effort if he utilizes appropriate ready-made statistics, that is, results of estimates, tests, and analyses that have already been made with regard to the subject at hand.

For students of business and economics, the best single source of descriptive estimates relating to the United States is, perhaps, the *Statistical Abstract of the United States,* which is published annually by the Bureau of the Census. This volume draws upon a multitude of sources, both governmental and private. The bibliography of sources at the back of each volume is arranged alphabetically by subjects and serves as a guide to additional data or more detailed information than is contained in the *Abstract* itself.

Current monthly and quarterly data on income, production, prices, wages, employment, trade, and so on are contained in the *Survey of Current Business,* which is issued monthly by the U.S. Department of Commerce. For statistics with coverage on a local geographical basis, one should see the *County and City Data Book,* also published by the Department of Commerce, but appearing only about once every three years.

As far as more specialized governmental statistics are concerned, those agencies which regulate or promote a given sector of the economy always have a great deal of statistical material available. In the field of land transportation, for example, the important regulatory agency is the Interstate Commerce Commission; in air transportation, the Federal Aviation Agency; in finance, the Federal Reserve Board and the Securities and Exchange Commission; in personnel and labor, the Department of Labor; and in marketing, the Department of Commerce.

In the international field, perhaps the one best general source of ready-made statistics is the *Statistical Yearbook,* published by the Statistical Office of the United Nations. Foreign governments and special agencies such as the International Bank for Reconstruction and Development also collect and publish statistical data on international trade and economic development.

If detailed lists of sources are desired, one may consult, in addition to the *Statistical Abstract of the United States*, the list appearing in F. E. Croxton and D. J. Cowden, *Applied General Statistics*, 2d ed. (Englewood Cliffs, N.J., Prentice-Hall, Inc., 1955), Appendix U, p. 823.

A brief list of sources relating to business forecasting, originally compiled by Maurice S. Bernstein, appears in Nyles V. Reinfeld, *Production Control* (Englewood Cliffs, N.J., Prentice-Hall, Inc., 1959), pp. 95–6.

SUMMARY

The major sections of a statistical report are (1) a statement of circumstances giving rise to the study and the purposes it seeks to achieve, (2) a description of methods and procedures, (3) a statement of the findings, and (4) the conclusions and recommendations.

In some reports, which are primarily for the purposes of conveying current information on a well-known topic, the first section may be omitted. Sometimes section (4) is divided, with a brief statement of the main conclusions and recommendations being given at the beginning of the report. A busy executive may insist upon such an arrangement.

Two important aids to good statistical reporting are tables and graphs. Basically, tables consist of figures arranged in rows and columns. Simple informal tables may be inserted parenthetically in the text of the report. They are not given numbers or titles, nor are they ruled.

A formal table possesses a number and a title and the following additional main parts: stub, box head (containing spanners and column heads), field, source note, and footnotes. In such a table, data may be classified according to two or more categories.

In addition to the graphical devices employed previously in connection with frequency distributions and time series, we have such things as column charts, bar charts, pie charts, picture diagrams, and statistical maps. Each of these graphical forms has several modifications, which make them adaptable to a wide range of types of data.

Ready-made statistics are the results of statistical studies that have already been carried out. A great mass of such statistics, as well as a long list of sources of such data, are given in the *Statistical Abstract of the United States*. Other lists of sources may be found in certain statistical textbooks.

SELECTED REFERENCES

JENKINSON, Bruce L., *Bureau of the Census Manual of Tabular Presentation* (Washington, D.C., U.S. Government Printing Office, 1950).

SCHMID, Calvin F., *Handbook of Graphic Presentation* (New York, The Ronald Press Co., 1954), Chs. IV–IX.

APPENDIX **A**

REVIEW OF

COMMON LOGARITHMS

COMMON LOGARITHMS are simply exponents of the number 10. Some logarithms having whole-number values have been set out in the following table:

No.	Number expressed as a power of 10	Logarithmic notation
.001	10^{-3}	$\log .001 = -3$
.01	10^{-2}	$\log .01 = -2$
.1	10^{-1}	$\log .1 = -1$
1	10^0	$\log 1 = 0$
10	10^1	$\log 10 = 1$
100	10^2	$\log 100 = 2$
1000	10^3	$\log 1000 = 3$

From the table above, we see that the logarithm of .01 is -2 and that the logarithm of 1000 is 3. Now in order to find logarithms of numbers lying between such values as .001 and .01, between 10 and 100, and so on, we must use a more extensive table, such as the one given on pages 345, 346.

To take an example, let us show how to find the logarithm of 8.63. We locate 86 in the extreme left-hand column of the table, then move across the row until we are directly under 3. The value we find is 9360. This is the *mantissa* of the logarithm we seek. That is, it is the part of the log lying to the right of the decimal point. The portion of the log to the left of the decimal point is called the *characteristic* and is found by inspecting a table of whole-number logarithms, such as that given above. Since 8.63 lies between 1 and 10 its characteristic will be 0, for the corresponding exponent of 10 is between 0 and 1. Thus log 8.63 = .9360. Log 86.3 would equal 1.9360, for now we have a number between 10 and 100. In general, *for numbers equal to or greater than 1, the characteristic is one less than the number of digits to the left of the decimal point.*

Suppose now that the number in question lies between 0 and 1. In order for such a number to be expressed as a power of 10, the exponent on 10 would have to be negative. This means, of course, that the logarithm would be negative. Take, for example, the number .0358. We find 35 in the extreme left-hand column of the table and move across to the right until we are directly beneath 8. The mantissa, then, is 5539. Now .0358 is between .01 and .1, so the characteristic will have to be -2. Looking at our original number, we find that *the characteristic is one more (in absolute value) than the number of zeros between the decimal point and the first digit larger than 0*, a rule which holds in general for numbers between 0 and 1. Thus we might be tempted to write log .0358 = -2.5539. But since all mantissas in the table are positive, we write $8.5539 - 10$. This device enables us to save a great deal of space in the log table, for if we introduced negative mantissas into the table, we would—to give just one example—have to have separate entries for log 358 and log .0358.

We are now in a position to discuss the use of logarithms in computations. Logarithms, of course, obey the laws of exponents. The logarithm of the product of several numbers, then, is the sum of their logs. The log of the quotient of two numbers is the difference of their logs. The log of the nth root of a number is $1/n$ times the log of the number. The logarithm of a power of a number is the power multiplied by the log of the number. Having found the log of an answer, we can find the answer itself by looking up the appropriate antilog, that is, the number corresponding to the logarithm.

1. *Multiplication.*

Multiply 796.5×35.86.

Log $(796.5 \times 35.86) = $ log $796.5 + $ log 35.86.

Log 796.5 is between log 796.0 and log 797.0.

The mantissa for 796.0 = 9009.

The mantissa for 797.0 = 9015.

The difference between the mantissas is 6. Since the number we desire (796.5) is $\frac{5}{10}$ of the distance between 796.0 and 797.0, we add $\frac{5}{10}$ of 6, or 3, to the mantissa of 796.0 to get the mantissa of 796.5, this result being $9009 + 3 = 9012$.[1] Now, log $796.5 = 2.9012$, the characteristic being 2, for 796.5 is between 100 and 1000.

---

[1] We may also accomplish an interpolation of this type by referring to the numbers printed in small type on the right side of the table. These small numbers themselves form a *table of proportional parts*. In the example at hand, we locate the last digit of 796.5, that is, 5, in the top row of the table of proportional parts. Then

Using similar methods, we find that the mantissa for 35.86 = 5539 + 7.2 = 55462 and that log 35.86 = 1.55462.

The logarithm of the required answer is found as follows:

$$\log (796.5 \times 35.86) = 2.9012 + 1.55462 = 4.45582$$

Now we must find the antilog of 4.45582. In the log table, we find that the mantissa, 45582, is between 4548 and 4564, so our antilog is between 285 and 286. The mantissa, 45582, is 10.2/16 of the distance between 4548 and 4564. Thus our answer is 10.2/16 of the distance between 285 and 286, so we add .64 to 285 to get 285.64.[2] Since we have a characteristic of 4 in the log of our answer, we will have 5 places to the left of the decimal point in the answer. With the decimal point properly located, then, the result is 28,564. That is, 796.5 × 35.86 = 28,564, or 28,560, our answer being accurate only to 4 significant digits.

2. *Division.*

Divide 78.6 by 93.2, that is, $\dfrac{78.6}{93.2}$.

$$\text{Log}\,\frac{78.6}{93.2} = \log 78.6 - \log 93.2.$$

The mantissa of 78.6 = 8954, and log 78.6 = 1.8954.
The mantissa of 93.2 = 9694, and log 93.2 = 1.9694.

$$\text{Log}\,\frac{78.6}{93.2} = 1.8954 - 1.9694.$$

Now since all mantissas in the table are positive, we must make an adjustment so that this difference will be positive. This adjustment merely involves adding 10 to and subtracting 10 from 1.8954. We have

$$11.8954 - 10$$
$$-1.9694$$
$$\overline{}$$
$$9.9260 - 10$$

To find the required answer, we must now find the antilog of 9.9260 − 10. In the table, we find that the mantissa, 9260, is between the tabular values of 9258 and 9263. These correspond respectively to the numbers 843 and 844. Since 9260 is 2/5 of the distance between 9258 and 9263, we add .4 to 843 to get 843.4 for our antilog. But now we must take into account the characteristic of −1 in the logarithm of our answer.

---

we move down the column headed by 5 until we are in line with the row containing the mantissa of 796. The number in this position is 3, so we add 3 to the mantissa (9009 + 3 = 9012).

[2] In finding an antilog by interpolation, we may also use the table of proportional parts. For the example at hand, we locate the row of the table that is in line with the row containing the mantissas 4548 and 4564. In this row we locate the number which is closest to 10.2, this being 11. We then note that the column containing 11 is headed by 7, which is the final significant digit in the antilogarithm. We write the antilog, in this case, as 28,570, which is approximately equal to 28,564.

Such a characteristic indicates an antilog between 1 and .1. Thus our answer is .8434, which is accurate to three significant digits.

3. *Extracting a root.*

Find the cube root of 212.8, that is, $\sqrt[3]{212.8}$ or 212.8.$^{1/3}$

The laws of exponents tell us that $\log \sqrt[3]{212.8} = \dfrac{\log 212.8}{3}$.

From the table, we find that the mantissa for $\log 212.8 = 3263 + 16.8$, so that $\log 212.8 = 2.32798$. Thus the logarithm of our answer is $2.32798/3 = .77599$. The antilog of .77599 is between 596 and 597, the mantissa for the former being 7752 and for the latter 7760. The mantissa .77599 is 7.9/8 of the distance between 7752 and 7760, so the required antilog is 7.9/8 of the distance between 596 and 597 or $596 + .988 = 596.988$. The remaining problem is to locate the decimal point. In the logarithm of our answer (.77599) the characteristic is 0. Thus our antilog lies between 1 and 10. The correct answer then is 5.96988, which is approximately the cube root of 212.8.

4. *Raising a number to a power.*

Raise 13 to the 3d power, that is, find 13^3.

The laws of exponents tell us that $\log 13^3 = 3 \log 13$.

From the table, we find that $\log 13 = 1.1139$.

Thus $3 \log 13 = 3 \times 1.1139 = 3.3417$.

Antilog $3.3417 = 2196.5$. (The exact cube of 13 is 2197.)

These four operations should be sufficient for most of the computations that the student will encounter in elementary statistics. If the individual steps involved slip his mind, he should remember that common logarithms are exponents to the base 10. From this basic fact and the laws of exponents all of the computational rules follow.

APPENDIX B

REVIEW OF

SQUARE ROOTS

THOSE STUDENTS who forget about square roots seem to do a particularly good job on these two matters: (1) the location of the decimal point in the root, and (2) the distinction between the "odd case" and the "even case."

The first matter is easily handled if we start at the decimal point in the number and group the digits in pairs, proceeding in both directions from the decimal point. A single digit on the extreme left is counted as a "pair." A zero is added to form a pair if a single digit appears on the extreme right. Consider taking the square root of 698.834. We pair off the digits as follows:

$$6'98.83'40$$

Now the following rule will always enable us to locate the decimal point properly: For each pair of digits in the number, there will be one digit in the square root. Thus the root of 698.834 will have two digits to the left of the decimal point. This root is ± 26.435469, if carried to six decimal places. (Roots will usually have to have at least two more significant digits than the number in order to get the required degree of accuracy.)

The first digit in the root is easily found. If the first "pair" on the left of the number is a perfect square, the first digit in the root will be the square root of this perfect square. If the first "pair" is not a perfect square, we find the largest perfect square which will divide the "pair." The root of this perfect square is the first digit in the root of the number. For example, the first digit in the root of 946 is 3. The first digit in the root of .0345 is 1. The remaining digits are readily found by trial and error if a computing machine is available. Or the entire root may be read from a table such as that shown on page 347. Logarithms may, of course, be used to find square roots.

To take another example, consider the number .00497. The square root of this number will have a zero immediately after the decimal point and then a 7. The root to 6 significant digits is ±.0704982. Notice that the positive root is larger than the number itself. Such will always be the case for numbers between 0 and 1.

Consider now the root of .0497. We may be tempted to conclude that the root of this number is identical with the root of .00497 except for the decimal point. Such thinking is due to a confusion of the "odd case" with the "even case," indicating that we have arrived at the second well-forgotten matter. (The square root of .0497, incidentally, is ±.2229350 and that of .00497 is ±.0704982.)

Consider first, numbers between 0 and 1. Those which have an *even* number of zeros between the decimal point and the next digit larger than zero are included in the "even case" and have identical roots except for the decimal point. Similarly, numbers having an *odd* number of zeros between the decimal point and the next digit larger than zero will have identical roots except for the decimal point. Such numbers are covered by the "odd case."

Now, for positive numbers which do not lie between 0 and 1, the "odd case" includes those having an odd number of digits to the left of the decimal point and the "even case" includes those having an even number of digits to the left of the decimal point.

Numbers having no digits to the left of the decimal point and no zeros immediately after the decimal point are included in the even case.

An illustration of the two cases follows:

Odd case		Even case	
No.	*Square root*	*No.*	*Square root*
19,650	140.1785	196,500	443.283
196.5	14.01785	1965	44.3283
1.965	1.401785	19.65	4.43283
.01965	.1401785	.1965	.443283
.0001965	.01401785	.001965	.0443283

Having refreshed his memory on these matters, the student should have no trouble in using the table of squares and square roots which begins on page 347.

TABLES

TABLE I

Areas Under the Normal Curve Between the Ordinate
at the Mean and the Ordinate at Z [1]

(expressed as proportions of the total area under the curve)

Z	.00	.01	.02	.03	.04	.05	.06	.07	.08	.09
0.0	.0000	.0040	.0080	.0120	.0159	.0199	.0239	.0279	.0319	.0359
0.1	.0398	.0438	.0478	.0517	.0557	.0596	.0636	.0675	.0714	.0753
0.2	.0793	.0832	.0871	.0910	.0948	.0987	.1026	.1064	.1103	.1141
0.3	.1179	.1217	.1255	.1293	.1331	.1368	.1406	.1443	.1480	.1517
0.4	.1554	.1591	.1628	.1664	.1700	.1736	.1772	.1808	.1844	.1879
0.5	.1915	.1950	.1985	.2019	.2054	.2088	.2123	.2157	.2190	.2224
0.6	.2257	.2291	.2324	.2357	.2389	.2422	.2454	.2486	.2518	.2549
0.7	.2580	.2612	.2642	.2673	.2704	.2734	.2764	.2794	.2823	.2852
0.8	.2881	.2910	.2939	.2967	.2995	.3023	.3051	.3078	.3106	.3133
0.9	.3159	.3186	.3212	.3238	.3264	.3289	.3315	.3340	.3365	.3389
1.0	.3413	.3438	.3461	.3485	.3508	.3531	.3554	.3577	.3599	.3621
1.1	.3643	.3665	.3686	.3718	.3729	.3749	.3770	.3790	.3810	.3830
1.2	.3849	.3869	.3888	.3907	.3925	.3944	.3962	.3980	.3997	.4015
1.3	.4032	.4049	.4066	.4083	.4099	.4115	.4131	.4147	.4162	.4177
1.4	.4192	.4207	.4222	.4236	.4251	.4265	.4279	.4292	.4306	.4319
1.5	.4332	.4345	.4357	.4370	.4382	.4394	.4406	.4418	4430	.4441
1.6	.4452	.4463	.4474	.4485	.4495	.4505	.4515	.4525	.4535	.4545
1.7	.4554	.4564	.4573	.4582	.4591	.4599	.4608	.4616	.4625	.4633
1.8	.4641	.4649	.4656	.4664	.4671	.4678	.4686	.4693	.4699	.4706
1.9	.4713	.4719	.4726	.4732	.4738	.4744	.4750	.4758	.4762	.4767
2.0	.4772	.4778	.4783	.4788	.4793	.4798	.4803	.4808	.4812	.4817
2.1	.4821	.4826	.4830	.4834	.4838	.4842	.4846	.4850	.4854	.4857
2.2	.4861	.4865	.4868	.4871	.4875	.4878	.4881	.4884	.4887	.4890
2.3	.4893	.4896	.4898	.4901	.4904	.4906	.4909	.4911	.4913	.4916
2.4	.4918	.4920	.4922	.4925	.4927	.4929	.4931	.4932	.4934	.4936
2.5	.4938	.4940	.4941	.4943	.4945	.4946	.4948	.4949	.4951	.4952
2.6	.4953	.4955	.4956	.4957	.4959	.4960	.4961	.4962	.4963	.4964
2.7	.4965	.4966	.4967	.4968	.4969	.4970	.4971	.4972	.4973	.4974
2.8	.4974	.4975	.4976	.4977	.4977	.4978	.4979	.4980	.4980	.4981
2.9	.4981	.4982	.4983	.4984	.4984	.4984	.4985	.4985	.4986	.4986
3.0	.49865									
3.5	.4997647									
4.0	.4999683									

[1] This table is taken from Harold O. Rugg, *Statistical Methods Applied to Education* (Boston, Houghton Mifflin Company, 1917), pp. 389–90, by permission of the publishers.

TABLE II

The "t" Distribution [1]

(probability that | "t" | is exceeded)

df	.10	.05	.02	.01	.001
1	6.314	12.706	31.821	63.657	636.619
2	2.920	4.303	6.965	9.925	31.598
3	2.353	3.182	4.541	5.841	12.924
4	2.132	2.776	3.747	4.604	8.610
5	2.015	2.571	3.365	4.032	6.869
6	1.943	2.447	3.143	4.707	5.959
7	1.895	2.365	2.998	3.499	5.408
8	1.860	2.306	2.896	3.355	5.041
9	1.833	2.262	2.821	3.250	4.781
10	1.812	2.228	2.764	3.169	4.587
11	1.796	2.201	2.718	3.106	4.437
12	1.782	2.179	2.681	3.055	4.318
13	1.771	2.160	2.650	3.012	4.221
14	1.761	2.145	2.624	2.977	4.140
15	1.753	2.131	2.602	2.947	4.073
16	1.746	2.120	2.583	2.921	4.015
17	1.740	2.110	2.567	2.898	3.965
18	1.734	2.101	2.552	2.878	3.922
19	1.729	2.093	2.539	2.861	3.883
20	1.725	2.086	2.528	2.845	3.850
21	1.721	2.080	2.518	2.831	3.819
22	1.717	2.074	2.508	2.819	3.792
23	1.714	2.069	2.500	2.807	3.767
24	1.711	2.064	2.492	2.797	3.745
25	1.708	2.060	2.485	2.787	3.725
26	1.706	2.056	2.479	2.779	3.707
27	1.703	2.052	2.473	2.771	3.690
28	1.701	2.048	2.467	2.763	3.674
29	1.699	2.045	2.462	2.756	3.659
30	1.697	2.042	2.457	2.750	3.646
∞	1.645	1.960	2.326	2.576	3.291

[1] This table is abridged from Table III of Fisher and Yates, *Statistical Tables for Biological, Agricultural, and Medical Research*, 5th ed., published by Oliver and Boyd Ltd., Edinburgh, by permission of the authors and publishers.

TABLE III

Page of Random Digits [1]

31827	80191	43585	20270	74558	48961	90052	02750	82718	27982
92204	68347	84735	32061	47876	42152	89344	82877	44440	61944
72608	47319	85449	66261	38104	76120	66105	86843	17467	79969
71171	34112	21904	22894	46802	68360	67676	37401	50290	46941
30238	58381	06203	10840	07664	84061	78870	19046	94038	74214
97806	63153	46986	88540	26772	51091	60122	13542	29098	02527
68901	15231	70325	54459	74210	33550	67053	03497	00764	50007
51517	35148	82482	85693	34742	79244	54316	59097	05238	71302
96035	69002	34342	01936	91700	87950	36445	27181	94249	35572
40704	12590	78982	10013	72214	98454	63763	75478	24327	74597
99130	52082	16513	04318	44844	62677	52651	92644	60732	8278^1
71335	76694	81253	49676	62672	77020	33251	77045	66312	2003^8
13116	26616	14165	91983	19943	51068	33249	54613	76240	9918^0
97727	69749	70411	30598	83133	74098	05019	92651	23968	39257
55499	59891	93900	73882	25113	59388	43088	23301	32577	52791
68114	62784	03503	02342	33585	79067	62339	67327	50998	48054
10644	70253	87979	40870	51988	92913	41660	58484	48654	81809
63563	42705	55463	28808	32994	93355	85549	85878	05904	85119
50696	67283	43473	16233	06090	37524	02533	41551	86849	63729
38518	61790	07851	50846	59824	61794	38329	16693	74317	87486
29835	05742	96097	41131	44163	56513	17119	69346	05420	06509
81722	66318	35983	03825	65327	00154	32181	50676	88628	92081
76493	58045	96750	07129	28694	35174	95039	09874	53959	79355
49335	20556	69838	18227	50454	68776	00591	81476	95160	32618
32626	25525	16767	87974	58254	09435	16945	70276	45279	49740
31413	49624	17412	92485	88605	17066	49553	43131	83541	54640
30882	36088	10376	15157	23479	92796	08852	98101	43943	44458
41294	09786	32189	23352	72569	43449	42922	91977	57528	49302
17888	24568	43374	48671	62219	17537	23896	10865	64795	21522
84534	85628	24040	62091	52814	00627	38812	37041	53031	62065
84770	38718	43464	28531	51519	98086	26105	98067	75599	05821
57412	03967	67914	47176	77597	98660	53675	83472	08001	75477
64826	46172	01491	06483	17601	86795	48441	79485	38864	89016
76411	41221	57763	52366	06071	32907	65560	31382	38259	13439
52345	55303	85463	56129	92052	58633	91461	13864	56921	23004
89904	07019	11723	27044	91405	04809	58411	56670	09970	31461
79283	35627	79392	14301	64037	26769	21626	82401	36774	88633
48682	88664	43008	32795	31584	98842	23352	88054	24483	93679
76037	32852	87414	96027	98954	42626	80580	93418	71767	88077
17517	46860	09293	41303	06117	13912	46878	38007	08537	27855
83388	12208	91115	21707	13677	90780	32243	09065	21672	39205
55719	99276	72750	18190	51008	70429	34917	50515	86410	87268
24435	18058	05772	72162	34936	62984	78068	06540	12552	72151
54699	57233	62385	34763	55021	47298	60832	32583	42662	00155
10678	53085	81841	14499	40856	34563	60072	28619	65728	72342
59680	53378	61676	67807	03084	19757	93934	80627	44152	21253
44014	55930	28617	75065	82315	92855	00405	22571	77823	38423
33995	38895	35776	76418	62458	17011	44858	56450	38343	31087
75524	91815	79153	32915	41471	14944	69944	17231	15667	48228
68239	39427	42908	78396	31568	38097	68515	14236	46656	90676

[1] By permission from Rand Corporation, *A Million Random Digits with 100,000 Normal Deviates* (Glencoe, Ill., The Free Press, 1955), p. 137.

TABLE IV

Control Chart Factors [1]

| Sample size | $\bar{X}$ chart | | | σ chart | | | | | | R chart | | | | |
| | Factors for control limits | | | Factor for center line | Factors for control limits | | | | Factor for center line | Factors for control limits | | | |
n	A	A_1	A_2	c_2	B_1	B_2	B_3	B_4	d_2	D_1	D_2	D_3	D_4
2	2.121	3.760	1.880	0.5642	0	1.843	0	3.267	1.128	0	3.686	0	3.267
3	1.732	2.394	1.023	0.7236	0	1.858	0	2.568	1.693	0	4.358	0	2.575
4	1.500	1.880	0.729	0.7979	0	1.808	0	2.266	2.059	0	4.698	0	2.282
5	1.342	1.596	0.577	0.8407	0	1.756	0	2.089	2.326	0	4.918	0	2.115
6	1.225	1.410	0.483	0.8686	0.026	1.711	0.030	1.970	2.534	0	5.078	0	2.004
7	1.134	1.277	0.419	0.8882	0.105	1.672	0.118	1.882	2.704	0.205	5.203	0.076	1.924
8	1.061	1.175	0.373	0.9027	0.167	1.638	0.185	1.815	2.847	0.387	5.307	0.136	1.864
9	1.000	1.094	0.337	0.9139	0.219	1.609	0.239	1.761	2.970	0.546	5.394	0.184	1.816
10	0.949	1.028	0.308	0.9227	0.262	1.584	0.284	1.716	3.078	0.687	5.469	0.223	1.777
11	0.905	0.973	0.285	0.9300	0.299	1.561	0.321	1.679	3.173	0.812	5.534	0.256	1.744
12	0.866	0.925	0.266	0.9359	0.331	1.541	0.354	1.646	3.258	0.924	5.592	0.284	1.716
13	0.832	0.884	0.249	0.9410	0.359	1.523	0.382	1.618	3.336	1.026	5.646	0.308	1.692
14	0.802	0.848	0.235	0.9453	0.384	1.507	0.406	1.594	3.407	1.121	5.693	0.329	1.671
15	0.775	0.816	0.223	0.9490	0.406	1.492	0.428	1.572	3.472	1.207	5.737	0.348	1.652
16	0.750	0.788	0.212	0.9523	0.427	1.478	0.448	1.552	3.532	1.285	5.779	0.364	1.636
17	0.728	0.762	0.203	0.9551	0.445	1.465	0.466	1.534	3.588	1.359	5.817	0.379	1.621
18	0.707	0.738	0.194	0.9576	0.461	1.454	0.482	1.518	3.640	1.426	5.854	0.392	1.608
19	0.688	0.717	0.187	0.9599	0.477	1.443	0.497	1.503	3.689	1.490	5.888	0.404	1.596
20	0.671	0.697	0.180	0.9619	0.491	1.433	0.510	1.490	3.735	1.548	5.922	0.414	1.586

[1] Tables IV and IV-A by permission from American Society for Testing Materials, *ASTM Manual on Quality Control of Materials* (Special Technical Publication 15–C, Philadelphia, 1951), pp. 63, 72.

TABLE IV-A

Formulas for Control Limits and Center Lines

Chart	Standards given		Analysis of past data	
	Center line	Limits	Center line	Limits
$\overline{X}$	$\overline{X}'$	$\overline{X}' \pm A\sigma'$	$\overline{\overline{X}}$	$\overline{\overline{X}} \pm A_1\bar{\sigma}$ or $\overline{\overline{X}} \pm A_2\overline{R}$
σ	$c_2\sigma'$	$B_1\sigma'$, $B_2\sigma'$	$\bar{\sigma}$	$B_3\bar{\sigma}$, $B_4\bar{\sigma}$
R	$d_2\sigma'$	$D_1\sigma'$, $D_2\sigma'$	$\overline{R}$	$D_3\overline{R}$, $D_4\overline{R}$

TABLE V

Common Logarithms [1]

No.	0	1	2	3	4	5	6	7	8	9	1 2 3	4 5 6	7 8 9
10	0000	0043	0086	0128	0170	0212	0253	0294	0334	0374	4 8 12	17 21 25	29 33 37
11	0414	0453	0492	0531	0569	0607	0645	0682	0719	0755	4 8 11	15 19 23	26 30 34
12	0792	0828	0864	0899	0934	0969	1004	1038	1072	1106	3 7 10	14 17 21	24 28 31
13	1139	1173	1206	1239	1271	1303	1335	1367	1399	1430	3 6 10	13 16 19	23 26 29
14	1461	1492	1523	1553	1584	1614	1644	1673	1703	1732	3 6 9	12 15 18	21 24 27
15	1761	1790	1818	1847	1875	1903	1931	1959	1987	2014	3 6 8	11 14 17	20 22 25
16	2041	2068	2095	2122	2148	2175	2201	2227	2253	2279	3 5 8	11 13 16	18 21 24
17	2304	2330	2355	2380	2405	2430	2455	2480	2504	2529	2 5 7	10 12 15	17 20 22
18	2553	2577	2601	2625	2648	2672	2695	2718	2742	2765	2 5 7	9 12 14	16 19 21
19	2788	2810	2833	2856	2878	2900	2923	2945	2967	2989	2 4 7	9 11 13	16 18 20
20	3010	3032	3054	3075	3096	3118	3139	3160	3181	3201	2 4 6	8 11 13	15 17 19
21	3222	3243	3263	3284	3304	3324	3345	3365	3385	3404	2 4 6	8 10 12	14 16 18
22	3424	3444	3464	3483	3502	3522	3541	3560	3579	3598	2 4 6	8 10 12	14 15 17
23	3617	3636	3655	3674	3692	3711	3729	3747	3766	3784	2 4 6	7 9 11	13 15 17
24	3802	3820	3838	3856	3874	3892	3909	3927	3945	3962	2 4 5	7 9 11	12 14 16
25	3979	3997	4014	4031	4048	4065	4082	4099	4116	4133	2 3 5	7 9 10	12 14 15
26	4150	4166	4183	4200	4216	4232	4249	4265	4281	4298	2 3 5	7 8 10	11 13 15
27	4314	4330	4346	4362	4378	4393	4409	4425	4440	4456	2 3 5	6 8 9	11 13 14
28	4472	4487	4502	4518	4533	4548	4564	4579	4594	4609	2 3 5	6 8 9	11 12 14
29	4624	4639	4654	4669	4683	4698	4713	4728	4742	4757	1 3 4	6 7 9	10 12 13
30	4771	4786	4800	4814	4829	4843	4857	4871	4886	4900	1 3 4	6 7 9	10 11 13
31	4914	4928	4942	4955	4969	4983	4997	5011	5024	5038	1 3 4	6 7 8	10 11 12
32	5051	5065	5079	5092	5105	5119	5132	5145	5159	5172	1 3 4	5 7 8	9 11 12
33	5185	5198	5211	5224	5237	5250	5263	5276	5289	5302	1 3 4	5 6 8	9 10 12
34	5315	5328	5340	5353	5366	5378	5391	5403	5416	5428	1 3 4	5 6 8	9 10 11
35	5441	5453	5465	5478	5490	5502	5514	5527	5539	5551	1 2 4	5 6 7	9 10 11
36	5563	5575	5587	5599	5611	5623	5635	5647	5658	5670	1 2 4	5 6 7	8 10 11
37	5682	5694	5705	5717	5729	5740	5752	5763	5775	5786	1 2 3	5 6 7	8 9 10
38	5798	5809	5821	5832	5843	5855	5866	5877	5888	5899	1 2 3	5 6 7	8 9 10
39	5911	5922	5933	5944	5955	5966	5977	5988	5999	6010	1 2 3	4 5 7	8 9 10
40	6021	6031	6042	6053	6064	6075	6085	6096	6107	6117	1 2 3	4 5 6	8 9 10
41	6128	6138	6149	6160	6170	6180	6191	6201	6212	6222	1 2 3	4 5 6	7 8 9
42	6232	6243	6253	6263	6274	6284	6294	6304	6314	6325	1 2 3	4 5 6	7 8 9
43	6335	6345	6355	6365	6375	6386	6395	6405	6415	6425	1 2 3	4 5 6	7 8 9
44	6435	6444	6454	6464	6474	6484	6493	6503	6513	6522	1 2 3	4 5 6	7 8 9
45	6532	6542	6551	6561	6571	6580	6590	6599	6609	6618	1 2 3	4 5 6	7 8 9
46	6628	6637	6646	6656	6665	6675	6684	6693	6702	6712	1 2 3	4 5 6	7 7 8
47	6721	6730	6739	6749	6758	6767	6776	6785	6794	6803	1 2 3	4 5 5	6 7 8
48	6812	6821	6830	6839	6848	6857	6866	6875	6884	6893	1 2 3	4 4 5	6 7 8
49	6902	6911	6920	6928	6937	6946	6955	6964	6972	6981	1 2 3	4 4 5	6 7 8
50	6990	6998	7007	7016	7024	7033	7042	7050	7059	7067	1 2 3	3 4 5	6 7 8
51	7076	7084	7093	7101	7110	7118	7126	7135	7143	7152	1 2 3	3 4 5	6 7 8
52	7160	7168	7177	7185	7193	7202	7210	7218	7226	7235	1 2 2	3 4 5	6 7 7
53	7243	7251	7259	7267	7275	7284	7292	7300	7308	7316	1 2 2	3 4 5	6 6 7
54	7324	7332	7340	7348	7356	7364	7372	7380	7388	7396	1 2 2	3 4 5	6 6 7
·	0	1	2	3	4	5	6	7	8	9	1 2 3	4 5 6	7 8 9

[1] By permission from William F. Ehret, *Smith's College Chemistry,* 7th ed. (New York, Appleton-Century-Crofts, Inc., 1960).

TABLE V—(Continued)

Common Logarithms

No.	0	1	2	3	4	5	6	7	8	9	1	2	3	4	5	6	7	8	9
55	7404	7412	7419	7427	7435	7443	7451	7459	7466	7474	1	2	2	3	4	5	5	6	7
56	7482	7490	7497	7505	7513	7520	7528	7536	7543	7551	1	2	2	3	4	5	5	6	7
57	7559	7566	7574	7582	7589	7597	7604	7612	7619	7627	1	2	2	3	4	5	5	6	7
58	7634	7642	7649	7657	7664	7672	7679	7686	7694	7701	1	1	2	3	4	4	5	6	7
59	7709	7716	7723	7731	7738	7745	7752	7760	7767	7774	1	1	2	3	4	4	5	6	7
60	7782	7789	7796	7803	7810	7818	7825	7832	7839	7846	1	1	2	3	4	4	5·6	6
61	7853	7860	7868	7875	7882	7889	7896	7903	7910	7917	1	1	2	3	4	4	5.6	6
62	7924	7931	7938	7945	7952	7959	7966	7973	7980	7987	1	1	2	3	3	4	5	6	6
63	7992	8000	8007	8014	8021	8028	8035	8041	8048	8055	1	1	2	3	3	4	5	5	6
64	8062	8069	8075	8082	8089	8096	8102	8109	8116	8122	1	1	2	3	3	4	5	5	6
65	8129	8136	8142	8149	8156	8162	8169	8176	8182	8189	1	1	2	3	3	4	5	5	6
66	8195	8202	8209	8215	8222	8228	8235	8241	8248	8254	1	1	2	3	3	4	5	5	6
67	8261	8267	8274	8280	8287	8293	8299	8306	8312	8319	1	1	2	3	3	4	5	5	6
68	8325	8331	8338	8344	8351	8357	8363	8370	8376	8382	1	1	2	3	3	4	4	5	6
69	8388	8395	8401	8407	8414	8420	8426	8432	8439	8445	1	1	2	2	3	4	4	5	6
70	8451	8457	8463	8470	8476	8482	8488	8494	8500	8506	1	1	2	2	3	4	4	5	6
71	8513	8519	8525	8531	8537	8543	8549	8555	8561	8567	1	1	2	2	3	4	4	5	5
72	8573	8579	8585	8591	8597	8603	8609	8615	8621	8627	1	1	2	2	3	4	4	5	5
73	8633	8639	8645	8651	8657	8663	8669	8675	8681	8686	1	1	2	2	3	4	4	5	5
74	8692	8698	8704	8710	8716	8722	8727	8733	8739	8745	1	1	2	2	3	4	4	5	5
75	8751	8756	8762	8768	8774	8779	8785	8791	8797	8802	1	1	2	2	3	3	4	5	5
76	8808	8814	8820	8825	8831	8837	8842	8848	8854	8859	1	1	2	2	3	3	4	5	5
77	8865	8871	8876	8882	8887	8893	8899	8904	8910	8915	1	1	2	2	3	3	4	4	5
78	8921	8927	8932	8938	8943	8949	8954	8960	8965	8971	1	1	2	2	3	3	4	4	5
79	8976	8982	8987	8993	8998	9004	9009	9015	9020	9025	1	1	2	2	3	3	4	4	5
80	9031	9036	9042	9047	9053	9058	9063	9069	9074	9079	1	1	2	2	3	3	4	4	5
81	9085	9090	9096	9101	9106	9112	9117	9122	9128	9133	1	1	2	2	3	3	4	4	5
82	9138	9143	9149	9154	9159	9165	9170	9175	9180	9186	1	1	2	2	3	3	4	4	5
83	9191	9196	9201	9206	9212	9217	9222	9227	9232	9238	1	1	2	2	3	3	4	4	5
84	9243	9248	9253	9258	9263	9269	9274	9279	9284	9289	1	1	2	2	3	3	4	4	5
85	9294	9299	9304	9309	9315	9320	9325	9330	9335	9340	1	1	2	2	3	3	4	4	5
86	9345	9350	9355	9360	9365	9370	9375	9380	9385	9390	1	1	2	2	3	3	4	4	5
87	9395	9400	9405	9410	9415	9420	9425	9430	9435	9440	0	1	1	2	2	3	3	4	4
88	9445	9450	9455	9460	9465	9469	9474	9479	9484	9489	0	1	1	2	2	3	3	4	4
89	9494	9499	9504	9509	9513	9518	9523	9528	9533	9538	0	1	1	2	2	3	3	4	4
90	9542	9547	9552	9557	9562	9566	9571	9576	9581	9586	0	1	1	2	2	3	3	4	4
91	9590	9595	9600	9605	9609	9614	9619	9624	9628	9633	0	1	1	2	2	3	3	4	4
92	9638	9643	9647	9652	9657	9661	9666	9671	9675	9680	0	1	1	2	2	3	3	4	4
93	9685	9689	9694	9699	9703	9708	9713	9717	9722	9727	0	1	1	2	2	3	3	4	4
94	9731	9736	9741	9745	9750	9754	9759	9763	9768	9773	0	1	1	2	2	3	3	4	4
95	9777	9782	9786	9791	9795	9800	9805	9809	9814	9818	0	1	1	2	2	3	3	4	4
96	9823	9827	9832	9836	9841	9845	9850	9854	9859	9863	0	1	1	2	2	3	3	4	4
97	9868	9872	9877	9881	9886	9890	9894	9899	9903	9908	0	1	1	2	2	3	3	4	4
98	9912	9917	9921	9926	9930	9934	9939	9943	9948	9952	0	1	1	2	2	3	3	4	4
99	9956	9961	9965	9969	9974	9978	9983	9987	9991	9996	0	1	1	2	2	3	3	3	4
	0	1	2	3	4	5	6	7	8	9	1	2	3	4	5	6	7	8	9

TABLE VI

Squares, Square Roots, and Reciprocals [1]

N	N^2	$\sqrt{N}$	$\frac{1}{N}$	N	N^2	$\sqrt{N}$	$\frac{1}{N}$
1	1	1.0000		50	2500	7.0711	.020000
2	4	1.4142	.500000	51	2601	7.1414	.019608
3	9	1.7321	.333333	52	2704	7.2111	.019231
4	16	2.0000	.250000	53	2809	7.2801	.018868
				54	2916	7.3485	.018519
5	25	2.2361	.200000	55	3025	7.4162	.018182
6	36	2.4495	.166667	56	3136	7.4833	.017857
7	49	2.6458	.142857	57	3249	7.5498	.017544
8	64	2.8284	.125000	58	3364	7.6158	.017241
9	81	3.0000	.111111	59	3481	7.6811	.016949
10	100	3.1623	.100000	60	3600	7.7460	.016667
11	121	3.3166	.090909	61	3721	7.8102	.016393
12	144	3.4641	.083333	62	3844	7.8740	.016129
13	169	3.6056	.076923	63	3969	7.9373	.015873
14	196	3.7417	.071429	64	4096	8.0000	.015625
15	225	3.8730	.066667	65	4225	8.0623	.015385
16	256	4.0000	.062500	66	4356	8.1240	.015152
17	289	4.1231	.058824	67	4489	8.1854	.014925
18	324	4.2426	.055556	68	4624	8.2462	.014706
19	361	4.3589	.052632	69	4761	8.3066	.014493
20	400	4.4721	.050000	70	4900	8.3666	.014286
21	441	4.5826	.047619	71	5041	8.4261	.014085
22	484	4.6904	.045455	72	5184	8.4853	.013889
23	529	4.7958	.043478	73	5329	8.5440	.013699
24	576	4.8990	.041667	74	5476	8.6023	.013514
25	625	5.0000	.040000	75	5625	8.6603	.013333
26	676	5.0990	.038462	76	5776	8.7178	.013158
27	729	5.1962	.037037	77	5929	8.7750	.012987
28	784	5.2915	.035714	78	6084	8.8318	.012821
29	841	5.3852	.034483	79	6241	8.8882	.012658
30	900	5.4772	.033333	80	6400	8.9443	.012500
31	961	5.5678	.032258	81	6561	9.0000	.012346
32	1024	5.6569	.031250	82	6724	9.0554	.012195
33	1089	5.7446	.030303	83	6889	9.1104	.012048
34	1156	5.8310	.029412	84	7056	9.1652	.011905
35	1225	5.9161	.028571	85	7225	9.2195	.011765
36	1296	6.0000	.027778	86	7396	9.2736	.011628
37	1369	6.0828	.027027	87	7569	9.3274	.011494
38	1444	6.1644	.026316	88	7744	9.3808	.011364
39	1521	6.2450	.025641	89	7921	9.4340	.011236
40	1600	6.3246	.025000	90	8100	9.4868	.011111
41	1681	6.4031	.024390	91	8281	9.5394	.010989
42	1764	6.4807	.023810	92	8464	9.5917	.010870
43	1849	6.5574	.023256	93	8649	9.6437	.010753
44	1936	6.6332	.022727	94	8836	9.6954	.010638
45	2025	6.7082	.022222	95	9025	9.7468	.010526
46	2116	6.7823	.021739	96	9216	9.7980	.010417
47	2209	6.8557	.021277	97	9409	9.8489	.010309
48	2304	6.9282	.020833	98	9604	9.8995	.010204
49	2401	7.0000	.020408	99	9801	9.9499	.010101

[1] By permission from James E. Wert, Charles O. Neidt, and J. Stanley Ahmann, *Statistical Methods in Educational and Psychological Research* (New York, Appleton-Century-Crofts, Inc., 1954).

TABLES

TABLE VI—(Continued)

Squares, Square Roots, and Reciprocals

N	N^2	$\sqrt{N}$	$\frac{1}{N}$	N	N^2	$\sqrt{N}$	$\frac{1}{N}$
100	10000	10.0000	.010000	150	22500	12.2474	.006667
101	10201	10.0499	.009901	151	22801	12.2882	.006623
102	10404	10.0995	.009804	152	23104	12.3288	.006579
103	10609	10.1489	.009709	153	23409	12.3693	.006536
104	10816	10.1980	.009615	154	23716	12.4097	.006494
105	11025	10.2470	.009524	155	24025	12.4499	.006452
106	11236	10.2956	.009434	156	24336	12.4900	.006410
107	11449	10.3441	.009346	157	24649	12.5300	.006369
108	11664	10.3923	.009259	158	24964	12.5698	.006329
109	11881	10.4403	.009174	159	25281	12.6095	.006289
110	12100	10.4881	.009091	160	25600	12.6491	.006250
111	12321	10.5357	.009009	161	25921	12.6886	.006211
112	12544	10.5830	.008929	162	26244	12.7279	.006173
113	12769	10.6301	.008850	163	26569	12.7671	.006135
114	12996	10.6771	.008772	164	26896	12.8062	.006098
115	13225	10.7238	.008696	165	27225	12.8452	.006061
116	13456	10.7703	.008621	166	27556	12.8841	.006024
117	13689	10.8167	.008547	167	27889	12.9228	.005988
118	13924	10.8628	.008475	168	28224	12.9615	.005952
119	14161	10.9087	.008403	169	28561	13.0000	.005917
120	14400	10.9545	.008333	170	28900	13.0384	.005882
121	14641	11.0000	.008264	171	29241	13.0767	.005848
122	14884	11.0454	.008197	172	29584	13.1149	.005814
123	15129	11.0905	.008130	173	29929	13.1529	.005780
124	15376	11.1355	.008065	174	30276	13.1909	.005747
125	15625	11.1803	.008000	175	30625	13.2288	.005714
126	15876	11.2250	.007937	176	30976	13.2665	.005682
127	16129	11.2694	.007874	177	31329	13.3041	.005650
128	16384	11.3137	.007813	178	31684	13.3417	.005618
129	16641	11.3578	.007752	179	32041	13.3791	.005587
130	16900	11.4018	.007692	180	32400	13.4164	.005556
131	17161	11.4455	.007634	181	32761	13.4536	.005525
132	17424	11.4891	.007576	182	33124	13.4907	.005495
133	17689	11.5326	.007519	183	33498	13.5277	.005464
134	17956	11.5758	.007463	184	33856	13.5647	.005435
135	18225	11.6190	.007407	185	34225	13.6015	.005405
136	18496	11.6619	.007353	186	34596'	13.6382	.005376
137	18769	11.7047	.007299	187	34969	13.6748	.005348
138	19044	11.7473	.007246	188	35344	13.7113	.005319
139	19321	11.7898	.007194	189	35721	13.7477	.005291
140	19600	11.8322	.007143	190	36100	13.7840	.005263
141	19881	11.8743	.007092	191	36481	13.8203	.005236
142	20164	11.9164	.007042	192	36864	13.8564	.005208
143	20449	11.9583	.006993	193	37249	13.8924	.005181
144	20736	12.0000	.006944	194	37636	13.9284	.005155
145	21025	12.0416	.006897	195	38025	13.9642	.005128
146	21316	12.0830	.006849	196	38416	14.0000	.005102
147	21609	12.1244	.006803	197	38809	14.0357	.005076
148	21904	12.1655	.006757	198	39204	14.0712	.005051
149	22201	12.2066	.006711	199	39601	14.1067	.005025

TABLE VI—(Continued)

Squares, Square Roots, and Reciprocals

N	N^2	$\sqrt{N}$	$\frac{1}{N}$	N	N^2	$\sqrt{N}$	$\frac{1}{N}$
200	40000	14.1421	.005000	250	62500	15.8114	.004000
201	40401	14.1774	.004975	251	63001	15.8430	.003984
202	40804	14.2127	.004950	252	63504	15.8745	.003968
203	41209	14.2478	.004926	253	64009	15.9060	.003953
204	41616	14.2829	.004902	254	64516	15.9374	.003937
205	42025	14.3178	.004878	255	65025	15.9687	.003922
206	42436	14.3527	.004854	256	65536	16.0000	.003906
207	42849	14.3875	.004831	257	66049	16.0312	.003891
208	43264	14.4222	.004808	258	66564	16.0624	.003876
209	43681	14.4568	.004785	259	67081	16.0935	.003861
210	44100	14.4914	.004762	260	67600	16.1245	.003846
211	44521	14.5258	.004739	261	68121	16.1555	.003831
212	44944	14.5602	.004717	262	68644	16.1864	.003817
213	45369	14.5945	.004695	263	69169	16.2173	.003802
214	45796	14.6287	.004673	264	69696	16.2481	.003788
215	46225	14.6629	.004651	265	70225	16.2788	.003774
216	46656	14.6969	.004630	266	70756	16.3095	.003759
217	47089	14.7309	.004608	267	71289	16.3401	.003745
218	47524	14.7648	.004587	268	71824	16.3707	.003731
219	47961	14.7986	.004566	269	72361	16.4012	.003717
220	48400	14.8324	.004545	270	72900	16.4317	.003704
221	48841	14.8661	.004525	271	73441	16.4621	.003690
222	49284	14.8997	.004505	272	73984	16.4924	.003676
223	49729	14.9332	.004484	273	74529	16.5227	.003663
224	50176	14.9666	.004464	274	75076	16.5529	.003650
225	50625	15.0000	.004444	275	75625	16.5831	.003636
226	51076	15.0333	.004425	276	76176	16.6132	.003623
227	51529	15.0665	.004405	277	76729	16.6433	.003610
228	51984	15.0997	.004386	278	77284	16.6733	.003597
229	52441	15.1327	.004367	279	77841	16.7033	.003584
230	52900	15.1658	.004348	280	78400	16.7332	.003571
231	53361	15.1987	.004329	281	78961	16.7631	.003559
232	53824	15.2315	.004310	282	79524	16.7929	.003546
233	54289	15.2643	.004292	283	80089	16.8226	.003534
234	54756	15.2971	.004274	284	80656	16.8523	.003521
235	55225	15.3297	.004255	285	81225	16.8819	.003509
236	55696	15.3623	.004237	286	81796	16.9115	.003497
237	56169	15.3948	.004219	287	82369	16.9411	.003484
238	56644	15.4272	.004202	288	82944	16.9706	.003472
239	57121	15.4596	.004184	289	83521	17.0000	.003460
240	57600	15.4919	.004167	290	84100	17.0294	.003448
241	58081	15.5242	.004149	291	84681	17.0587	.003436
242	58564	15.5563	.004132	292	85264	17.0880	.003425
243	59049	15.5885	.004115	293	85849	17.1172	.003413
244	59536	15.6205	.004098	294	86436	17.1464	.003401
245	60025	15.6525	.004082	295	87025	17.1756	.003390
246	60516	15.6844	.004065	296	87616	17.2047	.003378
247	61009	15.7162	.004049	297	88209	17.2337	.003367
248	61504	15.7480	.004032	298	88804	17.2627	.003356
249	62001	15.7797	.004016	299	89401	17.2916	.003344

TABLE VI—(Continued)

Squares, Square Roots, and Reciprocals

N	N^2	$\sqrt{N}$	$\frac{1}{N}$	N	N^2	$\sqrt{N}$	$\frac{1}{N}$
300	90000	17.3205	.003333	350	122500	18.7083	.002857
301	90601	17.3494	.003322	351	123201	18.7350	.002849
302	91204	17.3781	.003311	352	123904	18.7617	.002841
303	91809	17.4069	.003300	353	124609	18.7883	.002833
304	92416	17.4356	.003289	354	125316	18.8149	.002825
305	93025	17.4642	.003279	355	126025	18.8414	.002817
306	93636	17.4929	.003268	356	126736	18.8680	.002809
307	94249	17.5214	.003257	357	127449	18.8944	.002801
308	94864	17.5499	.003247	358	128164	18.9209	.002793
309	95481	17.5784	.003236	359	128881	18.9473	.002786
310	96100	17.6068	.003226	360	129600	18.9737	.002778
311	96721	17.6352	.003215	361	130321	19.0000	.002770
312	97344	17.6635	.003205	362	131044	19.0263	.002762
313	97969	17.6918	.003195	363	131769	10.0526	.002755
314	98596	17.7200	.003185	364	132496	19.0788	.002747
315	99225	17.7482	.003175	365	133225	19.1050	.002740
316	99856	17.7764	.003165	366	133956	19.1311	.002732
317	100489	17.8045	.003155	367	134689	19.1572	.002725
318	101124	17.8326	.003145	368	135424	19.1833	.002717
319	101761	17.8606	.003135	369	136161	19.2094	.002710
320	102400	17.8885	.003125	370	136900	19.2354	.002703
321	103041	17.9165	.003115	371	137641	19.2614	.002695
322	103684	17.9444	.003106	372	138384	19.2873	.002688
323	104329	17.9722	.003096	373	139129	19.3132	.002681
324	104976	18.0000	.003086	374	139876	19.3391	.002674
325	105625	18.0278	.003077	375	140625	19.3649	.002667
326	106276	18.0555	.003067	376	141376	19.3907	.002660
327	106929	18.0831	.003058	377	142129	19.4165	.002653
328	107584	18.1108	.003049	378	142884	19.4422	.002646
329	108241	18.1384	.003040	379	143641	19.4679	.002639
330	108900	18.1659	.003030	380	144400	19.4936	.002632
331	109561	18.1934	.003021	381	145161	19.5192	.002625
332	110224	18.2209	.003012	382	145924	19.5448	.002618
333	110889	18.2483	.003003	383	146689	19.5704	.002611
334	111556	18.2757	.002994	384	147456	19.5959	.002604
335	112225	18.3030	.002985	385	148225	19.6214	.002597
336	112896	18.3303	.002976	386	148996	19.6469	.002591
337	113569	18.3576	.002967	387	149769	19.6723	.002584
338	114244	18.3848	.002959	388	150544	19.6977	.002577
339	114921	18.4120	.002950	389	151321	19.7231	.002571
340	115600	18.4391	.002941	390	152100	19.7484	.002564
341	116281	18.4662	.002933	391	152881	19.7737	.002558
342	116964	18.4932	.002924	392	153664	19.7990	.002551
343	117649	18.5203	.002915	393	154449	19.8242	.002545
344	118336	18.5472	.002907	394	155236	19.8494	.002538
345	119025	18.5742	.002899	395	156025	19.8746	.002532
346	119716	18.6011	.002890	396	156816	19.8997	.002525
347	120409	18.6279	.002882	397	157609	19.9249	.002519
348	121104	18.6548	.002874	398	158404	19.9499	.002513
349	121801	18.6815	.002865	399	159201	19.9750	.002506

TABLE VI—(Continued)

Squares, Square Roots, and Reciprocals

N	N^2	$\sqrt{N}$	$\frac{1}{N}$	N	N^2	$\sqrt{N}$	$\frac{1}{N}$
400	160000	20.0000	.002500	450	202500	21.2132	.002222
401	160801	20.0250	.002494	451	203401	21.2368	.002217
402	161604	20.0499	.002488	452	204304	21.2603	.002212
403	162409	20.0749	.002481	453	205209	21.2838	.002208
404	163216	20.0998	.002475	454	206116	21.3073	.002203
405	164025	20.1246	.002469	455	207025	21.3307	.002198
406	164836	20.1494	.002463	456	207936	21.3542	.002193
407	165649	20.1742	.002457	457	208849	21.3776	.002188
408	166464	20.1990	.002451	458	209764	21.4009	.002183
409	167281	20.2237	.002445	459	210681	21.4243	.002179
410	168100	20.2485	.002439	460	211600	21.4476	.002174
411	168921	20.2731	.002433	461	212521	21.4709	.002169
412	169744	20.2978	.002427	462	213444	21.4942	.002165
413	170569	20.3224	.002421	463	214369	21.5174	.002160
414	171396	20.3470	.002415	464	215296	21.5407	.002155
415	172225	20.3715	.002410	465	216225	21.5639	.002151
416	173056	20.3961	.002404	466	217156	21.5870	.002146
417	173889	20.4206	.002398	467	218089	21.6102	.002141
418	174724	20.4450	.002392	468	219024	21.6333	.002137
419	175561	20.4695	.002387	469	219961	21.6564	.002132
420	176400	20.4939	.002381	470	220900	21.6795	.002128
421	177241	20.5183	.002375	471	221841	21.7025	.002123
422	178084	20.5426	.002370	472	222784	21.7256	.002119
423	178929	20.5670	.002364	473	223729	21.7486	.002114
424	179776	20.5913	.002358	474	224676	21.7715	.002110
425	180625	20.6155	.002353	475	225625	21.7945	.002105
426	181476	20.6398	.002347	476	226576	21.8174	.002101
427	182329	20.6640	.002342	477	227529	21.8403	.002096
428	183184	20.6882	.002336	478	228484	21.8632	.002092
429	184041	20.7123	.002331	479	229441	21.8861	.002088
430	184900	20.7364	.002326	480	230400	21.9089	.002083
431	185761	20.7605	.002320	481	231361	21.9317	.002079
432	186624	20.7846	.002315	482	232324	21.9545	.002075
433	187489	20.8087	.002309	483	233289	21.9773	.002070
434	188356	20.8327	.002304	484	234256	22.0000	.002066
435	189225	20.8567	.002299	485	235225	22.0227	.002062
436	190096	20.8806	.002294	486	236196	22.0454	.002058
437	190969	20.9045	.002288	487	237169	22.0681	.002053
438	191844	20.9284	.002283	488	238144	22.0907	.002049
439	192721	20.9523	.002278	489	239121	22.1133	.002045
440	193600	20.9762	.002273	490	240100	22.1359	.002041
441	194481	21.0000	.002268	491	241081	22.1585	.002037
442	195364	21.0238	.002262	492	242064	22.1811	.002033
443	196249	21.0476	.002257	493	243049	22.2036	.002028
444	197136	21.0713	.002252	494	244036	22.2261	.002024
445	198025	21.0950	.002247	495	245025	22.2486	.002020
446	198916	21.1187	.002242	496	246016	22.2711	.002016
447	199809	21.1424	.002237	497	247009	22.2935	.002012
448	200704	21.1660	.002232	498	248004	22.3159	.002008
449	201601	21.1896	.002227	499	249001	22.3383	.002004

TABLE VI—(Continued)

Squares, Square Roots, and Reciprocals

N	N²	√N	1/N	N	N²	√N	1/N
500	250000	22.3607	.002000	550	302500	23.4521	.001818
501	251001	22.3830	.001996	551	303601	23.4734	.001815
502	252004	22.4054	.001992	552	304704	23.4947	.001812
503	253009	22.4277	.001988	553	305809	23.5160	.001808
504	254016	22.4499	.001984	554	306916	23.5372	.001805
505	255025	22.4722	.001980	555	308025	23.5584	.001802
506	256036	22.4944	.001976	556	309136	23.5797	.001799
507	257049	22.5167	.001972	557	310249	23.6008	.001795
508	258064	22.5389	.001969	558	311364	23.6220	.001792
509	259081	22.5610	.001965	559	312481	23.6432	.001789
510	260100	22.5832	.001961	560	313600	23.6643	.001786
511	261121	22.6053	.001957	561	314721	23.6854	.001783
512	262144	22.6274	.001953	562	315844	23.7065	.001779
513	263169	22.6495	.001949	563	316969	23.7276	.001776
514	264196	22.6716	.001946	564	318096	23.7487	.001773
515	265225	22.6936	.001942	565	319225	23.7697	.001770
516	226256	22.7156	.001938	566	320356	23.7908	.001767
517	267289	22.7376	.001934	567	321489	23.8118	.001764
518	268324	22.7596	.001931	568	322624	23.8328	.001761
519	269361	22.7816	.001927	569	323761	23.8537	.001757
520	270400	22.8035	.001923	570	324900	23.8747	.001754
521	271441	22.8254	.001919	571	326041	23.8956	.001751
522	272484	22.8473	.001916	572	327184	23.9165	.001748
523	273529	22.8692	.001912	573	328329	23.9374	.001745
524	274576	22.8910	.001908	574	329476	23.9583	.001742
525	275625	22.9129	.001905	575	330625	23.9792	.001739
526	276676	22.9347	.001901	576	331776	24.0000	.001736
527	277729	22.9565	.001898	577	332929	24.0208	.001733
528	278784	22.9783	.001894	578	334084	24.0416	.001730
529	279841	23.0000	.001890	579	335241	24.0624	.001727
530	280900	23.0217	.001887	580	336400	24.0832	.001724
531	281961	23.0434	.001883	581	337561	24.1039	.001721
532	283024	23.0651	.001880	582	338724	24.1247	.001718
533	284089	23.0868	.001876	583	339889	24.1454	.001715
534	285156	23.1084	.001873	584	341056	24.1661	.001712
535	286225	23.1301	.001869	585	342225	24.1877	.001709
536	287296	23.1517	.001866	586	343396	24.2074	.001706
537	288369	23.1733	.001862	587	344569	24.2281	.001704
538	289444	23.1948	.001859	588	345744	24.2487	.001701
539	290521	23.2164	.001855	589	346921	24.2693	.001698
540	291600	23.2379	.001852	590	348100	24.2899	.001695
541	292681	23.2594	.001848	591	349281	24.3105	.001692
542	293764	23.2809	.001845	592	350464	24.3311	.001689
543	294849	23.3024	.001842	593	351649	24.3516	.001686
544	295936	23.3238	.001838	594	352836	24.3721	.001684
545	297025	23.3452	.001835	595	354025	24.3926	.001681
546	298116	23.3666	.001832	596	355216	24.4131	.001678
547	299209	23.3880	.001828	597	356409	24.4336	.001675
548	300304	23.4094	.001825	598	357604	24.4540	.001672
549	301401	23.4307	.001821	599	358801	24.4745	.001669

TABLE VI—(Continued)

Squares, Square Roots, and Reciprocals

N	N^2	$\sqrt{N}$	$\frac{1}{N}$	N	N^2	$\sqrt{N}$	$\frac{1}{N}$
600	360000	24.4949	.001667	650	422500	25.4951	.001538
601	361201	24.5153	.001664	651	423801	25.5147	.001536
602	362404	24.5357	.001661	652	425104	25.5343	.001534
603	363609	24.5561	.001658	653	426409	25.5539	.001531
604	364816	24.5764	.001656	654	427716	25.5734	.001529
605	366025	24.5967	.001653	655	429025	25.5930	.001527
606	367236	24.6171	.001650	656	430336	25.6125	.001524
607	368449	24.6374	.001647	657	431649	25.6320	.001522
608	369664	24.6577	.001645	658	432964	25.6515	.001520
609	370881	24.6779	.001642	659	434281	25.6710	.001517
610	372100	24.6982	.001639	660	435600	25.6905	.001515
611	373321	24.7184	.001637	661	436921	25.7099	.001513
612	374544	24.7386	.001634	662	438244	25.7294	.001511
613	375769	24.7588	.001631	663	439569	25.7488	.001508
614	376996	24.7790	.001629	664	440896	25.7682	.001506
615	378225	24.7992	.001626	665	442225	25.7876	.001504
616	379456	24.8193	.001623	666	443556	25.8070	.001502
617	380689	24.8395	.001621	667	444889	25.8263	.001499
618	381924	24.8596	.001618	668	446224	25.8457	.001497
619	383161	24.8797	.001616	669	447561	25.8650	.001495
620	384400	24.8998	.001613	670	448900	25.8844	.001493
621	385641	24.9199	.001610	671	450241	25.9037	.001490
622	386884	24.9399	.001608	672	451584	25.9230	.001488
623	388129	24.9600	.001605	673	452929	25.9422	.001486
624	389376	24.9800	.001603	674	454276	25.9615	.001484
625	390625	25.0000	.001600	675	455625	25.9808	.001481
626	391876	25.0200	.001597	676	456976	26.0000	.001479
627	393129	25.0400	.001595	677	458329	26.0192	.001477
628	394384	25.0599	.001592	678	459684	26.0384	.001475
629	395641	25.0799	.001590	679	461041	26.0576	.001473
630	396900	25.0998	.001587	680	462400	26.0768	.001471
631	398161	25.1197	.001585	681	463761	26.0960	.001468
632	399424	25.1396	.001582	682	465124	26.1151	.001466
633	400689	25.1595	.001580	683	466489	26.1343	.001464
634	401956	25.1794	.001577	684	467856	26.1534	.001462
635	403225	25.1992	.001575	685	469225	26.1725	.001460
636	404496	25.2190	.001572	686	470596	26.1916	.001458
637	405769	25.2389	.001570	687	471969	26.2107	.001456
638	407044	25.2587	.001567	688	473344	26.2298	.001453
639	408321	25.2784	.001565	689	474721	26.2488	.001451
640	409600	25.2982	.001563	690	476100	26.2679	.001449
641	410881	25.3180	.001560	691	477481	26.2869	.001447
642	412164	25.3377	.001558	692	478864	26.3059	.001445
643	413449	25.3574	.001555	693	480249	26.3249	.001443
644	414736	25.3772	.001553	694	481636	26.3439	.001441
645	416025	25.3969	.001550	695	483025	26.3629	.001439
646	417316	25.4165	.001548	696	484416	26.3818	.001437
647	418609	25.4362	.001546	697	485809	26.4008	.001435
648	419904	25.4558	.001543	698	487204	26.4197	.001433
649	421201	25.4755	.001541	699	488601	26.4386	.001431

TABLE VI—(Continued)

Squares, Square Roots, and Reciprocals

N	N^2	$\sqrt{N}$	$\frac{1}{N}$	N	N^2	$\sqrt{N}$	$\frac{1}{N}$
700	490000	26.4575	.001429	750	562500	27.3861	.001333
701	491401	26.4764	.001427	751	564001	27.4044	.001332
702	492804	26.4953	.001425	752	565504	27.4226	.001330
703	494209	26.5141	.001422	753	567009	27.4408	.001328
704	495616	26.5330	.001420	754	568516	27.4591	.001326
705	497025	26.5518	.001418	755	570025	27.4773	.001325
706	498436	26.5707	.001416	756	571536	27.4955	.001323
707	499849	26.5895	.001414	757	573049	27.5136	.001321
708	501264	26.6083	.001412	758	574564	27.5318	.001319
709	502681	26.6271	.001410	759	576081	27.5500	.001318
710	504100	26.6458	.001408	760	577600	27.5681	.001316
711	505521	26.6646	.001406	761	579121	27.5862	.001314
712	506944	26.6833	.001404	762	580644	27.6043	.001312
713	508369	26.7021	.001403	763	582169	27.6225	.001311
714	509796	26.7208	.001401	764	583696	27.6405	.001309
715	511225	26.7395	.001399	765	585225	27.6586	.001307
716	512656	26.7582	.001397	766	586756	27.6767	.001305
717	514089	26.7769	.001395	767	588289	27.6948	.001304
718	515524	26.7955	.001393	768	589824	27.7128	.001302
719	516961	26.8142	.001391	769	591361	27.7308	.001300
720	518400	26.8328	.001389	770	592900	27.7489	.001299
721	519841	26.8514	.001387	771	594441	27.7669	.001297
722	521284	26.8701	.001385	772	595984	27.7849	.001295
723	522729	26.8887	.001383	773	597529	27.8029	.001294
724	524176	26.9072	.001381	774	599076	27.8209	.001292
725	525625	26.9258	.001379	775	600625	27.8388	.001290
726	527076	26.9444	.001377	776	602176	27.8568	.001289
727	528529	26.9629	.001376	777	603729	27.8747	.001287
728	529984	26.9815	.001374	778	605284	27.8927	.001285
729	531441	27.0000	.001372	779	606841	27.9106	.001284
730	532900	27.0185	.001370	780	608400	27.9285	.001282
731	534361	27.0370	.001368	781	609961	27.9464	.001280
732	535824	27.0555	.001366	782	611524	27.9643	.001279
733	537289	27.0740	.001364	783	613089	27.9821	.001277
734	538756	27.0924	.001362	784	614656	28.0000	.001276
735	540225	27.1109	.001361	785	616225	28.0179	.001274
736	541696	27.1293	.001359	786	617796	28.0357	.001272
737	543169	27.1477	.001357	787	619369	28.0535	.001271
738	544644	27.1662	.001355	788	620944	28.0713	.001269
739	546121	27.1846	.001353	789	622521	28.0891	.001267
740	547600	27.2029	.001351	790	624100	28.1069	.001266
741	549081	27.2213	.001350	791	625681	28.1247	.001264
742	550564	27.2397	.001348	792	627264	28.1425	.001263
743	552049	27.2580	.001346	793	628849	28.1603	.001261
744	553536	27.2764	.001344	794	630436	28.1780	.001259
745	555025	27.2947	.001342	795	632025	28.1957	.001258
746	556516	27.3130	.001340	796	633616	28.2135	.001256
747	558009	27.3313	.001339	797	635209	28.2312	.001255
748	559504	27.3496	.001337	798	636804	28.2489	.001253
749	561001	27.3679	.001335	799	638401	28.2666	.001252

TABLE VI—(Continued)

Squares, Square Roots, and Reciprocals

N	N^2	$\sqrt{N}$	$\dfrac{1}{N}$	N	N^2	$\sqrt{N}$	$\dfrac{1}{N}$
800	640000	28.2843	.001250	850	722500	29.1548	.001176
801	641601	28.3019	.001248	851	724201	29.1719	.001175
802	643204	28.3196	.001247	852	725904	29.1890	.001174
803	644809	28.3373	.001245	853	727609	29.2062	.001172
804	646416	28.3549	.001244	854	729316	29.2233	.001171
805	648025	28.3725	.001242	855	731025	29.2404	.001170
806	649636	28.3901	.001241	856	732736	29.2575	.001168
807	651249	28.4077	.001239	857	734449	29.2746	.001167
808	652864	28.4253	.001238	858	736164	29.2916	.001166
809	654481	28.4429	.001236	859	737881	29.3087	.001164
810	656100	28.4605	.001235	860	739600	29.3258	.001163
811	657721	28.4781	.001233	861	741321	29.3428	.001161
812	659344	28.4956	.001232	862	743044	29.3598	.001160
813	660969	28.5132	.001230	863	744769	29.3769	.001159
814	662596	28.5307	.001229	864	746496	29.3939	.001157
815	664225	28.5482	.001227	865	748225	29.4109	.001156
816	665856	28.5657	.001225	866	749956	29.4279	.001155
817	667489	28.5832	.001224	867	751689	29.4449	.001153
818	669124	28.6007	.001222	868	753424	29.4618	.001152
819	670761	28.6182	.001221	869	755161	29.4788	.001151
820	672400	28.6356	.001220	870	756900	29.4958	.001149
821	674041	28.6531	.001218	871	758641	29.5127	.001148
822	675684	28.6705	.001217	872	760384	29.5296	.001147
823	677329	28.6880	.001215	873	762129	29.5466	.001145
824	678976	28.7054	.001214	874	763876	29.5635	.001144
825	680625	28.7228	.001212	875	765625	29.5804	.001143
826	682276	28.7402	.001211	876	767376	29.5973	.001142
827	683929	28.7576	.001209	877	769129	29.6142	.001140
828	685584	28.7750	.001208	878	770884	29.6311	.001139
829	687241	28.7924	.001206	879	772641	29.6479	.001138
830	688900	28.8097	.001205	880	774400	29.6648	.001136
831	690561	28.8271	.001203	881	776161	29.6816	.001135
832	692224	28.8444	.001202	882	777924	29.6985	.001134
833	693889	28.8617	.001200	883	779689	29.7153	.001133
834	695556	28.8791	.001199	884	781456	29.7321	.001131
835	697225	28.8964	.001198	885	783225	29.7489	.001130
836	698896	28.9137	.001196	886	784996	29.7658	.001129
837	700569	28.9310	.001195	887	786769	29.7825	.001127
838	702244	28.9482	.001193	888	788544	29.7993	.001126
839	703921	28.9655	.001192	889	790321	29.8161	.001125
840	705600	28.9828	.001190	890	792100	29.8329	.001124
841	707281	29.0000	.001189	891	793881	29.8496	.001122
842	708964	29.0172	.001188	892	795664	29.8664	.001121
843	710649	29.0345	.001186	893	797449	29.8831	.001120
844	712336	29.0517	.001185	894	799236	29.8998	.001119
845	714025	29.0689	.001183	895	801025	29.9166	.001117
846	715716	29.0861	.001182	896	802816	29.9333	.001116
847	717409	29.1033	.001181	897	804609	29.9500	.001115
848	719104	29.1204	.001179	898	806404	29.9666	.001114
849	720801	29.1376	.001178	899	808201	29.9833	.001112

TABLE VI—(Continued)

Squares, Square Roots, and Reciprocals

N	N^2	$\sqrt{N}$	$\frac{1}{N}$	N	N^2	$\sqrt{N}$	$\frac{1}{N}$
900	810000	30.0000	.001111	950	902500	30.8221	.001053
901	811801	30.0167	.001110	951	904401	30.8383	.001052
902	813604	30.0333	.001109	952	906304	30.8545	.001050
903	815409	30.0500	.001107	953	908209	30.8707	.001049
904	817216	30.0666	.001106	954	910116	30.8869	.001048
905	819025	30.0832	.001105	955	912025	30.9031	.001047
906	820836	30.0998	.001104	956	913936	30.9192	.001046
907	822649	30.1164	.001103	957	915849	30.9354	.001045
908	824464	30.1330	.001101	958	917764	30.9516	.001044
909	826281	30.1496	.001100	959	919681	30.9677	.001043
910	828100	30.1662	.001099	960	921600	30.9839	.001042
911	829921	30.1828	.001098	961	923521	31.0000	.001041
912	831744	30.1993	.001096	962	925444	31.0161	.001040
913	833569	30.2159	.001095	963	927369	31.0322	.001038
914	835396	30.2324	.001094	964	929296	31.0483	.001037
915	837225	30.2490	.001093	965	931225	31.0644	.001036
916	839056	30.2655	.001092	966	933156	31.0805	.001035
917	840889	30.2820	.001091	967	935089	31.0966	.001034
918	842724	30.2985	.001089	968	937024	31.1127	.001033
919	844561	30.3150	.001088	969	938961	31.1288	.001032
920	846400	30.3315	.001087	970	940900	31.1448	.001031
921	848241	30.3480	.001086	971	942841	31.1609	.001030
922	850084	30.3645	.001085	972	944784	31.1769	.001029
923	851929	30.3809	.001083	973	946729	31.1929	.001028
924	853776	30.3974	.001082	974	948676	31.2090	.001027
925	855625	30.4138	.001081	975	950625	31.2250	.001026
926	857476	30.4302	.001080	976	952576	31.2410	.001025
927	859329	30.4467	.001079	977	954529	31.2570	.001024
928	861184	30.4631	.001078	978	956484	31.2730	.001022
929	863041	30.4795	.001076	979	958441	31.2890	.001021
930	864900	30.4959	.001075	980	960400	31.3050	.001020
931	866761	30.5123	.001074	981	962361	31.3209	.001019
932	868624	30.5287	.001073	982	964324	31.3369	.001018
933	870489	30.5450	.001072	983	966289	31.3528	.001017
934	872356	30.5614	.001071	984	968256	31.3688	.001016
935	874225	30.5778	.001070	985	970225	31.3847	.001015
936	876096	30.5941	.001068	986	972196	31.4006	.001014
937	877969	30.6105	.001067	987	974169	31.4166	.001013
938	879844	30.6268	.001066	988	976144	31.4325	.001012
939	881721	30.6431	.001065	989	978121	31.4484	.001011
940	883600	30.6594	.001064	990	980100	31.4643	.001010
941	885481	30.6757	.001063	991	982081	31.4802	.001009
942	887364	30.6920	.001062	992	984064	31.4960	.001008
943	889249	30.7083	.001060	993	986049	31.5119	.001007
944	891136	30.7246	.001059	994	988036	31.5278	.001006
945	893025	30.7409	.001058	995	990025	31.5436	.001005
946	894916	30.7571	.001057	996	992016	31.5595	.001004
947	896809	30.7734	.001056	997	994009	31.5753	.001003
948	898704	30.7896	.001055	998	996004	31.5911	.001002
949	900601	30.8058	.001054	999	998001	31.6070	.001001
				1000	1000000	31.6228	.001000

LIST OF
PRINCIPAL FORMULAS

Arithmetic mean, binomial distribution: $\mu = nP$

Arithmetic mean, finite population, ungrouped data: $\mu = \dfrac{\Sigma X_i}{N}$

Arithmetic mean, sample of grouped data, long method: $\bar{x} = \dfrac{\Sigma f_i x_i}{n}$

or: $\bar{x} = \Sigma\left(\dfrac{f_i}{n}\right) x_i$

Arithmetic mean, sample of grouped data, short method: $\bar{x} = x_0 + \dfrac{\Sigma f_i v_i}{n} c$

Arithmetic mean, sample of ungrouped data, long method: $\bar{x} = \dfrac{\Sigma x_i}{n}$

Arithmetic mean, sample of ungrouped data, short method: $\bar{x} = x_0 + \dfrac{\Sigma u_i}{n}$

Binomial distribution: $Pr(x) = \dbinom{n}{x} P^x Q^{n-x}$

Coefficient of determination: $r^2 = \dfrac{[\Sigma(x_i - \bar{x})(y_i - \bar{y})]^2}{\Sigma(x_i - \bar{x})^2 \Sigma(y_i - \bar{y})^2}$

$$= \dfrac{(n\Sigma x_i y_i - \Sigma x_i \Sigma y_i)^2}{[(n\Sigma x_i^2 - (\Sigma x_i)^2][n\Sigma y_i^2 - (\Sigma y_i)^2]}$$

Coefficient of variation, sample of ungrouped data: $cv = \dfrac{s}{\bar{x}}$

Confidence interval for estimating a total, large sample: $N\bar{x} \pm Z \cdot Ns/\sqrt{n}$

Confidence interval for estimating μ, large sample: $\bar{x} \pm Z \cdot s/\sqrt{n}$

Confidence interval for estimating μ, small sample: $\bar{x} \pm t \cdot s/\sqrt{n}$

Confidence interval for estimating the mean
y value for a given x value in linear
regression:

$$y' \pm t \cdot s_E \sqrt{\frac{1}{n} + \frac{(x_c - \bar{x})^2}{\Sigma(x_i - \bar{x})^2}}$$

Fisher's ideal index:

$$I = \sqrt{\text{Laspeyres} \times \text{Paasche}}$$

Geometric mean, sample of ungrouped data:

$$gm = \sqrt[n]{x_1 \cdot x_2 \cdot x_3 \cdots x_n}$$

Harmonic mean, sample of ungrouped data:

$$hm = \frac{n}{\Sigma(1/x_i)}$$

Laspeyres price index:

$$I = \frac{\Sigma p_n q_0}{\Sigma p_0 q_0} \times 100$$

Linear regression line:

$$y' = a + bx$$

Linear trend line:

$$T = a + bx$$

Median, sample of grouped data:

$$m = B_L + \frac{g}{f_m} c$$

Normal equations, straight line of least squares:

$$\Sigma y_i = na + b\Sigma x_i$$

$$\Sigma x_i y_i = a\Sigma x_i + b\Sigma x_i^2$$

Paasche price index:

$$I = \frac{\Sigma p_n q_n}{\Sigma p_0 q_n} \times 100$$

Pearsonian coefficient of correlation:

$$r = \frac{s_{xy}}{s_x s_y}$$

$$= \frac{\Sigma(x_i - \bar{x})(y_i - \bar{y})}{\sqrt{\Sigma(x_i - \bar{x})^2}\sqrt{\Sigma(y_i - \bar{y})^2}}$$

Poisson distribution:

$$Pr(x) = \frac{e^{-\lambda}\lambda^x}{x!}$$

Spearman's coefficient of rank correlation:

$$r_r = 1 - \frac{6\Sigma d_i^2}{n^3 - n}$$

Standard error of the mean, estimated:

$$s_{\bar{x}} = \frac{s}{\sqrt{n}}$$

Standard error of the mean, true:

$$\sigma_{\bar{x}} = \frac{\sigma}{\sqrt{n}}$$

Standard error of a proportion, estimated:

$$s_p = \sqrt{\frac{pa}{n}}$$

Standard error of a proportion, true:

$$\sigma_p = \sqrt{\frac{PQ}{n}}$$

Standard error of estimate: $s_E = \sqrt{\dfrac{\Sigma(y_i - y')^2}{n - 2}}$

t, computed value: $t = \dfrac{\bar{x} - \mu_0}{s/\sqrt{n}}$

Value index: $I_v = \dfrac{\Sigma p_n q_n}{\Sigma p_0 q_0} \times 100$

Variance, finite population, ungrouped: $\sigma^2 = \dfrac{\Sigma(X_i - \mu)^2}{N}$

Variance, finite population, ungrouped, second form: $S^2 = \dfrac{\Sigma(X_i - \mu)^2}{N - 1}$

Variance, sample of grouped data, long method: $s^2 = \dfrac{\Sigma f_i(x_i - \bar{x})^2}{n - 1}$

Variance, sample of grouped data, short method: $s^2 = \left[\dfrac{\Sigma f_i v_i^2 - \dfrac{(\Sigma f_i v_i)^2}{n}}{n - 1}\right] c^2$

Variance, sample of ungrouped data, long method: $s^2 = \dfrac{\Sigma(x_i - \bar{x})^2}{n - 1}$

Variance, sample of ungrouped data, short method: $s^2 = \dfrac{\Sigma x_i^2 - \dfrac{(\Sigma x_i)^2}{n}}{n - 1}$

$= \dfrac{\Sigma u_i^2 - \dfrac{(\Sigma u_i)^2}{n}}{n - 1}$

Variance, binomial distribution: $\sigma^2 = nPQ$

Weighted mean of price relatives: $I = \dfrac{\Sigma \left(\dfrac{p_n}{p_0}\right) w}{\Sigma w} \times 100$

Z, approximate computed value: $Z \doteq \dfrac{\bar{x} - \mu_0}{s/\sqrt{n}}$

Z, approximate computed value, normal curve
approximation to the binomial distribution: $Z \doteq \dfrac{x \pm \frac{1}{2} - u}{\sigma}$

Z, approximate computed value, normal curve approximation to the modified binomial distribution: $Z \doteq \dfrac{p \pm \dfrac{1}{2n} - P_0}{\sqrt{\dfrac{PQ}{n}}}$

INDEX